Mastering Muscles & Movement

SECOND EDITION

A Brain-Friendly System for Learning
Musculoskeletal Anatomy and Basic Kinesiology

What professionals are saying about Mastering Muscles & Movement

"Mastering Muscles & Movement makes human anatomy and kinesiology highly accessible to the reader. The information is presented in a format that accelerates the learning process and creates a long-term functional memory for the student. Accompanied with the study cards, Mastering Muscles & Movement makes learning fun and simple. I highly recommend this book for undergraduate to post-graduate students as well as practitioners in the field of healing arts and musculoskeletal medicine."

Avilio Halme, MPT, COMS

"Mastering Muscles and Movement presents an innovative and practical learning tool for students of Anatomy and Kinesiology. It is the first book that I have seen that actually demonstrates the steps to successful memorization and information retention. It gives you the sense that you are looking through the notes of the best student in class and learning their secret code. The simple, quick access to detailed content and the excellent selection of study tools will make this a book that students reach for first."

Ellen K. Geary MS, LAc

"Mastering Muscles and Movement outshines every other learning guide I have seen, and it is the ONLY book offering a system that maximizes the learning potential for every student of anatomy, kinesiology, massage therapy, physical therapy, etc. The layout, images, muscle groupings, and tables included in the system are pure genius. The author provides helpful online learning resources that add power and efficiency to the system. The clear and concise images allow for quick referencing of material. I'm impressed with the accuracy and level of detail included on innervation, attachment sites, actions, joints, and ligaments. There is so much information packed into this gem of a book! Additionally, it includes sections on the muscles of the face and jaw as well as the pelvic floor, two areas that are often overlooked in kinesiology textbooks. Mastering Muscles and Movement is truly in a class of its own and it is my first choice for instructing kinesiology courses and as a reference guide in my clinical practice."

Wren McLaughlin, PT, DPT, PRC, WCS, MS

---

www.studymuscles.com

Interactive apps and downloadable support materials are available at the companion website.

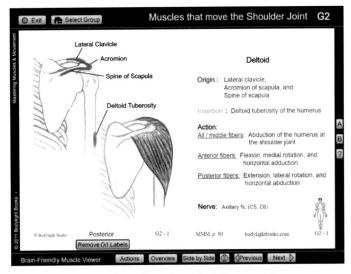

Brain-Friendly Muscle Viewer App

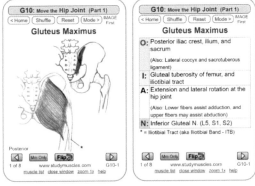

Flashcard App

Also...   Bony Landmark Flashcards
Study Questions
Interactive Atlas of Bones & Landmarks
Muscle Layering Slide Shows
And more!

Mastering
Muscles & Movement

SECOND EDITION

A Brain-Friendly System for Learning Musculoskeletal Anatomy and Basic Kinesiology

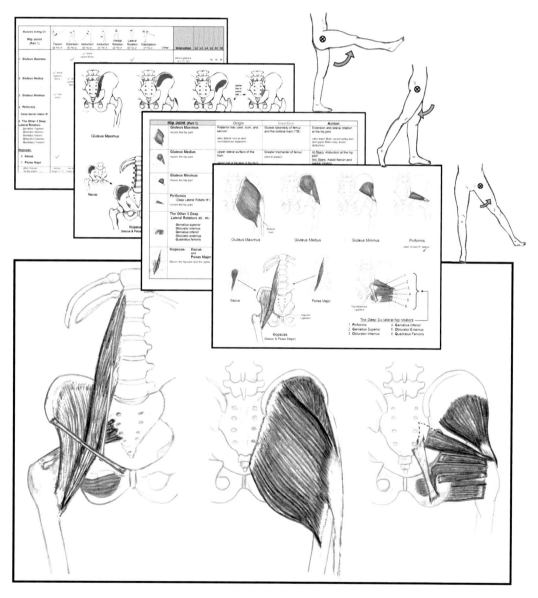

Written and illustrated by **David M. Campbell**

Bodylight Books
Bellingham, WA

Mastering Muscles and Movement

A Brain-Friendly System for Learning Musculoskeletal Anatomy and Basic Kinesiology

Second Edition

Published by

Bodylight Books
Bellingham, WA
United States of America

www.studymuscles.com
www.bodylightbooks.com

ISBN: 978-0-9788664-5-7

Library of Congress Control Number: 2021920972

FCS1084

Preface

Mastering Muscles & Movement – A Brain-Friendly System for Learning Musculoskeletal Anatomy and Basic Kinesiology, provides a unique, strategically organized approach for learning the muscles, bones, joints, movements, and motor innervation of the human body. As the subtitle implies, research in brain-based learning has been richly applied in the design of this book to facilitate understanding, memorization, and mastery of this body of knowledge.

Approach

This book provides a complete set of information for the study of musculoskeletal anatomy and basic kinesiology. While there are many books available that cover the subject, **Mastering Muscles & Movement** (MM&M) presents a fresh *approach* that is designed to leverage the natural ways the brain observes, learns, and recalls this type of information. Rather than employing the usual one-muscle-per-page format, this book treats *groups* of muscles as "movement families" and presents them in a way that provides a rich visual, verbal, and relational learning environment.

The result is a truly **brain-friendly** experience for the student. The myriad details and inter-relationships are easily recognized in simple and natural ways by the innovative arrangement of the muscle information on each page and from page-to-page. The reader comfortably stays aware of the bigger picture while studying any one item, easily compares and contrasts related features and facts, and is enabled to structure study time to play to strengths or to eliminate weaknesses.

Benefits

Some benefits of this approach are:

- Isolates and supports learning and repetition from many directions: visual, verbal, relational.

- Supports the brain in doing what it does best: Consistently encourages the reader, simply by the way the material is laid out and sized on the pages, to compare and contrast, see patterns, perceive interrelationships, and "come at" the information from different directions.

- Muscle and bone information and illustrations are arranged to allow easy and repetitive self-testing while studying.

- Precise and uncluttered presentation clarifies common misunderstandings, and illuminates facts and relationships that are often overlooked.

- While studying, the information is anchored in the brain with multiple "hooks", providing rich cross-neuronal connections that are important for easier recall of details and relationships.

- Material is clearly organized throughout, and has visual cues that always keep the reader aware of where they are within the greater body of knowledge contained in the book.

Audience

The first edition of MM&M has been successfully utilized by students learning massage therapy, yoga instruction, physical therapy, Pilates instruction, athletic training, and dance, as well as students in college undergraduate functional anatomy and anatomical kinesiology classes. This new second edition has incorporated many improvements suggested by students and instructors over the years. The format has been redesigned and new information and illustrations added, while maintaining the original brain-friendly organization and approach that has proved useful in the past.

For many students MM&M has served as a **course textbook**, while in other educational programs it has proved valuable as **supplemental material** (depending on the level of specialization required for the course). In addition, this book has served as an easily accessible **reference** on the shelf of practicing professionals. Finally, because of its clarity of organization and simplicity of approach, it is an excellent **quick-review** book for students who are preparing for examination, and for practicing professionals who want to refresh their knowledge before attending continuing education classes.

Organization

MM&M is organized in a way that flows through a course of study of the musculoskeletal system. The clearly delineated segments allow the reader to focus on a specific portion of information while staying oriented within the whole. Note that the muscle groups in Chapters 4-6 can be taught in any order. Each presentation is independent of the others, allowing instructors to structure their class to their preference.

Chapter 1 – Basic Information provides foundational information for the study of muscles and movement. It gives definitions of terms and establishes a system for describing and analyzing body movement. Basic information is provided for the main body systems that are related to the study of kinesiology: bones, joints, muscles, nerves, and fascia. Finally, it introduces some important kinesiology concepts.

Chapter 2 – Bones, Bony Landmarks, Joints, and Ligaments employs an atlas format to present detailed features of all the bones of the body. This provides a central location that can be quickly referred to while proceeding through learning the muscles of the body later in the book. It gives information about the overall skeleton, as well as details about each individual bone. Master lists of the joints of the body and ligaments of the body are also included. Note that detailed illustrations of the joints and ligaments are provided at the beginning of chapters 4 through 6 as appropriate for the upper extremity, axial skeleton and lower extremity divisions of the body.

Chapter 3 – Using the Brain-Friendly System to Optimize Your Learning is a must-read to prepare the reader to fully utilize the brain-friendly approach employed to describe all the muscles in Chapters 4, 5 and 6. Understanding how to proceed is an essential step to allow the learner to truly master the muscles and movements of the body. Chapter 3 also outlines the types of information to learn and how that information is used in practical applications.

Chapters 4, 5, and 6 provide the bulk of the muscles and movement information in a special format that emphasizes constantly comparing and contrasting facts and pictures. The unique organization allows the reader to comfortably understand, memorize and recall the muscles of the body and study their actions and innervations. This approach helps the brain build a rich neuronal network that will lead to true mastery of the subject.

Chapters 7 – Summary Tables provides a handy presentation that can be quickly referenced once the reader has learned all the muscles in chapters 4, 5, and 6. The tables also reconcile some of the overlaps or gaps that were necessarily created by dividing the muscles into 13 groups for chapters 4-6 (especially multi-joint muscles). These tables are very useful when assessing and analyzing a client's movement patterns or posture, when performing or teaching stretching or strengthening exercises, or when reviewing material prior to an exam. Chapter 7 also includes a comprehensive master table of the motor innervation of the entire musculoskeletal system of the body.

Chapter 8 – Study Aids gives a summary of the ancillary materials currently available on the companion website. These include downloadable PDF files and interactive apps, The end of the chapter also includes some general purpose worksheets that can be photocopied by the purchaser of the book for their personal use. Note that the online materials are likely to evolve over time, given the dynamic nature of the internet.

Ancillary Materials

Online materials based on the text and illustrations in **Mastering Muscles & Movement** are available at www.studymuscles.com to support both students and instructors.

Student materials include muscle and bone flashcards, muscle and bony landmark practice sheets, synergist/antagonist practice sheets, muscle tickets, study questions and other study aids. The study tools also include a muscle flashcard app and the **Brain-Friendly Muscle Viewer**, which is an interactive app that presents all the muscles in a style that matches the organization of the textbook.

The instructor resources include downloadable Powerpoint presentations, homework and quiz templates, study questions with keys, and other materials.

Mastering Muscles & Movement

Contents

Muscles – List by Group

Muscles are placed in groups based on the bones and joints they *move* as they contract.

----- Upper Extremity -----
(Chapter 4)

Group 1 – Scapula / Clavicle
Trapezius
Levator scapula
Rhomboid major & minor
Serratus anterior
Pectoralis minor
Subclavius

p. 75-82

1

Group 2 – Shoulder Joint
Deltoid
Supraspinatus
Infraspinatus
Teres minor
Subscapularis
Pectoralis major
Coracobrachialis
Latissimus dorsi
Teres major

p. 83-90

2

Group 3 – Elbow, Forearm
Biceps brachii
Brachialis
Brachioradialis
Pronator teres
Pronator quadratus
Triceps brachii
Anconeus
Supinator

p. 91-98

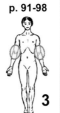
3

Group 4 – Wrist, Hand, Fingers
Flexor carpi radialis
Palmaris longus
Flexor carpi ulnaris
Flexor digitorum superficialis
Flexor digitorum profundus
Extensor carpi radialis longus
Extensor carpi radialis brevis
Extensor carpi ulnaris
Extensor digitorum
Extensor indicis

p. 99-106

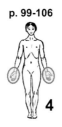
4

Group 5 – Thumb
Flexor pollicis longus
Flexor pollicis brevis
Opponens pollicis
Adductor pollicis
Abductor pollicis brevis
Abductor pollicis longus
Extensor pollicis longus
Extensor pollicis brevis

p. 107-113

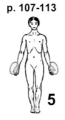
5

Bonus Group
Intrinsic muscles of the hand

p. 114-115

----- Axial Body -----
(Chapter 5)

Group 6 – Face, Jaw
Masseter
Temporalis
Lateral pterygoid
Medial pterygoid
Occipitofrontalis
Platysma
Suprahyoids Group
   Geniohyoid, Mylohyoid,
   Stylohyoid, Digastric
Infrahyoids Group
   Sternohyoid, Sternothyroid,
   Omohyoid, Thyrohyoid
Muscles of facial expression

p. 127-134

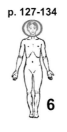
6

Group 7 – Neck, Head
Sternocleidomastoid
Scalenes group
Longus capitis & longus colli
Suboccipital group
   Rectus capitis posterior major
   Rectus capitis posterior minor
   Oblique capitis superior
   Oblique capitis inferior
Splenius capitis
Splenius cervicis
Semispinalis capitis
Levator scapula*
Trapezius, upper fibers*
   *(revisited for reversed O/I actions)

p. 135-142

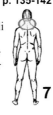
7

Group 8 – Spine
Spinalis
Longissimus
Iliocostalis
Semispinalis
Multifidus
Rotatores
Quadratus lumborum
Interspinales & Intertransversarii

p. 143-150

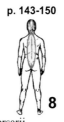
8

Group 9 – Thorax, Abdomen, Breathing
Rectus abdominis
External oblique
Internal oblique
Transverse abdominis
Diaphragm
External intercostals
Internal intercostals
Serratus posterior superior
Serratus posterior inferior
Levator costae
Transversus Thoracis

p. 151-157

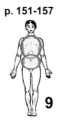
9

Bonus Group
Muscles of the pelvic floor and perineum

p. 158-159`

----- Lower Extremity -----
(Chapter 6)

Group 10 – Hip Joint (Part 1)
Gluteus maximus
Gluteus medius
Gluteus minimus
Piriformis (1st lateral rotator)
The other 5 lateral rotators
   Gemellus superior
   Obturator internus
   Gemellus inferior
   Obturator externus
   Quadratus femoris
Iliopsoas
   (Iliacus & Psoas major)

p. 167-174

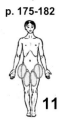
10

Group 11 – Hip Joint (Part 2)
Sartorius
Tensor fascia latae
Pectineus
Adductor brevis
Adductor longus
Adductor magnus
Gracilis

p. 175-182

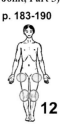
11

Group 12 – Knee (& Hip Joint, Part 3)
Rectus femoris
Vastus lateralis
Vastus intermedius
Vastus medialis
Biceps femoris
Semitendinosus
Semimembranosus
Popliteus

p. 183-190

12

Group 13 – Ankle, Foot, Toes
Gastrocnemius
Plantaris
Soleus
Tibialis posterior
Flexor digitorum longus
Flexor hallucis longus
Fibularis longus (peroneus)
Fibularis brevis (peroneus)
Tibialis anterior
Extensor digitorum longus
Extensor hallucis longus

p. 191-197

13

Bonus Group
Intrinsic muscles of the foot

p. 198-199

Muscles – Alphabetical List

Muscles – Alphabetical List

About the Information in This Book

Books on muscles and movement are notoriously inconsistent in the details of the muscle attachments, actions and innervation assigned to individual muscles. Variations in artistic renderings of muscles and other structures present an additional challenge when studying musculoskeletal anatomy. There are many valid reasons for these apparent inconsistencies, including human anatomical variation, measurement and analysis methods employed by anatomists, and editorial decision processes.

Suffice it to say, this book necessarily adds one more resource to the fray. As such, I will note the main resources and the process I used while making decisions about the information I present in this book. The Bibliography on page 231 lists the main resources used while developing the material. Some resources were influential in my artistic choices, while others were given varying degrees of influence in my decisions about factual muscle information (origin, insertion, action, innervation), as well as terminology and descriptions regarding physiology and kinesiology.

For muscle, nerve, bone, joint and ligament details, I studied and compared many sources, from introductory muscular system books to high-end anatomy atlases to comprehensive kinesiology textbooks (see bibliography). When differences were not easily reconciled, I turned to the highly detailed analyses of anatomy and function in the Travell and Simons manuals (ref. 33 and 39) and sometimes to newer peer-reviewed articles in the medical literature. In more difficult cases I made tables to compare sources and look for common ground, discussed the information with colleagues, consulted additional books and internet resources, and studied cadaver dissections.

After weighing all of the above, I then "flavored" the presentation based on my specific approach, i.e., to be **brain-friendly**. The information was then incrementally refined while seeing students' responses over many years of teaching kinesiology and cadaver anatomy. Please read the Preface on page *i*, and read Chapter 3 – "Using the Brain-Friendly System to Optimize Your Learning" to better understand the specific approach used in the Mastering Muscles & Movement system.

Acknowledgements

Over the many years I have been developing and improving this book there have been too many influences and contributors to name them all individually. However, the following is an attempt to "name a few" of the people who graciously helped me along the way.

Those making direct contribution to the process and/or content of this book (in alphabetical order): Pat Archer, Jack Blackburn, Elizabeth Fletcher Brown, Barb Collins, Jen Cosgrove, Gwen Crowell, Janae Fletcher, George Gottlieb, Avilio Halme, Kinsey Jackson, Liz Lamm, Whitney Lowe, Anna Mariano, Wren McLaughlin, Brenda Mitchell, Lisa Nelson, Eric Root, Helen Thayer, Diana Thompson, Kristin Torok, and my students and colleagues at the Spectrum Center School of Massage in WA state.

And finally for patience, love, support, expert editorial advice, and a little fun in between the hard work: Laurie Pitts.

About the Author/Illustrator

Dave Campbell, BS, LMT, has been an instructor of kinesiology and cadaver anatomy since 2001. He has been a manual therapy practitioner for over 30 years and has an enduring fascination with the intricacies of the human body, mind, and spirit. Dave maintains a bodywork practice at The Natural Health Clinic in Bellingham, WA, specializing in craniosacral therapy, organ- and nerve-specific fascial mobilization, and myofascial therapies.

Dave holds a B.S. in Mathematics from the University of California. A former engineer at the Fairchild Laboratory for AI Research in Palo Alto, CA, he developed his brain-friendly approach to teaching muscles and movement based on years of experience in the study of human perception, artificial intelligence, and graphic representation of scientific information.

Chapter 1
Basic Information

Introduction

The essential definition of the term **kinesiology** is "the study of movement". To study movement of the human body one must learn the muscles, their functions, the joints they cross, and the places on bones where they attach. That knowledge is then utilized in a variety of practical applications.

Chapter 1 – Basic Information provides foundational information and terminology that need to be understood before learning all the muscles that are presented later in the book. Once these basics are covered, the rest of the book proceeds as follows.

Chapter 2 – Bones, Bony Landmarks, Joints, and Ligaments employs an atlas format to present detailed features of all the bones of the body. This provides a central location that can be quickly referred to while studying the musculoskeletal system. Master lists of joints and ligaments are also included, which then refer to the more detailed information given in chapters 4 - 6.

Chapter 3 – Using the Brain-Friendly System to Optimize Your Learning is a must-read to prepare the reader to fully utilize the brain-friendly approach employed when describing all the muscles in Chapters 4 - 6. Understanding how to proceed is an essential step to allow the learner to truly master the muscles and movements of the body.

Chapters 4, 5, and 6 provide the bulk of the muscles and movement information in a special format that emphasizes constantly comparing and contrasting facts and pictures. The unique organization allows the reader to comfortably understand, memorize and recall the muscles of the body and study their actions and innervations.

Chapter 7 – Summary Tables provides a handy set of summary action and innervation tables that can be quickly referenced once the reader has learned all the muscles in chapters 4, 5, and 6.

Anatomical Terms

Anatomical Position

Anatomical position is a standing posture in which the parts of the body are placed in specific ways. It provides a *reference position* that is used as the basis to name and describe body movements, positions, and directions. The components of anatomical position are:

- Erect posture
- Face forward
- Feet forward
- Arms at sides
- Palms of hands forward
- Fingers and thumbs in extension (straight, not closed in fists).

A vertical line called the **midline** divides the body into right and left symmetrical halves. Note that the body is not symmetrical from front to back, so the midline does not apply when viewing the body from the side.

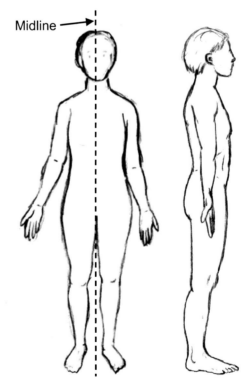

Midline →

Anatomical Position

Terms of Direction and Position

The following terms are used to describe the relationships of one body structure to another, and to clarify body positions and movements. These terms are defined for a person standing in anatomical position. Therefore, it is easiest to learn the terms while visualizing the body in that position. Once learned, the terms can be used to precisely describe body positions and directions no matter what orientation the body is in.

Superior / Cranial (also cephalad) – Closer to the head; situated above another structure. Example: The right lung is *superior* to the liver. **Inferior / Caudal** – Closer to the feet; situated below another structure. Example: The umbilicus (belly button) is *inferior* to the chin. The terms *cranial* and *caudal* are primarily used when referring to the head, neck and torso.	**Proximal** – Nearer to the trunk or point of origin of a limb. Example: The knee is *proximal* to the foot. **Distal** – Further from the root of a limb. Example: The hand is *distal* to the elbow. The terms *proximal* and *distal* are primarily used when referring to the arms and legs.
Anterior / Ventral – Front of the body, or a structure closer to the front than another structure. Example: The abdomen is *anterior* to the spine. **Posterior / Dorsal** – Back of the body, or a structure closer to the back than another structure. Example: The spine is *posterior* to the sternum (breast bone). The terms *ventral* and *dorsal* are primarily used when referring to the head, neck and torso.	**Deep** – Beneath or inward from the surface of the body. Example: Muscles are *deep* to the skin, and bones are deep to the muscles. **Superficial** – Near the surface, or closer to the surface than another structure. Example: The muscles are *superficial* to the bones.
	Ipsilateral – Indicates that a structure is on the same side of the body as another structure. Example: The shoulder and ipsilateral hip moved toward each other. **Contralateral** – Refers to a structure being on the opposite side of the body from another structure. Example: Touch your foot with your contralateral hand.
Medial – Refers to a structure that is closer to the midline or median plane of the body. Example: The eyes are *medial* to the ears. **Lateral** – A structure that is further away from the midline. Example: The little toes are *lateral* to the big toes (in anatomical position).	**Supine** – Lying on the back (face up, belly exposed). **Prone** – Lying on the belly (face down, back exposed).

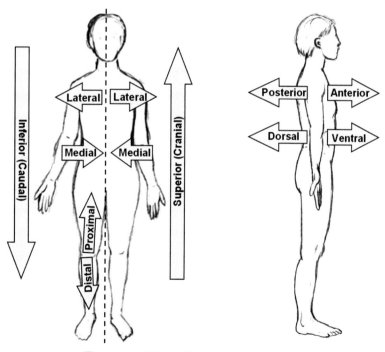

Terms of Direction and Position

Regions of the Body

The body can be divided into many regions. Knowing the names of regions allows efficient and precise communication when talking about locations on the body. Here are some regional terms that are useful when studying kinesiology:

Cranial	- head	Lumbar	- lower back
Cervical	- neck	Sacral	- base of spine, tail bone
Thoracic	- upper trunk, ribcage	Inguinal	- where lower abdomen meets thigh
Supraclavicular	- above the clavicle	Pubic	- genital region
Axillary	- armpit	Gluteal	- buttocks
Pectoral	- upper chest	Femoral	- thigh
Abdominal	- area between ribs and pubis	Patellar	- kneecap, front of knee
Brachial	- arm (upper arm)	Popliteal	- behind knee
Antebrachial	- forearm	Crural	- leg (below knee)
Cubital	- elbow	Sural	- calf of leg
Antecubital	- front of elbow	Dorsum	- top of foot, also back of hand
Palmar	- palm side of hand	Plantar	- bottom (sole) of foot

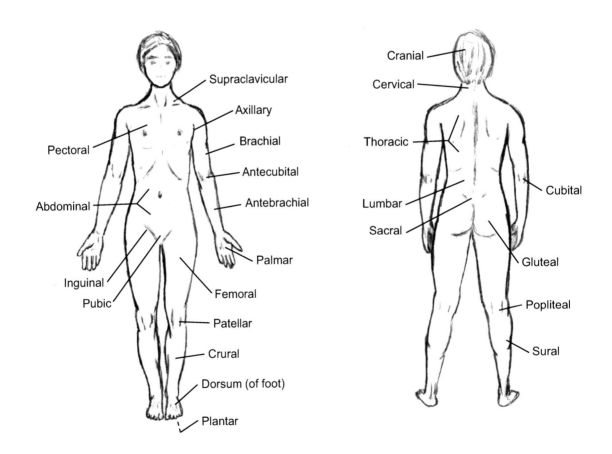

Regions of the Body

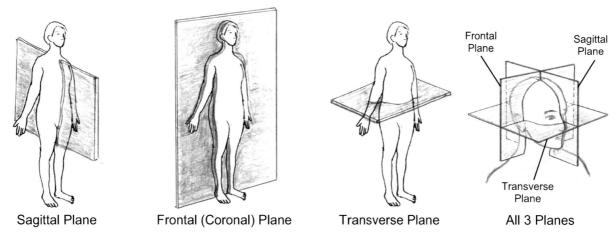

| Sagittal Plane | Frontal (Coronal) Plane | Transverse Plane | All 3 Planes |

The Three Cardinal Planes

Planes

A **plane** is an imaginary flat surface (visualize a pane of glass or flat piece of cardboard). Basic body movements are defined to occur *in* one of three **cardinal planes**:

Sagittal Plane – A vertical plane passing from front to back, dividing the body into right and left portions. A special sagittal plane called the **median plane** (also called the **midsagittal plane**) passes through the midline and divides the body into equal halves. Forward and backward body movements occur in the sagittal plane.

Frontal (Coronal) Plane – A vertical plane extending from side to side, dividing the body into anterior and posterior portions. Side-to-side movements occur in the frontal plane.

Transverse Plane – A horizontal plane that divides the body into upper and lower portions. Rotational or twisting movements occur in the transverse plane.

Moving In a Plane: To visualize a body part moving in a plane, first place the plane so it passes through the joint that is moving. Pick a point on the body part that is doing a certain action, and that point will stay in contact with the plane throughout the movement. For example, if you are going to bend the neck and trunk forward (flexion of the spine), then place a sagittal plane at the midline of the body so it passes through the joints along the spine. Note that your nose lies in the plane, and as you flex forward notice how the tip of your nose travels (it stays *in* the plane).

Moving Out of a Plane: Moving in one of the vertical planes constitutes moving *out* of the other vertical plane. For example, moving from anatomical position in the sagittal plane causes movement out of the frontal plane. In the above spine flexion example, your nose moves forward out of the frontal plane.

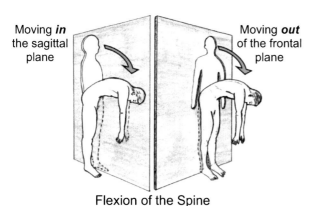

Moving *in* the sagittal plane

Moving *out* of the frontal plane

Flexion of the Spine

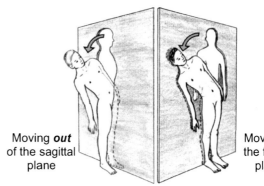

Moving *out* of the sagittal plane

Moving *in* the frontal plane

Side Bending of the Spine

Moving In a Plane vs. Moving Out of a Plane

Movement Definitions (Actions)

The terms defined in this section enable clear and concise description of the movements (also called actions) of all parts of the body. These terms, like the terms of position and direction on page 3, are initially defined and most easily learned referring to a body in anatomical position. They may then be used to describe movements of the body in any orientation or position. It is useful to think of actions as matched in pairs of opposing actions.

Action Pairs

Defining the action of a body part moving in space involves two components: (1) specify the joint where the body part is connected to the body, and (2) observe the plane in which the body part is moving. The body part can then move in one direction or the opposite direction while staying within that plane. These two opposing movements are called an **action pair**. When observing a body part moving, it is important to stay aware that there is always an opposing movement possible. Below are examples of the action pairs possible when the humerus is moving at the shoulder joint.

Action Pairs at the Shoulder Joint

Main Actions

Main actions are "standard" actions that apply to many parts of the body. Two bones meet at a joint, and they stay in contact at that joint as one bone moves relative to the other bone. The moving bone stays in one of the three cardinal planes as it moves, defining the action. The main actions are listed in the table below, and illustrated on page 7.

Main Actions

Moving in the:	Action Pairs	Applies to:
Sagittal plane	Flexion Extension	Limbs, neck, and torso
Frontal plane	Abduction Adduction	Limbs
	Lateral Flexion to the right Lateral Flexion to the left	Neck, torso
Transverse plane	Lateral Rotation Medial Rotation	Limbs
	Right Rotation Left Rotation	Neck, torso

Special-Purpose Actions

These are separately named actions that apply to specific structures of the body. They have special names either because they do not fit the "standard" movements described above, or simply to clarify unique types of movement that occur with certain structures. Special-purpose actions are listed in the table below, and illustrated on page 8.

Special-Purpose Actions

Action Pair	Applies to:
Pronation Supination	Forearm
Plantar flexion Dorsiflexion	Ankle
Inversion Eversion	Subtalar joint (below ankle)
Protraction Retraction	Scapula, mandible
Elevation Depression	Scapula, mandible, ribs
Upward Rotation Downward Rotation	Scapula
Radial Deviation Ulnar Deviation	Wrist
Horizontal Abduction Horizontal Adduction	Shoulder joint
Circumduction	A combination action at ball & socket and ellipsoid joints

Main Actions (shown as action pairs)

 = Direction of movement
 = Location of joint that is moving

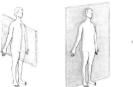

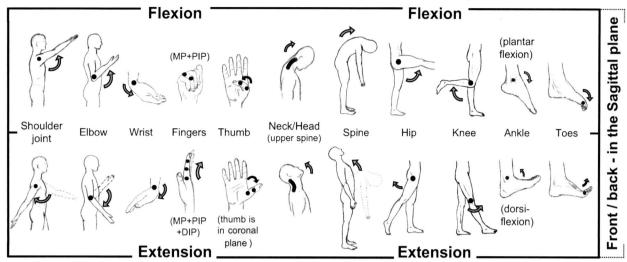

Front / back - in the Sagittal plane

| Flexion | | | | | | Flexion | | | | |

Shoulder joint — Elbow — Wrist — Fingers (MP+PIP) — Thumb — Neck/Head (upper spine) — Spine — Hip — Knee — Ankle (plantar flexion) — Toes

Extension — (MP+PIP +DIP) — (thumb is in coronal plane) — (dorsi-flexion) — Extension

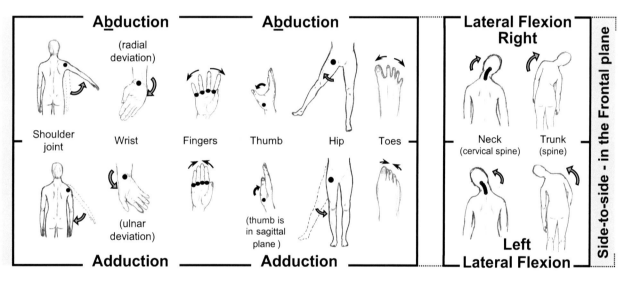

Side-to-side - in the Frontal plane

| Abduction | | Abduction | | Lateral Flexion Right |

Shoulder joint — Wrist (radial deviation) — Fingers — Thumb — Hip — Toes

Adduction — (ulnar deviation) — (thumb is in sagittal plane) — Adduction

Neck (cervical spine) — Trunk (spine)

Left Lateral Flexion

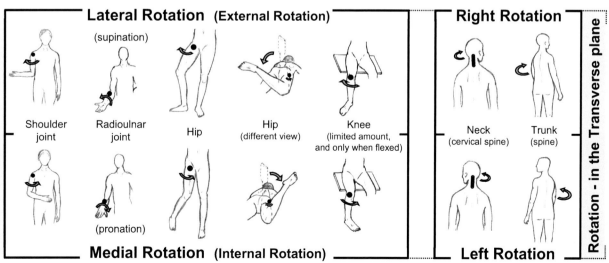

Rotation - in the Transverse plane

| Lateral Rotation (External Rotation) | | | | | Right Rotation |

Shoulder joint — Radioulnar joint (supination) — Hip — Hip (different view) — Knee (limited amount, and only when flexed)

Medial Rotation (Internal Rotation) — (pronation)

Neck (cervical spine) — Trunk (spine)

Left Rotation

Special-Purpose Actions (shown as action pairs)

↱ = Direction of movement
⊛ = Location of joint that is moving

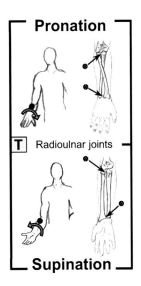

Pronation

T Radioulnar joints

Supination

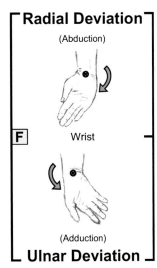

Radial Deviation

(Abduction)

F Wrist

(Adduction)

Ulnar Deviation

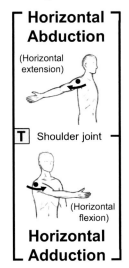

Horizontal Abduction

(Horizontal extension)

T Shoulder joint

(Horizontal flexion)

Horizontal Adduction

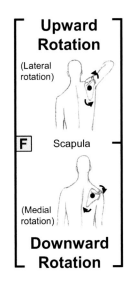

Upward Rotation

(Lateral rotation)

F Scapula

(Medial rotation)

Downward Rotation

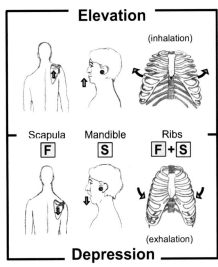

Elevation

(inhalation)

Scapula F Mandible S Ribs F+S

(exhalation)

Depression

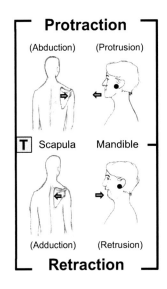

Protraction

(Abduction) (Protrusion)

T Scapula Mandible

(Adduction) (Retrusion)

Retraction

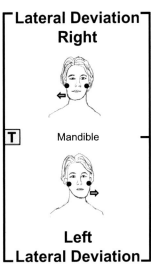

Lateral Deviation Right

T Mandible

Left Lateral Deviation

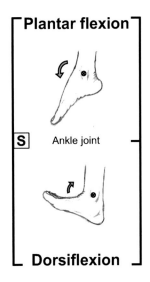

Plantar flexion

S Ankle joint

Dorsiflexion

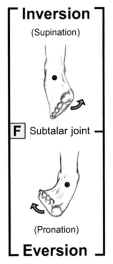

Inversion

(Supination)

F Subtalar joint

(Pronation)

Eversion

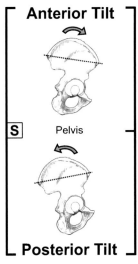

Anterior Tilt

S Pelvis

Posterior Tilt

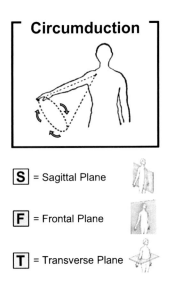

Circumduction

S = Sagittal Plane

F = Frontal Plane

T = Transverse Plane

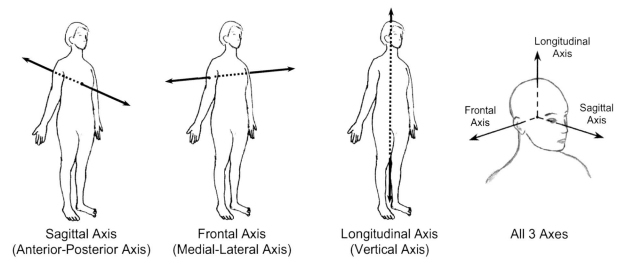

| Sagittal Axis (Anterior-Posterior Axis) | Frontal Axis (Medial-Lateral Axis) | Longitudinal Axis (Vertical Axis) | All 3 Axes |

The Three Axes of Rotation

Axis of Rotation

Movements are defined to occur *in* a plane and *about* an axis. The plane and axis are positioned so that they both pass through the joint that is moving. The concept of moving in a plane was discussed earlier in this chapter on page 5. This section will now define the **axis of rotation**. Then, the next section will describe how to put a plane and axis together to set up a more complete system for describing movements.

Three Axes

An **axis** is a straight line around which an object rotates (plural is axes). Visualize an arrow sticking through a target or a wagon axle that the wheels rotate around. Three axes at right angles establish an axis system for describing body movements in three dimensions. The figure above shows these axes in relation to the body in anatomical position. The two horizontal axes are named for the planes in which they lie. For easier understanding, the axes are also named to indicate the direction they travel.

1. **Sagittal Axis** – A horizontal front-to-back line, lying in the sagittal plane and at right angles to the frontal plane. This axis is also called the **Anterior-Posterior axis** (AP axis).

2. **Frontal Axis** – A horizontal side-to-side line, lying in the frontal plane and at right angles to the sagittal plane. This axis is also called the **Medial-Lateral axis** (ML axis).

3. **Longitudinal Axis** – A vertical top-to-bottom line, lying at right angles to the transverse plane. This axis is also referred to as the **Vertical axis**.

Moving About an Axis

To visualize moving about an axis, consider an axis skewering a block of wood (see figure below). Assume the hole the axis is going through is loose enough to allow the block to spin on the axis. The block spinning on the axis is moving in a plane that is perpendicular (at right angles) to the axis. Much like a wheel on the axle of a car, the block is prevented from moving in any other direction.

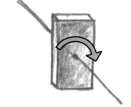

Anterior-Posterior axis sticking through a Frontal plane

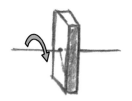

Medial-Lateral axis sticking through a Sagittal plane

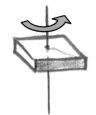

Longitudinal axis sticking through a Transverse plane

Rotational Movement About Each Axis

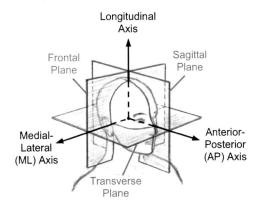

Longitudinal Axis

Frontal Plane

Sagittal Plane

Medial-Lateral (ML) Axis

Anterior-Posterior (AP) Axis

Transverse Plane

Planes and Axes – A System for Describing Movement

As a body part moves in a given plane, the joint turns about an axis. The axis is perpendicular (at right angles) to the plane, and the axis passes through the joint that is turning as the movement progresses. The figure below illustrates the three planes and their associated right-angle axes, along with some examples of actions for each (from page 7). The three plane-axis combinations are:

1. A sagittal plane goes with a medial-lateral axis (ML axis).
2. A frontal plane goes with an anterior-posterior axis (AP axis).
3. A transverse plane goes with a longitudinal axis (vertical axis).

When talking about movement, the plane is usually named when describing a body part moving through space, and the axis is used when describing what the joint is doing at the point where the two bones articulate. For example, "When Brenda's arm swung forward in the sagittal plane, the shoulder joint was turning about a medial-lateral (frontal) axis."

Non-Planar and Non-Axial Movements

Many movements a person does in real life are complex and not purely in one cardinal plane. The plane and axis system defined above, however, allows us to categorize and analyze body movement for the study of kinesiology.

For example, movements that do not fit into the simple 3-plane/3-axis system are:

- Oblique/diagonal/circular movements: They are described as combinations and sequences of the basic planar movements. For example, moving an arm out from the body at an angle has components in sagittal and frontal planes.

- Specialty action pairs: Elevation/depression, protraction/retraction, lateral deviation (see page 8) are sliding or gliding movements, i.e., they don't turn about an axis. These movements are separately named and applied as "exceptions" to the basic 3-axis system.

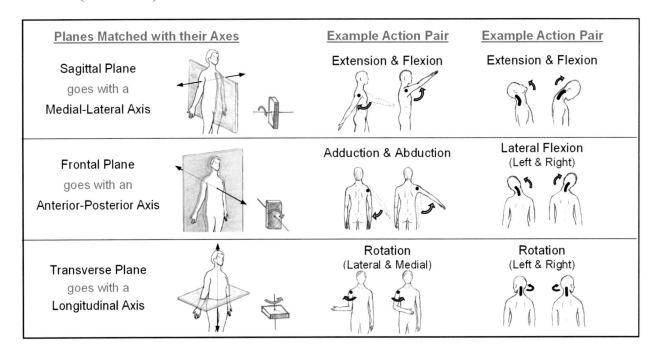

Planes Matched with their Axes	Example Action Pair	Example Action Pair
Sagittal Plane goes with a **Medial-Lateral Axis**	Extension & Flexion	Extension & Flexion
Frontal Plane goes with an **Anterior-Posterior Axis**	Adduction & Abduction	Lateral Flexion (Left & Right)
Transverse Plane goes with a **Longitudinal Axis**	Rotation (Lateral & Medial)	Rotation (Left & Right)

Skeletal System – The Bones

This section gives a brief overview of the skeletal system, which is made up of bones and cartilage. The human body has (at least) 206 bones. The bones are connected to each other at the joints to form the skeleton, which is the internal framework of the body. The joints, also called articulations, will be discussed in the next section.

Skeleton

A complete skeleton is shown on page 12. A primary function of the skeleton is to give support and shape to the rest of the body. It also provides protection for vital organs such as the heart, lungs, brain, and spinal cord. The bones also perform physiological functions, such as storing calcium and producing red blood cells. Finally, and most important for the study of kinesiology, bones and joints form a system of levers that muscles attach to and pull on to create body movement.

The human skeleton is organized into two major divisions:

Axial Skeleton – The central structure of the body: Head, spine, ribcage (80 bones).

Appendicular Skeleton – The extremities: Shoulder girdles, arms and hands, hip bones, legs and feet (126 bones).

Basic List of Bones

Below is a basic list of bones to get started. A complete list of bones and an atlas giving details about each bone of the body are presented in **Chapter 2 – Bones, Bony Landmarks, Joints, and Ligaments**. As we present the muscles in each area of the body in Chapters 4, 5 and 6, we'll add more details about the bones in that part of the body, and will refer back to pertinent pictures in Chapter 2.

Axial Skeleton

Skull:
  Cranial bones:
    Occiput, Parietal, Temporal, Frontal, Sphenoid, Ethmoid

  Facial bones:
    Zygomatic, Maxilla, Nasal, Lacrimal, Palatine, Vomer, Inferior Nasal Concha Mandible

Hyoid

Spine:
  Cervical Vertebrae
  Thoracic Vertebrae
  Lumbar Vertebrae
  Sacrum
  Coccyx

Ribs
Sternum

Appendicular Skeleton

Upper Extremity:
  Clavicle
  Scapula
  Humerus
  Ulna
  Radius
  Carpals
  Metacarpals
  Phalanges of the hand

Lower Extremity:
  Hip (coxal) bone:
        Ilium
        Ischium
        Pubis
  Femur
  Patella
  Tibia
  Fibula
  Tarsals
  Metatarsals
  Phalanges of the foot

The Skeletal System

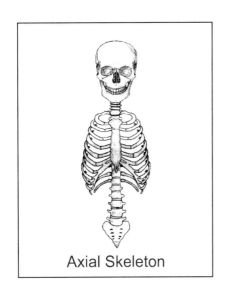

Axial Skeleton

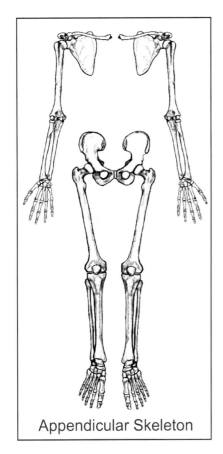

Appendicular Skeleton

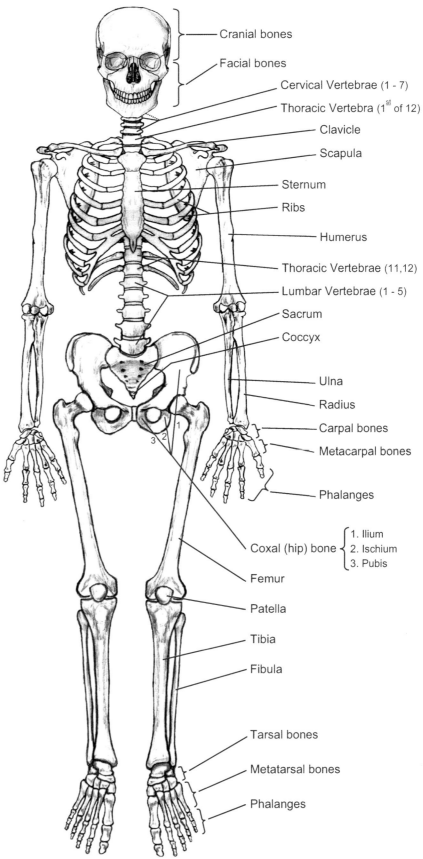

Cranial bones

Facial bones

Cervical Vertebrae (1 - 7)

Thoracic Vertebra (1st of 12)

Clavicle

Scapula

Sternum

Ribs

Humerus

Thoracic Vertebrae (11,12)

Lumbar Vertebrae (1 - 5)

Sacrum

Coccyx

Ulna

Radius

Carpal bones

Metacarpal bones

Phalanges

Coxal (hip) bone { 1. Ilium 2. Ischium 3. Pubis

Femur

Patella

Tibia

Fibula

Tarsal bones

Metatarsal bones

Phalanges

Classification of Bones by Shape

One way bones are classified is by their general shapes. Shape categories are based on the physical attributes of the bones, but the shapes also indicate certain functional or physiological features as well. For example, long bones function as levers for muscles to pull on and move body parts. Or physiologically, flat bones produce more red blood cells than other shapes. Most bones can be placed in one of the five categories shown in the table. However, some individual bones do not easily fit into one of these categories.

Bony Landmarks

Bony landmarks are words that name specific locations and features on bones. These words are used when identifying origins and insertions of muscles, i.e., the places where muscles attach to bones. Naming bony landmarks also creates a precise method for referring to other features of bones, such as specific holes, grooves and edges. **Chapter 2 – Bones, Bony Landmarks, Joints, and Ligaments** has detailed illustrations for all bony landmarks used in this book. The figure to the right shows a few sample bony landmark drawings (see Chapter 2 for full size versions).

Bones – Classified by Shape

Shape	Description	Examples
Long Bones	Shaft with widened articulating ends	Humerus, fibula, phalanges
Short Bones	More or less cube-shaped	Carpal bones, most tarsal bones
Flat Bones	Have flat broad surfaces	Scapula, ribs, ilium, parietal
Irregular Bones	"Other" varied shapes	Vertebrae, sphenoid, calcaneus
Sesamoid Bones	Oval, small, suspended in tendon	Patella, a pair under base of big toe

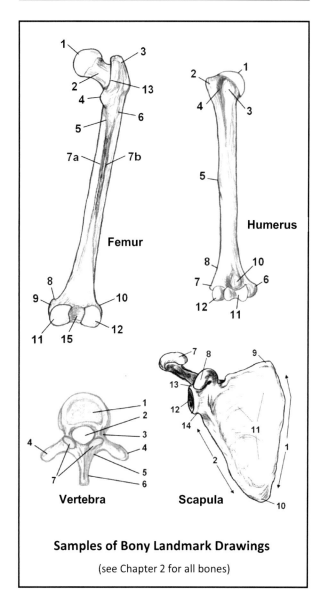

Samples of Bony Landmark Drawings

(see Chapter 2 for all bones)

Some Common Bony Landmark Terms

Term	Description	Examples
Process	A part of a bone that "sticks out"	#8 on Scapula, #4, #6 on Vertebra
Tubercle, Tuberosity	A bump or bulging place on a bone	#2, #5 on Humerus
Fossa	A smooth, flat part of a bone (often slightly concave)	#11 on Scapula
Head	Enlarged rounded end of a long bone	#1 on Femur, #1 on Humerus
Condyle	Dual rounded ends of a bone that articulate with the next bone	#11, #12 on Femur
Epicondyle	A place on a long bone just above the condyle	#9, #10 on Femur, #6, #7 on Humerus
Foramen	A hole in a bone: Vessels, nerves or other structures pass through the hole	#2 on Vertebra

Articular System – The Joints

A **joint** (also called an **articulation**) is the point of contact between two bones, between a cartilage structure and a bone, or between teeth and bones. Joints are the structures that allow the individual "rigid" bones of the skeleton to assemble into a freely moving body.

Throughout this book a special symbol ◄► is used to indicate the meeting point of the bones that make up a joint. For example, the tibiofemoral joint is the connection of the femur and the tibia at the knee. This could be represented by "femur ◄► tibia", or for greater detail, "condyles of femur ◄► condyles of tibia".

Broad Classifications of Joints - by Structure and Function

Joint structure determines function. The physical **structure of a joint** includes the shape of the articulating surfaces of the bones, how tightly they fit, and the types of tissue that hold the bones together. The **function of a joint** indicates how it moves (or doesn't move). There are three broad categories of joints:

Joints – Classified by Structure and Function

Function	Structure	Examples
Synarthrotic (immovable)	Fibrous	Cranial sutures, Teeth in sockets, 1st rib ◄► sternum
Amphiarthrotic (slightly moveable)	Cartilagenous	Intervertebral discs, Pubic symphysis, Manubrium ◄► Body of of sternum sternum
Diarthrotic (freely moveable)	Synovial	Most joints in the body. Synovial joints are described in detail below.

Stability vs. Mobility Trade-off

Stability is the ability of the body to maintain its integrity and form and to resist injury. **Mobility** is the ability of the body to move freely as required for the activities of life. A joint may allow a great deal of motion, as in the shoulder, or very little motion as in the tibiofibular joint. All joints function within

an inherent trade-off: Joints that are more moveable provide less stability, while joints that are more stable tend to have less movement ability.

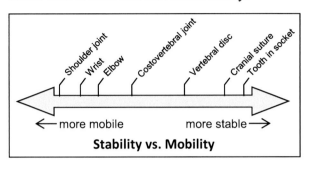

Stability vs. Mobility

Synovial Joints – Structure

Synovial joints are freely moveable (diarthrotic) because the bones are not securely connected by fibrous or cartilaginous tissue. Instead, there is a cavity that holds slippery synovial fluid between the bones. All synovial joints have the following structural components:

- Two bones that articulate
- Articular cartilage on each bone
- Joint capsule (fibrous outer shell, reinforced by ligaments)
- Synovial membrane (inner lining of capsule, secretes synovial fluid)
- Joint cavity
- Synovial fluid (in the cavity)

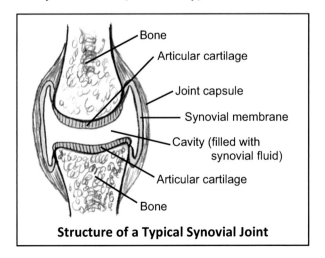

Structure of a Typical Synovial Joint

Accessory Structures for Synovial Joints

In addition to the basic joint capsule, synovial joints may be supported by one or more **accessory structures**. These structures include ligaments, cartilage pads, bursae, and fat pad "packing material".

Ligaments – Strong connective tissue bands that connect bone to bone and provide protection against the joint moving too far and becoming damaged. Most ligaments are outside the joint capsule (extracapsular ligaments) and span the bones that make up the joint. In addition, ligaments can be embedded within the fibrous material of the joint capsule itself, or can be completely inside the joint cavity (intracapsular ligaments).

Cartilage pads (small disc, meniscus, labrum) – Extra padding, protection, shaping, and containment inside the synovial cavity.

Bursae – A bursa (plural is bursae) is a sac containing synovial fluid. The composition of the sac is similar to a joint capsule, i.e., thin fibrous connective tissue lined with a synovial membrane that secretes synovial fluid. These fluid-filled sacs serve as shock absorbers or reduce friction between moving structures, and are primarily located where a muscle or tendon may rub on a bone.

Six Types of Synovial Joints

There are six types of synovial joints, based on commonality of bone shapes and supporting structures. Each type has a characteristic bone-shape/capsule/ligament arrangement that allows a certain set of actions. The joints of the body and their types are shown on a skeleton on page 17.

A mnemonic that may help you remember the six types is BS-PHEGS.

The Six Types of Synovial Joints

	Joint Type	Description	# of Axes	Action Pairs	Examples
BS	Ball & Socket	A rounded end on one bone fits into a cupped socket on the other bone	Triaxial	Flexion, Extension Abduction, Adduction Medial & Lateral Rotation	Glenohumeral joint (shoulder joint), Coxal joint (hip joint)
P	Pivot	A rounded projection on one bone fits into a ring formed by bone and ligament	Uniaxial	Rotation (Medial and Lateral Rotation, or Right and Left Rotation)	Radioulnar joint, Atlantoaxial joint (dens part)
H	Hinge	Cylindrical surfaces fit together like a door hinge	Uniaxial	Flexion, Extension	Humeroulnar joint, Interphalangeal joint
E	Ellipsoid or Condyloid	A shallow rounded end on one bone meets an oval depression on another bone	Biaxial	Flexion, Extension Abduction, Adduction (Ellipsoid is more oval shaped, condyloid is more spherical)	Radiocarpal joint, Atlanto-occipital joint, Metacarpophalangeal joint
G	Gliding or Plane	Flat or slightly curved surfaces allow sliding in all directions	Non-axial	Gliding	Intervertebral facet joints, Intercarpal joints Intertarsal joints Acromioclavicular joint
S	Saddle	Surfaces resemble saddles – convex one way and concave the other	Biaxial+	Flexion, Extension Abduction, Adduction, Opposition (facilitated by a specialized type of rotation)	Carpometacarpal joint #1 (base of thumb near the wrist)

To introduce the features of synovial joints, the following table presents the joints of the upper extremity, beginning with the glenohumeral joint and moving distally. Note that many of the joint names are created by simply naming the bones that make up the joint. For example, the articulation between the humerus and ulna is called the humeroulnar joint.

The upper extremity contains at least one of each type of synovial joint. In the table below, compare the actions of each joint with the six joint types (BS-PHEGS) listed on the previous page.

The joints of the upper and lower extremities and the axial skeleton are described in detail later in this book, as they relate to the groups of muscles in Chapters 4 through 6.

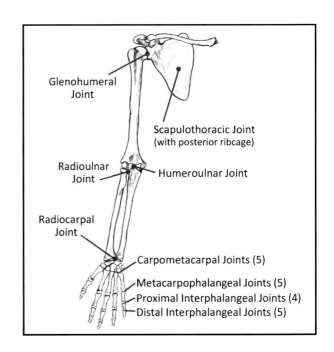

Joints of the Upper Extremity

Joint Name	Common Name	Bones Involved (& specific bony landmarks)		Type of Joint	Actions
Glenohumeral Joint	Shoulder joint	Scapula (glenoid fossa)	◄► Humerus (head)	Ball & Socket	Flexion, Extension Abduction, Adduction Rotation (medial & lateral) Horizontal Abduction Horizontal Adduction
Scapulothoracic Joint	Shoulder blade	Scapula (subscapular fossa) -with muscles sandwiched between-	◄► Ribs (posterior surfaces)	"False" Joint, (Functional Joint)	Elevation, Depression Abduction, Adduction Rotation (upward & downward)
Humeroulnar Joint	Elbow	Humerus (trochlea)	◄► Ulna (trochlear notch)	Hinge	Flexion, Extension
Radioulnar Joint (proximal)	Forearm	Radius (head)	◄► Ulna (radial notch)	Pivot	Supination, Pronation (i.e., rotations)
Radiocarpal Joint	Wrist	Radius (distal end)	◄► Carpal bones (proximal row)	Ellipsoid	Flexion, Extension Abduction, Adduction
Carpometacarpal Joints – digits #2-#5: fingers	Mid-palm of the hand	Carpal bones (distal row)	◄► Metacarpals (bases)	Gliding	Gliding
Carpometacarpal Joint – digit #1: thumb	Base of thumb at the wrist	Carpal bone (trapezium)	◄► Metacarpal #1 (base)	Saddle	Flexion, Extension Abduction, Adduction Opposition
Metacarpophalangeal Joints	Knuckles of the hand	Metacarpals (heads)	◄► Phalanges (bases)	Condyloid	Flexion, Extension Abduction, Adduction
Interphalangeal Joints (PIP-Proximal Interphalan..) (DIP-Distal Interphalangeal)	Fingers	Phalanges (heads)	◄► Phalanges (bases)	Hinge	Flexion, Extension

The symbol ◄► indicates two structures connecting at a joint.

Joints of the Body and Their Types

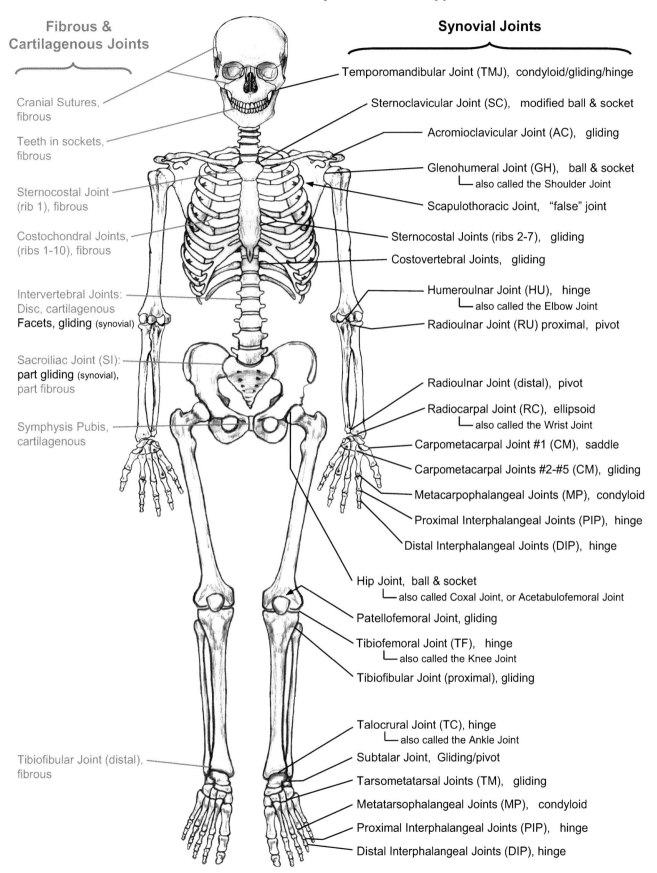

Fibrous & Cartilagenous Joints

Cranial Sutures, fibrous

Teeth in sockets, fibrous

Sternocostal Joint (rib 1), fibrous

Costochondral Joints, (ribs 1-10), fibrous

Intervertebral Joints: Disc, cartilagenous **Facets, gliding** (synovial)

Sacroiliac Joint (SI): **part gliding** (synovial), part fibrous

Symphysis Pubis, cartilagenous

Tibiofibular Joint (distal), fibrous

Synovial Joints

Temporomandibular Joint (TMJ), condyloid/gliding/hinge

Sternoclavicular Joint (SC), modified ball & socket

Acromioclavicular Joint (AC), gliding

Glenohumeral Joint (GH), ball & socket
└─ also called the Shoulder Joint

Scapulothoracic Joint, "false" joint

Sternocostal Joints (ribs 2-7), gliding

Costovertebral Joints, gliding

Humeroulnar Joint (HU), hinge
└─ also called the Elbow Joint

Radioulnar Joint (RU) proximal, pivot

Radioulnar Joint (distal), pivot

Radiocarpal Joint (RC), ellipsoid
└─ also called the Wrist Joint

Carpometacarpal Joint #1 (CM), saddle

Carpometacarpal Joints #2-#5 (CM), gliding

Metacarpophalangeal Joints (MP), condyloid

Proximal Interphalangeal Joints (PIP), hinge

Distal Interphalangeal Joints (DIP), hinge

Hip Joint, ball & socket
└─ also called Coxal Joint, or Acetabulofemoral Joint

Patellofemoral Joint, gliding

Tibiofemoral Joint (TF), hinge
└─ also called the Knee Joint

Tibiofibular Joint (proximal), gliding

Talocrural Joint (TC), hinge
└─ also called the Ankle Joint

Subtalar Joint, Gliding/pivot

Tarsometatarsal Joints (TM), gliding

Metatarsophalangeal Joints (MP), condyloid

Proximal Interphalangeal Joints (PIP), hinge

Distal Interphalangeal Joints (DIP), hinge

Range of Motion (ROM)

Range of motion (ROM) is a term that applies to each joint in the body. ROM is the amount of motion, usually expressed in degrees, allowed by the shape of the joint and the soft tissue surrounding it. The range is defined separately for each action the joint is capable of doing.

Each joint has a **normal range** through which it can move, e.g., from full extension to full flexion. The range is dictated by bone shapes, angles of articulation, and any inhibiting structures. Normal inhibiting structures include ligaments, joint capsule, muscle length, tissues, other bones, etc.

Abnormal ROM can mean that a pathology exists:

- Less than normal range (restricted, limited, what is stopping it?)
- More than normal range (hypermobile, loose, what is *not* stopping it that should?)

Recall the three axes of movement described earlier in this chapter (p. 9-10). ROM is considered <u>individually</u> for each axis of movement available for a joint. A pair of opposite actions take a joint through its full range of motion about an axis. For example, going from maximum flexion through to the limit of extension travels the full ROM (moving in the extension direction) for a joint moving around its medial-lateral axis.

When performing a movement at a joint for the purpose of assessing the body's capability, one observes whether the body part moves fully to the normal end of its range, and also whether the stopping mechanism at the end of the movement feels normal or not (the "end feel").

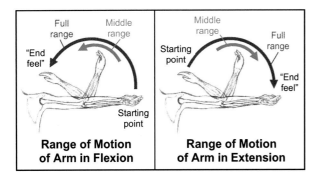

Range of Motion of Arm in Flexion

Range of Motion of Arm in Extension

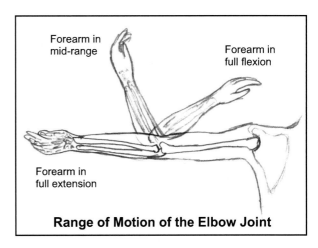

Range of Motion of the Elbow Joint

Most reference books list ROM as number of degrees moved from anatomical position for each half of an action pair. For example, a "normal" wrist joint allows 80° of flexion and 65° of extension from anatomical position.

Joint Degrees of Freedom

A joint's capability to move can be classified by how many of the three axes it can rotate around:

> **uniaxial** = 1 axis,
> **biaxial** = 2 axes,
> **triaxial** = all 3 axes

More axes mean the joint has more action pairs available and therefore more movement options.

Flexion & Extension pair = one axis
Abduction & Adduction pair = a second axis
Rotation pair = a third axis

So, for the six joint types (shown on page 15)....

1. A Ball and Socket is a triaxial joint: It does all three of the above action pairs.

2. A Pivot is a uniaxial joint: It does only rotation.

3. A Hinge is a uniaxial joint: It does only flexion/extension.

4. An Ellipsoid (or condyloid) is a biaxial joint: It does flexion/extension & abduction/adduction.

5. A Gliding is a non-axial joint: It does small gliding movements, not moving about an axis.

6. A Saddle is a biaxial+ joint: It does flexion/extension, abduction/adduction, and a limited form of rotation.

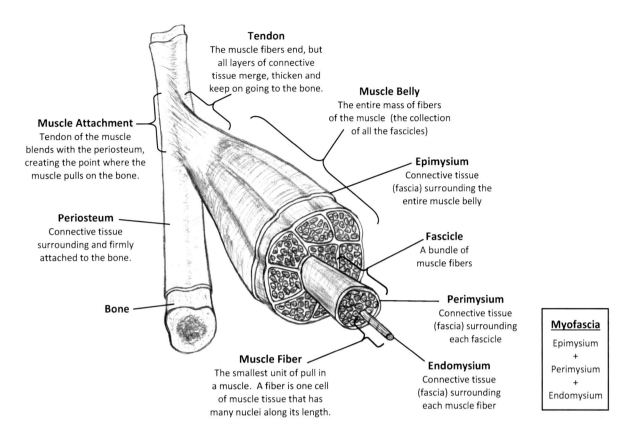

Tendon
The muscle fibers end, but all layers of connective tissue merge, thicken and keep on going to the bone.

Muscle Attachment
Tendon of the muscle blends with the periosteum, creating the point where the muscle pulls on the bone.

Periosteum
Connective tissue surrounding and firmly attached to the bone.

Bone

Muscle Belly
The entire mass of fibers of the muscle (the collection of all the fascicles)

Epimysium
Connective tissue (fascia) surrounding the entire muscle belly

Fascicle
A bundle of muscle fibers

Perimysium
Connective tissue (fascia) surrounding each fascicle

Muscle Fiber
The smallest unit of pull in a muscle. A fiber is one cell of muscle tissue that has many nuclei along its length.

Endomysium
Connective tissue (fascia) surrounding each muscle fiber

Myofascia
Epimysium
+
Perimysium
+
Endomysium

Anatomy of a Typical Skeletal Muscle

Muscular System – The Muscles

Anatomy and Function

The figure above shows the anatomical components of a typical skeletal muscle. In addition to the bundles of muscle fibers and layers of **myofascia**, each muscle has a rich supply of blood vessels and nerves. The muscle belly has a striated look and feel due to the muscle fibers being lined up with each other. Most muscle fibers run the entire length of the belly from tendon to tendon. Different arrangements of fibers directly affect the strength of pull, range of motion, and speed of movement created when the muscle contracts (discussed on the next page).

When relaxed, the muscle feels soft and has a neutral length and girth. When stimulated by the nervous system, the muscle contracts and the muscle belly feels firm/hard. If the bones are moveable, the muscle becomes shorter and thicker as it moves the bones closer together. Conversely, when stretched beyond the resting (neutral) state by an outside force, the muscle gets longer and thinner and develops a taut feel.

The **force-length relationship** specifies that muscles generate the greatest force when at their resting (mid-range) length, and are weaker when substantially shortened or lengthened. This is discussed further on page 33.

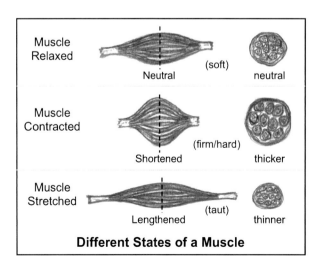

Muscle Relaxed — Neutral (soft) — neutral

Muscle Contracted — Shortened (firm/hard) — thicker

Muscle Stretched — Lengthened (taut) — thinner

Different States of a Muscle

Line of Pull

Generally, a muscle attaches to two bones and crosses the joint between those two bones (note, however, that there are many exceptions to this). The direction of the muscle fibers delineates a **line of pull** between the bones. When the muscle contracts, the bone that is more moveable moves toward the bone that is more stable and the joint rotates through an angle. If both bones are moveable, they move toward each other.

It is usually possible to visualize what body movements (actions) a muscle will create. First, observe the shape and fiber direction of the muscle and the points where its tendons attach to the bones. This creates a line of pull on the bones. Next, look where that line of pull is positioned relative to the joint between the bones. Finally, visualize how the bones will move around the joint when the line of pull shortens. Knowing the type of joint (see page 15) helps you know which actions are allowed.

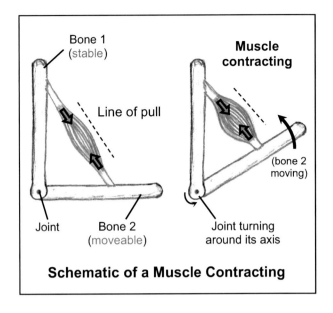

Schematic of a Muscle Contracting

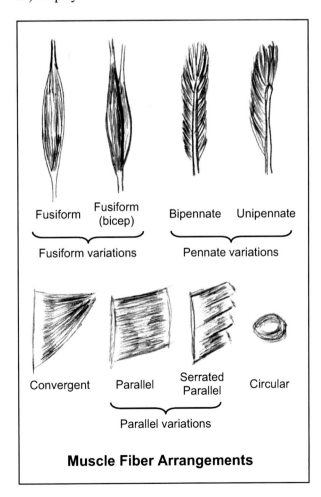

Muscle Fiber Arrangements

Fiber Arrangements

The arrangement of the muscle fibers has a direct influence on how a muscle pulls on its attached bones. Speed of movement, range of movement, strength of pull, and direction(s) of pull are all related to the fiber lengths and angles, as well as the number of fibers pulling together (more fibers = more strength). Here are the major categories:

1. **Fusiform** – Long fibers closing to a narrow tendon at each end. Can create long range and high speed of movement.

2. **Pennate** – Many short fibers connecting at oblique angle to a central tendon (creating a feather-like look). Has lots of fibers so is good for strength, but fibers are short so range is smaller.

3. **Convergent** – Narrow attachment one end, broad attachment other end. This creates a varying angle of pull, so different regions of fibers can create different actions.

4. **Parallel** – Wide with all parallel fibers; all fibers pull in the same direction. These muscles can be thin with fewer fibers or thick with more fibers (and therefore more strength).

5. **Circular** – Fibers squeeze in to close an opening.

Tendons and Attachments

The tendon portion of a muscle can have many shapes: narrow, broad, thick, thin, long, short, nonexistent. Here are some possibilities:

- Tendons at the two ends of a fusiform muscle attaching to a single point on each bone it pulls.

- Long tendon where space is limited. The muscle belly is far away from the bone attachment where the pulling force occurs. Long tendons going through narrow spaces usually travel in **synovial sheaths** to facilitate easy sliding.

- Tendon goes around a bend to reach the bone where it attaches, often gaining a "pulley" advantage by changing the direction from which it pulls on the bone.

- Muscle attaches to broad area on a bone. Little or no tendon portion; the fascia of the muscle fascicles blends right into the periosteum.

- Elongated, oblong, odd shaped area on a bone, or multiple bones.

- Attachment to interosseus membrane between two bones.

- Attachment to another muscle via fascia or aponeurosis. An **aponeurosis** is a broad, flat tendon that covers a relatively large area on the body.

With few exceptions, each muscle attaches (via its tendons) directly to the bones it moves. When a bone has several muscles attaching to it, the attachment sites fit together like puzzle pieces so each muscle has its own point where it pulls on the bone. See page 85 for an example showing the scapula and humerus attachments.

Muscles and Opposing Movements

For each action created by a muscle acting on a joint, there is an opposite action created by a muscle pulling on the joint from the opposite side of the body part. This was described as an **action pair** on page 6. The figure below uses the actions at the elbow joint of the biceps brachii and the opposing triceps brachii to illustrate this concept.

When the biceps brachii contracts it moves the forearm in flexion at the elbow. Meanwhile the triceps must relax and become longer to accommodate the action.

Conversely, when the triceps brachii contracts it creates extension at the elbow (the opposite action to flexion). To allow this, the biceps must relax and become longer.

The nervous system naturally helps this process by reflexively inhibiting a muscle from contracting if its opponent is being stimulated to contract (this is called **reciprocal inhibition**).

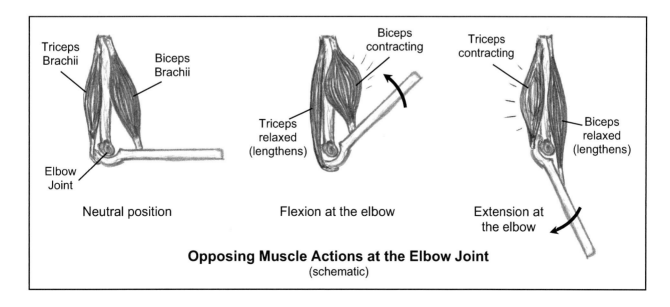

Opposing Muscle Actions at the Elbow Joint
(schematic)

Nervous System – The Nerves

This section gives a brief description of the nervous system as it relates to muscles and movement. The nervous system in its entirety is quite complex, and it is beyond the scope of this book to cover most of its features. Please refer to any good anatomy & physiology textbook for more complete information. To help understand this section, please preview the bony landmarks on pages 43-45.

The goal of this section is to give you an overview of how the nervous system is organized as it relates to the workings of skeletal muscles and the movements they create. Additionally, this section will define the terminology that is used in the "Innervation" portions of the B tables in Chapters 4, 5, and 6 ("B" tables are described on page 62). This terminology is also used in the Innervation Summary Table S-4 in Chapter 7.

Overall Organization

The human nervous system is divided into the **central nervous system**, which includes the brain and spinal cord, and the **peripheral nervous system**, which includes the nerves that carry signals to and from all the parts of the body. For the study of kinesiology, we are primarily interested in the nerves that activate muscles and cause movement (**motor nerves**). However, sensory nerves also play an important role, both in giving reasons for the body to want to move, and in providing feedback as a movement is in progress.

To understand where the nerves come from that activate muscles, we are interested in the brain stem and the spinal cord. The **brain stem** resides inside the cranial vault along with the rest of the brain. At its inferior end it becomes the **spinal cord** which passes through the foramen magnum at the base of the skull and travels down through the vertebral column.

Level by level down the vertebral column, groups of nerves emerge from each side of the spinal cord. At each space between two vertebrae, the nerves bundle together into **spinal nerve roots**, exit bilaterally from the vertebral column, and go out into the body. At the point of exit the nerves become part of the peripheral nervous system.

The figure at left illustrates the naming scheme used to identify nerve roots. The **cranial nerves**, which arise from the brain stem, are numbered with roman numerals I-XII, and the spinal nerve roots are numbered using vertebra-related identifiers C1-C8, T1-T12, L1-L5, and S1-S5.

Brain Stem

Foramen Magnum

C1

C7

T1

T12

L1

L5

Cranial Nerves

Cr. I–XII, arise from brain stem and exit through foramen in base of skull

Cervical Spinal Nerves

C1, exits above vertebra C1
C2-C8, exit below vertebrae C1-C7

Thoracic Spinal Nerves

T1-T12, exit below vertebrae T1-T12

Lumbar Spinal Nerves

L1-L5, exit below vertebrae L1-L5

Sacral Spinal Nerves

S1-S5, exit through foramen in the sacrum

Numbering of Cranial and Spinal Nerve Roots

Spinal Nerve Roots and Rami

The spinal cord passes down the vertebral column inside the **spinal canal** (also called the **vertebral canal**), which is created by the lined-up vertebral foramen of the vertebrae. At each place where two adjacent vertebrae meet, a side channel is created which allows nerves near that level to emerge from the spinal canal and go out into the body.

Intervertebral Foramen

The side-exit opening is called the **intervertebral foramen**, and it is formed by the meeting of the archways of the pedicle portions of the vertebrae above and below. Note that movements of the spine, such as flexion/extension, right/left rotation and lateral flexion, cause the shape of the intervertebral foramen to change as the pedicles of adjacent vertebrae move relative to each other. This, plus distortions in the discs, creates a dynamic environment of pressures and strains on the nerve roots.

Anatomy of Nerve Roots

At each segmental level several nerve roots arise from the anterior and posterior aspects of the spinal cord, wrap around laterally, and bundle into a single spinal nerve root on each side. The anterior roots contain motor nerves sending impulses out to the body, and the posterior roots contain sensory nerves bringing sensory signals from the body in to the spinal cord and up to the brain.

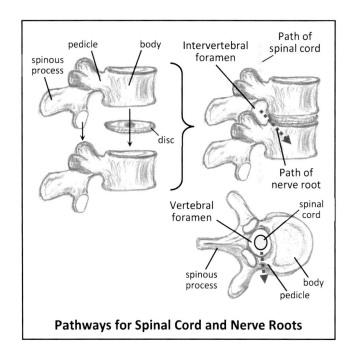

Pathways for Spinal Cord and Nerve Roots

Shortly after a spinal nerve root exits from the vertebral column, it begins branching to take nerves to different places out in the body. The initial split divides the root into two **primary rami** (branches). The **dorsal ramus** is smaller and carries nerves directly to the skin and muscles of the back. The **ventral ramus** is much larger because it contains more nerves to supply the relatively larger portion of the body that is anterior to the spine.

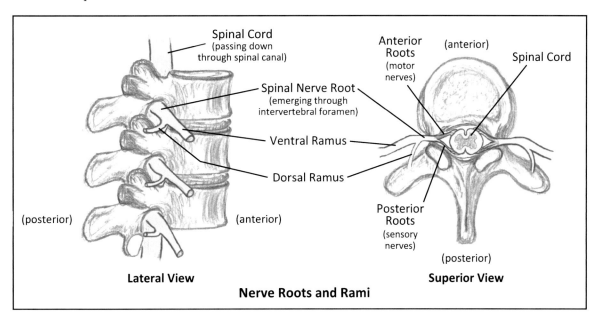

Lateral View   **Superior View**
Nerve Roots and Rami

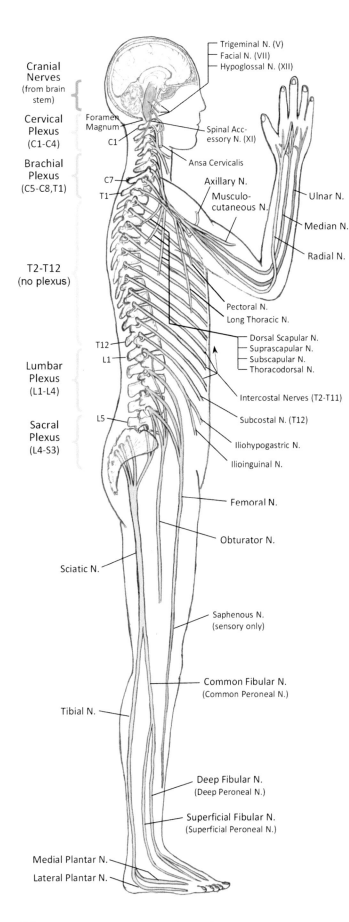

Cranial
Nerves
(from brain
stem)

Cervical
Plexus
(C1-C4)

Brachial
Plexus
(C5-C8,T1)

T2-T12
(no plexus)

Lumbar
Plexus
(L1-L4)

Sacral
Plexus
(L4-S3)

Foramen
Magnum

C1

C7

T1

T12

L1

L5

Sciatic N.

Tibial N.

Medial Plantar N.
Lateral Plantar N.

Trigeminal N. (V)
Facial N. (VII)
Hypoglossal N. (XII)

Spinal Acc-
essory N. (XI)

Ansa Cervicalis

Axillary N.
Musculo-
cutaneous N.

Ulnar N.

Median N.

Radial N.

Pectoral N.
Long Thoracic N.

Dorsal Scapular N.
Suprascapular N.
Subscapular N.
Thoracodorsal N.

Intercostal Nerves (T2-T11)

Subcostal N. (T12)

Iliohypogastric N.

Ilioinguinal N.

Femoral N.

Obturator N.

Saphenous N.
(sensory only)

Common Fibular N.
(Common Peroneal N.)

Deep Fibular N.
(Deep Peroneal N.)

Superficial Fibular N.
(Superficial Peroneal N.)

Nerve Plexuses and Naming of Major Nerves

This section completes the description of how the nervous system is organized as it relates to muscles and movement.

Plexuses

The ventral rami of spinal nerves (except for thoracic nerves T2-T12) cross-connect and mingle within their regions to create braid-like collections of nerves called **plexuses**. Each plexus supplies specific regions of the body, as seen in the illustration at left.

Nerve Plexuses

Plexus	Description
Cervical Plexus	Originates from segments C1-C4 and supplies muscles of the neck, upper shoulders, and diaphragm.
Brachial Plexus	Originates from segments C5-C8 and T1 and supplies muscles that move the shoulder girdle, upper limb, lower neck.
Lumbar Plexus	Originates from segments L1-L4 and supplies muscles of lower abdomen, anterior, medial and lateral aspects of the thigh.
Sacral Plexus	Originates from segments L4-L5 and S1-S3 and supplies the buttocks, perineum, posterior thighs, legs, and feet.

Note that the term **lumbosacral plexus** is often used to refer to the lumbar and sacral plexuses combined. Also note that nerve roots T2-T12 do not form a plexus. They individually travel out along the line of each rib.

Names of Major Nerves

Major nerves that carry multiple nerve bundles to specific body areas have names that help identify where they reside in the body. These major nerves are labeled in the illustration at left (Femoral N., etc.). The names are used when specifying the innervation of muscles. Many of the major nerves contain nerve bundles that arise from multiple spinal segments due to the cross linking that occurs in plexuses.

Dermatomes

A dermatome is an area of skin that is supplied by a single spinal segment. Skin sensations can be used to assess spinal nerves (see page 212).

How Nerves Work With Muscles

The main function of skeletal muscles is to contract and create movement by pulling on bones or other structures. Muscles only contract when they are stimulated by the **motor nerves** that supply them. Nerve impulses can be sent by the willful control of the brain to accomplish a desired movement (for example, to pick up a book), or by reflex actions that loop back directly from the spinal cord (for example, to jerk away from a flame when sensory receptors sense skin is getting burned).

Innervation

Each muscle of the body is activated by impulses from one or more motor nerves. The set of nerves that control a muscle are called its **innervation**. For example, the rectus femoris muscle is supplied by branches of the femoral nerve.

Motor nerves come from nerve roots that exit from the spine at one or more spinal segments. Also, some motor nerves come from cranial nerves. Therefore a more complete way to specify the innervation of a muscle is to give both its major nerve name and the spinal segments where the nerve originates. To complete the above example: the rectus femoris muscle's innervation is the femoral nerve originating from spinal segments L2, L3, and L4.

Knowing which muscles are innervated from a specific spinal segment can be used to assess nerve root pathology at that segment. A **myotome** is defined as the group of *muscles* that are served by a single spinal nerve root. The muscles can be tested for weakness (or paralysis) to see if the nerve root at that segment is compressed or damaged. Some useful myotome tests are described on page 34.

Motor Units

Each muscle fiber within a muscle has a branch of a motor axon from the nervous system connected to it. When the brain sends a nerve impulse down the motor axon, the muscle fiber reacts by trying to make itself shorter in length. This shortening force is called a **contraction**, and a muscle fiber contracts fully whenever it is stimulated. Each contraction is "all-or-none", meaning there are no gradations of strength of pull in any one muscle fiber.

A single motor axon divides into many small branches when it arrives at the muscle belly, and each small branch then connects to a single muscle fiber. Thus, the firing of one axon causes a number of fibers to contract. The fibers are typically *not* adjacent to each other. One motor nerve axon, its small branches, and the set of connected muscle fibers is called a **motor unit**.

Each motor unit creates a specific amount of pulling force based on the number of fibers contained in the motor unit (more fibers = more force). To gain more pulling force, the brain **recruits** more muscle fibers by firing the motor axons that connect to additional motor units.

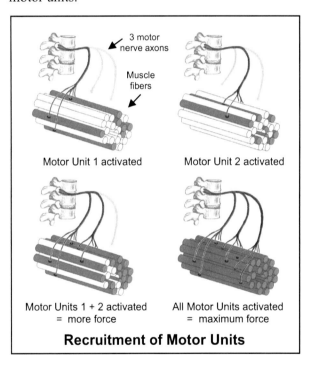

Recruitment of Motor Units

In addition to the motor nerves described above, **sensory nerves** also play an important role by providing feedback as a movement is in progress. Somatosensory nerves sense body movement and position in space (**proprioception**) and perceive such things as heat, pressure and pain. Additional information is gathered from the vestibular system, and from special senses such as sight and hearing. The brain continuously integrates all of the above information in order to orchestrate and continuously modify appropriate combinations of muscle contractions.

Fascial System – Separation, Connection, Integration

Previous sections have described the four anatomical systems of the body that most relate to the study of kinesiology and musculoskeletal anatomy: skeletal, articular, muscular and nervous systems. This section adds a brief introduction to **fascia**, a fifth system that ties it all together.

While traditionally not considered by anatomists to be a separate body system, fascia is now considered by many to be a system in its own right. During the past couple of decades, fascia has been the subject of an abundance of in-depth study as its features and utility have become more appreciated. It is beyond the scope of this book to delve into all the ways that fascia is important, but this section introduces some of the features of fascia as it relates to the study of muscles and movement.

Description

Fascia is a specific form of connective tissue that is made up of three main components: collagen, elastin and ground substance. Collagen fibers provide strength and resilience, elastin fibers add flexibility and elasticity, and ground substance is the fluid supporting environment.

It is called fascia because it forms thin sheets of tissue that cover body structures at all levels from major structures like muscle bellies and organs down to individual muscle and nerve fibers. Recent research has shown that fascial fibers even permeate into individual cells.

Fascia begins forming early in embryonic development and its formation guides, differentiates and interconnects the assembly of the developing body structures in the embryo. By the time a baby is born it has a full fascial system throughout its body. Throughout life, fascia guides and adapts as it supports the essential integrity of the body and all its parts. It is also essential for healing tissue injury, which can create scarring and other restrictions.

Types

Superficial Fascia: The dual layer hypodermis that anchors the skin to the underlying structures. It stores fat and water and creates passageways for nerves and vessels. In a few places it has muscles embedded within it, such as the platysma.

Deep Fascia: Traditionally, this term referred to the fascia surrounding and investing into muscles. More recently this term has been expanded to describe the interconnected network of fascia that exists throughout all body structures within the envelope of the superficial fascia.

Myofascia: The muscle-related subset of the deep fascia (described on page 19) which extends into tendons, aponeuroses, periosteum, and interfaces to ligaments and joint capsules.

Neurofascia: Meningeal layers surround the brain, spinal cord and proximal portion of spinal nerve roots, then at those nerve roots merge to become the neurofascia of the peripheral nervous system.

Visceral fascia and membranes: Contain and separate organs and vessels, and attach to the inner aspects of bones and innermost myofascial layers.

Separation

Fascia separates body structures from one another. It provides interfaces between structures that keep them in their own place while allowing structures to slide past each other as the body moves. This creates a dynamic stability for not only muscles vs neighboring muscles, but all tissues and structures that reside in close proximity to each other within the body.

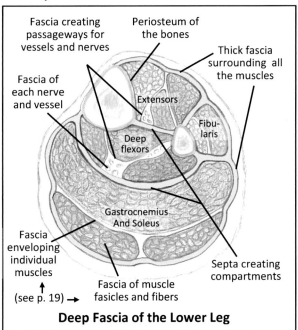

Fascia creating passageways for vessels and nerves

Periosteum of the bones

Thick fascia surrounding all the muscles

Fascia of each nerve and vessel

Extensors

Fibularis

Deep flexors

Fascia enveloping individual muscles

Gastrocnemius And Soleus

Septa creating compartments

(see p. 19) → Fascia of muscle fasicles and fibers

Deep Fascia of the Lower Leg

Connection

Fascia forms an interconnected tensional network that adapts its fiber arrangement and density according to local tensional demands. This section discusses two important functions of this network as they relate to muscles and movement.

Myofascial chains are groups of muscles and fascia that are linked through distinct fascial lines of connection. These lines travel through myofascia, tendons, joint capsules, ligaments, and periosteum of bones. Thus, muscles never really act in isolation. When a muscle contracts to pull on bones and create movement (or simply holds chronic tension), it also creates longer lines of tension through chains of myofascia. The figure below demonstrates two of these chains as described by Thomas Myers in his book *Anatomy Trains*[23].

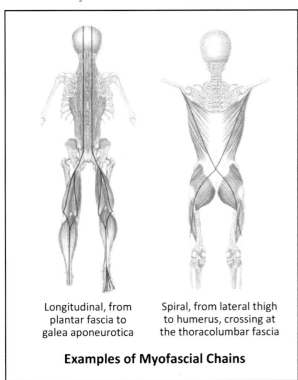

Longitudinal, from plantar fascia to galea aponeurotica

Spiral, from lateral thigh to humerus, crossing at the thoracolumbar fascia

Examples of Myofascial Chains

Myofascial chains have various functional implications, such as,

- Longitudinal and spiral chains create pathways for the mechanical communication of tension and compression. For example, in the longitudinal figure above, a restriction in the plantar fascia could influence such things as neck tension or headaches.

- Longitudinal and spiral chains facilitate a system of stretch and recoil of the fascia that greatly assists the efficiency and force transmission of muscle contractions during such activities as walking or throwing a ball. For example, observe the spiral line in the figure. During walking or running, the forward swing of an arm along with the contralateral leg pre-loads oblique tension into the lumbar fascia, which then via recoil assists the forward propulsion created when those limbs subsequently pull backward as a step is taken.

Integration

Fascia envelops and permeates all physical structures, forming a continuous "web" throughout the body. This creates the potential for direct mechanical communication between all body parts. Mechanical distortion information is transmitted much faster than nerve communication coming from, say, pressure or stretch receptors.

Fascia supports a body-wide system of **tensegrity** that adds a buoyant structural support from within, reducing the compressive load on the body from gravity and other forces.

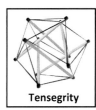

Tensegrity

Fascia is the brain's largest source of proprioceptive information, enhancing body-wide coordination.

Fascia is able to move and shape itself via smooth muscle fibers embedded within its matrix of collagen, elastin and ground substance (controlled via the autonomic nervous system).

Fascia defines conduits for blood and lymph vessels and nerve trunks, so restrictions in fascia can challenge the functioning of these structures.

Fascial pathologies come from trauma (physical or emotional), inflammation, or immobilization from postural issues and chronic tension/guarding.

Fascia References

To further explore fascia, refer to the following resources in the Bibliography on page 231: ref. # 2 (chapter 8), 10, 14, 15, 23, and 35.

Kinesiology Concepts

When muscles contract they, simply stated, shorten in the line of the fibers. This creates a pulling force at both ends of the muscle where it attaches to bone. Usually one end is attached to a more stable bone, so the other (more moveable) bone moves. Sometimes both bones are free, so they move toward each other.

Movement and Levers

1. Muscles pull bones around a joint (an axis for the movement passes through the joint).

2. Movement occurs by the opening, closing, rotating, and gliding of bones at the joints.

3. The bones act as **Levers,** and the muscles attach to and pull on these levers.

A leverage unit is made up of a lever (the bone) with an associated fulcrum, resistance, and effort.

F̲ Fulcrum = The joint connecting the two bones

R̲ Resistance = The load to be lifted or moved

E̲ Effort = The muscle pulling at attachment point

- **First-class lever –**
    - Joint (fulcrum) is between muscle and load.
    - Examples: Seesaw = balance, pry bar = power
    - For balance, as used in the body.

- **Second-class lever –**
    - Load (resistance) is between joint and muscle.
    - Example: Wheelbarrow
    - For power, with small range of motion.

- **Third-class lever –**
    - Muscle (effort) is between joint and load.
    - Examples: Shoveling, paddling a canoe
    - For speed and large range of motion (in the body, the point where the muscle pulls is near the joint).

        Third-class are by far the most common levers in the body.

A mnemonic that may help you remember the three levers is to name what is in the middle:

    Class 1, 2, 3 = F R E

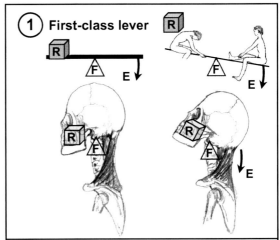

① First-class lever

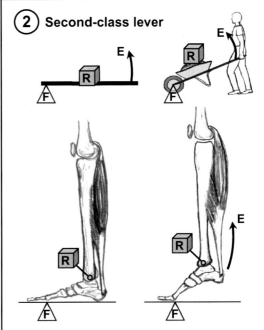

② Second-class lever

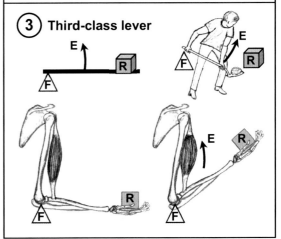

③ Third-class lever

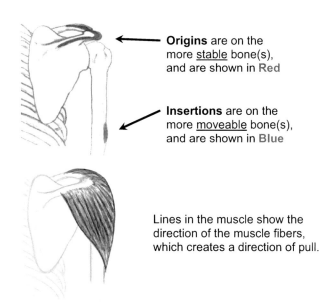

Origins are on the more <u>stable</u> bone(s), and are shown in Red

Insertions are on the more <u>moveable</u> bone(s), and are shown in Blue

Lines in the muscle show the direction of the muscle fibers, which creates a direction of pull.

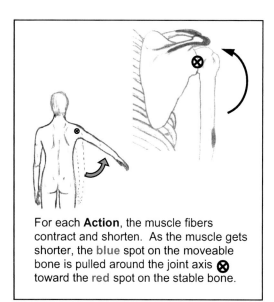

For each **Action**, the muscle fibers contract and shorten. As the muscle gets shorter, the blue spot on the moveable bone is pulled around the joint axis ⊗ toward the red spot on the stable bone.

Origin, Insertion and Action of the Deltoid Muscle

Functional Naming of Muscle Attachments

Muscle **Origin:** The muscle attachment to the more stable bone is called the *origin*. The origin is usually the more proximal attachment on a limb. On the axial skeleton, the origin is often the more inferior or more medial attachment, but there are many exceptions to this.

Muscle **Insertion:** The attachment to the more moveable bone is called the *insertion*. The insertion is usually the more distal attachment on a limb.

Muscle **Action:** The movements that the muscle creates when it contracts and shortens are called its *actions*. Actions occur at the joint (or joints) that exist between the bone of origin and the bone of insertion.

Origins and insertions are shown in red and blue on bone drawings in Chapters 4-6. Knowing the origin vs. insertion can help you visualize the basic action of a muscle when it contracts.

"Reversed O/I" Muscle Action

The origin, insertion, and action for a muscle are defined based on which bone moves when doing "normal" activities. In many cases, there are ways that the so-called "more moveable" bone can be stabilized, which makes the so-called "more stable" bone then become the moveable one. In that case we do *not* rename the origin and insertion, but instead simply refer to the action as a **reversed O/I action**.

The naming of Origin vs. Insertion are based on:

1. The "usual" movement created by the muscle
2. When moving from anatomical position
3. Usually an open chain movement (see page. 34)

"Reversed O/I" Use of the Muscle:

The stable vs. moveable bones swap roles:

- The origin bone becomes moveable while the insertion bone is held stable.
- In this case, we do <u>not</u> rename the origin and insertion – we simply say the muscle is being used in a "Reversed O/I" way.
- Usually a closed chain movement (see p. 34)

Flexion at the Hip Joint

"Usual" Action:
The Femur Moves

"Reverse O/I" Action:
The Trunk Moves

(Femur held stable)

Types of Muscle Contractions

There are three categories of muscle contractions – isotonic, isometric and tonic – with an important subdivision for isotonic contractions. Note that a muscle *contracting* means that the muscle fibers are actively "trying" to shorten because they are being stimulated by the motor nerves connected to them. How the bones actually move (or sometimes don't move), depends on what type of external forces are affecting the bones at the time.

1. Isotonic – The muscle is contracting (actively working) and the bones are *moving*. Just the fact that the bones move makes a contraction isotonic, regardless of which direction they are moving. There are two types of isotonic contractions, concentric and eccentric:

- **Concentric contraction** – *Creates* a movement, which is the action of the muscle. The muscle is working and is getting shorter, moving the bones toward each other.

  (also called active shortening)

- **Eccentric contraction** – *Controls* or slows down a movement that is going in the opposite direction of the action of the muscle. The muscle is working, but is getting longer while working because the opposing force is greater than the pulling force of the muscle.

  (also called a lengthening contraction)

2. Isometric – The muscle is contracting but the bones are *not moving*. No movement occurs either because the muscle force exactly matches the resistance (e.g., when holding a book motionless out in front of you), or because the muscle cannot overcome a stable object (e.g., pushing against a wall or trying to lift a 1000-pound weight off the ground).

3. Tonic – Sustained small sequencing contractions are occurring when the muscle is at rest, or is holding posture.

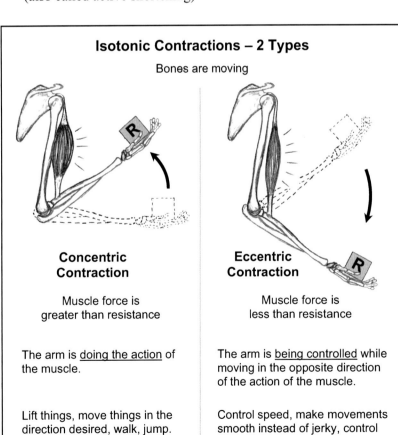

Isotonic Contractions – 2 Types

Bones are moving

Concentric Contraction

Muscle force is greater than resistance

The arm is doing the action of the muscle.

Lift things, move things in the direction desired, walk, jump.

Eccentric Contraction

Muscle force is less than resistance

The arm is being controlled while moving in the opposite direction of the action of the muscle.

Control speed, make movements smooth instead of jerky, control descent caused by gravity.

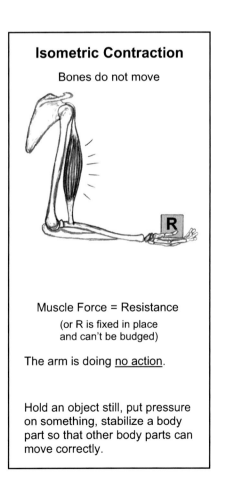

Isometric Contraction

Bones do not move

Muscle Force = Resistance

(or R is fixed in place and can't be budged)

The arm is doing no action.

Hold an object still, put pressure on something, stabilize a body part so that other body parts can move correctly.

Roles Muscles Play When Working Together

There are several roles a muscle can play when moving a part of the body in a given direction. Sometimes the muscle can be the main driving force of the action, and sometimes the muscle can play a supporting role such as stabilizing another part of the body, helping the action, or slowing down or controlling the smoothness of the action. Here are some roles that muscles can play:

Agonist

The main muscle(s) creating a desired action. Sometimes called "prime mover". There can be more than one agonist for a given action at a specific joint.

Antagonist

Opposes the action of the agonist, thus restricting or controlling the speed and smoothness of the movement. Must relax to allow agonist to shorten.

Synergist

Helps the agonist(s) with a desired movement.

- *Assist*: Helps with the movement, but with a weaker contribution than the agonist.

- *May assist*: Small contribution to the movement; only active when really needed, or only when certain bone angles make it useful.

- Note: The word *synergist* is also used to indicate <u>all</u> the muscles that contribute directly to a given action at a given joint, as in, "Name all the synergists that create flexion at the elbow."

Stabilizer

Stabilizes against unwanted movements, holding one part of the body steady while another part moves. For example, muscles stabilizing the scapula so the arm can move independently. Muscles that are stabilizing are also called *fixators*.

Neutralizer

Counteracts unwanted movements of a body part while it is moving. Involved in coordination, fine tuning the direction of a movement. For example, while hip flexor muscles are moving the thigh anteriorly, the adductor and abductor muscles keep the movement from drifting laterally or medially, respectively.

Using the Above Terms in Practice

Naming the synergists and antagonists for a muscle can only be done in the context of a *specific* action of that muscle at a specific joint. For example, biceps brachii is a synergist with brachialis in the action of *flexion* at the elbow joint, but biceps brachii is a synergist with supinator in the action of *supination* at the radioulnar joint (see page 96).

Also, notice that the agonists and antagonists trade roles for the two opposing movements of any action pair (action pairs are defined on page 6).

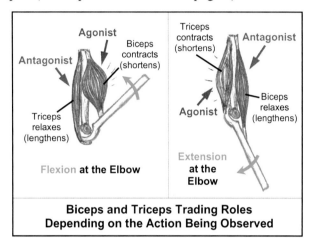

Biceps and Triceps Trading Roles Depending on the Action Being Observed

Biomechanics

Many mechanical factors are involved when a muscle contracts, affecting the way the bones move, the strength of the pulling force, the speed of the movement, and effects and stresses on other parts of the body. Analyzing these many factors is called the study of **biomechanics**. Biomechanical analysis is beyond the scope of this basic text, but as you learn the muscles and actions in this book you will be naturally applying many of the concepts that are formally organized in the field of biomechanics.

A few of the concepts involved are:

- Angle of pull of a muscle on a bone, or combined angles of pull of multiple muscles on a bone.

- Mechanical advantage created by position of muscle attachment in relation to the joint axis.

- Relationships changing as a joint moves through its range of motion.

- Working with gravity: Stability, equilibrium, balance, lifting objects or body parts.

Range of Motion – Applications and Procedures

Range of motion (ROM) was introduced earlier in this chapter on page 18. This section will expand on that subject and introduce additional terminology related to muscles and movement.

Uses of ROM

Moving parts of the body while considering range of motion is a useful practice in many situations. Movements can employ the full range or can involve a smaller distance within the range.

- For assessment – Use movement to test the client's body for capabilities and/or pathologies.

- For identification – Use movement while palpating to locate bony landmarks, specific muscles, and other body structures. Or, use resisted movement to engage a muscle to make it stand out from its neighboring structures.

- For treatment – Move the client's body parts as a component of a treatment technique.

- For safety – Having a clear knowledge of the movement capabilities of each body structure, or chain of structures, allows the practitioner to assess and treat a client without causing harm.

Approach

What you are thinking about and observing while applying ROM concepts determines the procedures used, the information gathered, and the therapeutic effects achieved. The following sections discuss different approaches and the associated ROM procedures.

ROM Focusing on a Joint

One of the simplest ways to use ROM is to assess the movement capabilities of a joint. This was described earlier in this chapter on page 18.

Applying ROM for a joint is done using passive movement. The practitioner moves the client's body parts in ways that take the two connecting bones through the anatomical movements (actions) that are allowed by the structure of the joint and its surrounding structures. Movement may be limited by the shape of abutting portions of bones, joint capsule, ligaments, or other soft tissue structures of the joint. Generally, joint ROM is assessed in only one plane of motion at a time.

ROM Focusing on a Muscle

When focusing on the structure and function of a muscle, more complex dimensions come into play. The following examples require that you have selected a specific muscle you wish to assess, treat, strengthen, or stretch.

Shortening a muscle, i.e., the bones are moving in a way that brings the bony attachments of the muscle closer together. This means you are performing the action of the muscle. For a muscle that has multiple actions, you can isolate one action or choose a motion that combines multiple actions.

Active Shortening – You instruct your client and they perform the movement using the muscle of interest.

Passive Shortening – The client relaxes while you move their body parts.

Resisted Shortening – The client actively contracts their muscle while you provide resistance. For the muscle to shorten, they must "win" the tug-of-war, thus creating an isotonic, concentric contraction. If their bones do not move, then an isometric contraction is created.

Lengthening a muscle, i.e., moving the bones to pull its bony attachments further apart from each other. This means you are performing the *opposite* of the action(s) of the muscle.

Active Lengthening – You instruct your client to do a movement that is the opposite of the muscle's action (they will be using the antagonist muscle), so the muscle of interest gets longer.

Passive Lengthening – You move the client's body parts in a way that makes the muscle belly longer. Sometimes the movement is well within their range of motion, and sometimes you may want to lengthen the muscle to the end of its range, i.e., stretch it, and possibly assess the end-feel.

Resisted Lengthening – The client actively contracts against your resistance, but you "win" the tug-of-war. This creates an isotonic, eccentric contraction of the muscle.

Using ROM with Multiple-Joint Muscles

When working with a muscle that crosses more than one joint, additional mechanics must be considered while shortening or lengthening that muscle.

Shortening
When a muscle shortens, it will create actions at *all* the joints it crosses (unless other muscles or forces inhibit action at some of the joints). For example, the biceps brachii creates both flexion at the elbow and supination of the forearm at the radioulnar joint. So, performing both elbow flexion and forearm supination at the same time will more fully shorten the biceps brachii. This is the classic pose of someone showing off their bulging biceps. Holding that pose and then pronating the forearm (turning the palm facing away) distinctly reduces the biceps bulge as the pronation lengthens out the biceps muscle belly.

Active insufficiency
When contracting a muscle, it cannot get short enough to close all the joints to their full range at the same time. One joint must be "opened back up" to allow the other joints to close further.

Example- Trying to make a tight fist (full finger flexion) when the wrist is flexed is not possible because the finger flexor muscles cannot shorten enough to fully flex both the fingers and the wrist at the same time. Straightening out the wrist allows making a tighter fist, and extending the wrist a little affords an even tighter fist.

Lengthening
When being lengthened, movement at each of the joints crossed adds together to increase the lengthening of the muscle. For example, the semitendinosus (one of the hamstring muscles) creates both flexion at the knee and extension at the hip joint. So, performing the *reverse* actions of knee extension and hip flexion at the same time will more fully lengthen the semitendinosus than if, say, only knee extension is performed.

Passive insufficiency
When lengthening or stretching a muscle, all the joints crossed by the muscle cannot be opened to their full range at the same time (the muscle can't become long enough to allow it). One joint must be

"backed off" to allow the other joints to open further.

Example- Stretching the hamstring muscles is done using knee extension combined with hip flexion. If done with the knee in full extension, only a limited amount of hip flexion is possible. To allow more hip flexion to occur, the knee must be "backed off" from its full extension position.

Other Movement-Related Terminology

Force-length Relationship
In general, a muscle can create a stronger pulling force when it is in the middle portion of its range of movement. If its fibers are shortened down too far, the internal contractile components (myofilaments) are overlapped too much and are not lined up for efficient force generation. Conversely, if the fibers are lengthened out too far, the internal contractile components are not overlapped enough to create substantial force.

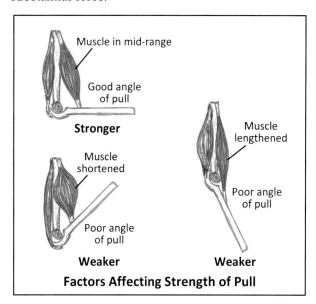

Factors Affecting Strength of Pull

Also, when a muscle is lengthened out, the joint is opened out, and the **angle of pull** on the bones may have reduced leverage and therefore a weaker force (see line of pull, page 20). Our brain learns to use the force-length relationship and the angle of pull to our advantage. When more strength is needed to accomplish the task at hand, we naturally adjust our body position to bring a muscle closer to its mid-range length and/or to improve the leverage afforded by the angle of pull.

Using ROM for Spinal Nerve Assessment

Testing muscles for weakness can be useful to assess for possible compression, damage, or other pathology of individual spinal nerve roots. **Myotomes** were briefly described earlier in this chapter on page 25. Resisted shortening ROM (page 32) is used for myotome-related assessment.

Many muscles are innervated by multiple nerve roots, so assessing a specific segmental root is somewhat of an art form. Practical experience over time has shown certain key muscle tests to be the most reliable for specific nerve roots. The following tables list some practical information from Donald Neumann's text *Kinesiology of the Musculoskeletal System* (bibliography ref. #28).

Testing Spinal Nerve Roots – Brachial Plexus

Root	Key Muscle	Movement to Resist for the Test
C5	Biceps brachii	Elbow flexion with forearm supinated
C5	Middle deltoid	Shoulder abduction
C6	Extensor carpi radialis longus	Wrist extension with radial deviation
C7	Triceps brachii	Elbow extension
C7	Extensor digitorum	Finger extension at MCP joint
C8	Flexor digitorum profundus	Finger flexion at DIP joint
T1	Dorsal and palmar interossei	Finger abduction and adduction

Testing Spinal Nerve Roots – Lumbosacral Plexus

Root	Key Muscle	Movement to Resist for the Test
L2	Iliopsoas	Hip flexion
L2	Adductor longus	Hip adduction
L3	Quadriceps	Knee extension
L4	Tibialis anterior	Ankle dorsiflexion
L5	Extensor digitorum longus	Toe extension
L5	Gluteus medius	Hip abduction
S1	Gluteus maximus	Hip extension with knee flexed
S1	Semitendinosus	Knee flexion and internal rotation
S2	Gastrocnemius and soleus	Ankle plantar flexion
S2	Flexor hallucis longus	Flexion of the big toe (hallux)
S3	Dorsal and plantar interossei	Toe abduction and adduction

Open Chain vs. Closed Chain Movements

An **open chain** movement is when the distal body part, usually the hand or foot, is free to move and not fixed to an object or the ground. With a **closed chain** movement, the distal part is fixed in place. Open vs. closed chain movements place different demands on the muscles and joints involved, as well as the roles other muscles play, such as stabilizing or neutralizing. An open-chain movement is

"simpler" and makes it easier to isolate the actions of a single muscle (see page 29). Closed-chain movements are more complex, involving multiple joints and muscles, but are the way muscles are frequently used in daily life.

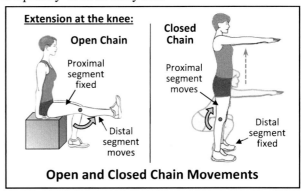

Open and Closed Chain Movements

Valgus and Varus

Valgus angulation and **varus angulation** are terms used to describe how adjacent bones in the arms and legs are lined up with each other in the frontal plane. The terms describe how the distal bone is angled relative to the proximal bone.

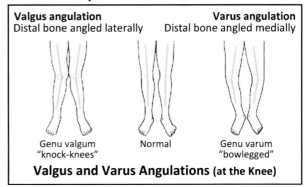

Valgus and Varus Angulations (at the Knee)

Since the two bones meet at a joint, **valgus force** and **varus force** describe stresses applied to joints. The terms valgus and varus are most frequently applied when observing angulations and forces at the elbow, wrist, fingers, knee, ankle, and toes.

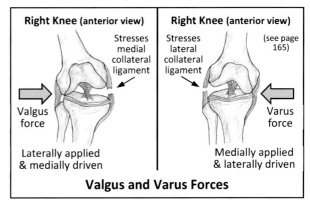

Valgus and Varus Forces

Bones, Bony Landmarks, Joints, and Ligaments

Introduction

Chapter 2 – Bones, Bony Landmarks, Joints, and Ligaments provides a central location in this book where all terminology on bones and joints is collected. This information is centralized in one location because you will need to refer to it frequently as you study the muscles in Chapters 4 through 6. This chapter includes an atlas of the **bones** of the body with **bony landmarks** labeled on them. Also included are full skeleton illustrations and tables and figures with summary information about **joints** and **ligaments**.

To fully learn the bones and bony landmarks, you should be able to recall the information from both **verbal** and **visual** directions. That is, when you *read* the name of a landmark you can visualize where it is on the bone, and conversely, when you *see* a place on a bone you can recall its bony landmark name.

Each page of bone drawings is arranged with the bones on one side of the page and a list of bone names, bony landmarks, and joints on the other side of the page. This arrangement allows you to cover the list of names to hide it, and then use the labels on the drawings to test yourself as you memorize the names. This facilitates learning the landmarks from a *visual* direction. To study the information from a *verbal* direction, you need the opposite arrangement. That is, remove the labels on the bone drawings, and then read each bony landmark name in the list and try to visualize where it is on the bone.

The Mastering Muscles & Movement support website (studymuscles.com) has downloadable pages of bony landmark drawings with labels removed to facilitate studying from both the visual and verbal directions.

Bones of the Human Body

Axial Skeleton	Appendicular Skeleton

Skull (22)
    Cranial Bones (8) –
        Frontal (1), Parietal (2),
        Temporal (2), Occiput (1),
        Sphenoid (1), Ethmoid (1)
 	
    Facial Bones (14) –
        Mandible (1), Zygomatic (2),
        Maxilla (2), Palatine (2),
        Nasal (2), Lacrimal (2),
        Vomer (1), Inferior Nasal Concha (2)
 	
Hyoid (1)
 	
Spine (26) –
    Cervical Vertebrae (7)
    Thoracic Vertebrae (12)
    Lumbar Vertebrae (5)
    Sacrum (5 V. fused)
    Coccyx (2-4 V. fused)
 	
Ribs (12 each side = 24) –
    7 true ribs (have direct connection to sternum)
    5 false ribs
        └ 3 connected to cartilage of rib 7
        └ 2 floating
 	
Sternum (1)
	Upper Extremity:
	Clavicle
	Scapula
	Humerus
	Ulna
	Radius
	Carpal bones (8) –
	        Scaphoid, Lunate, Triquetrum, Pisiform,
	        Trapezium, Trapezoid, Capitate, Hamate
	Metacarpal bones (5)
	Phalanges of the Hand (14) –
	        Digit #1 – Thumb (Pollux) has 2 phalanges
	        Digits #2-5 – Fingers, have 3 phalanges each
	Sesamoid bones of the hand
	
	Lower Extremity:
	Hip Bone (Ilium, Ischium and Pubis fused)
	Femur
	Patella
	Tibia
	Fibula
	Tarsal bones (7) –
	        Talus, Calcaneus, Cuboid,
	        Navicular, 1st, 2nd and 3rd Cuneiforms
	Metatarsal bones (5)
	Phalanges of the Foot (14) –
	        Digit #1 – Big toe (Hallux), has 2 phalanges
	        Digits #2-5 – Toes, have 3 phalanges each
	Sesamoid bones of the foot

The Skeletal System

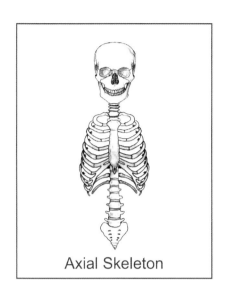

Axial Skeleton

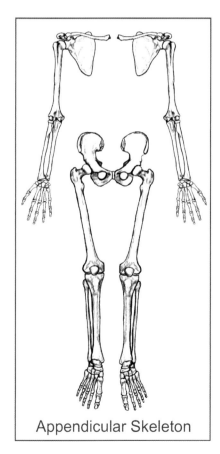

Appendicular Skeleton

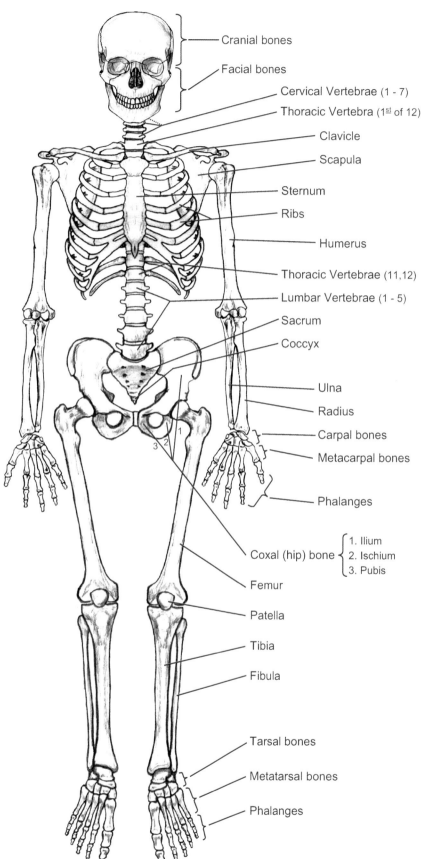

Cranial bones

Facial bones

Cervical Vertebrae (1 - 7)

Thoracic Vertebra (1st of 12)

Clavicle

Scapula

Sternum

Ribs

Humerus

Thoracic Vertebrae (11,12)

Lumbar Vertebrae (1 - 5)

Sacrum

Coccyx

Ulna

Radius

Carpal bones

Metacarpal bones

Phalanges

Coxal (hip) bone
1. Ilium
2. Ischium
3. Pubis

Femur

Patella

Tibia

Fibula

Tarsal bones

Metatarsal bones

Phalanges

The Skeletal System

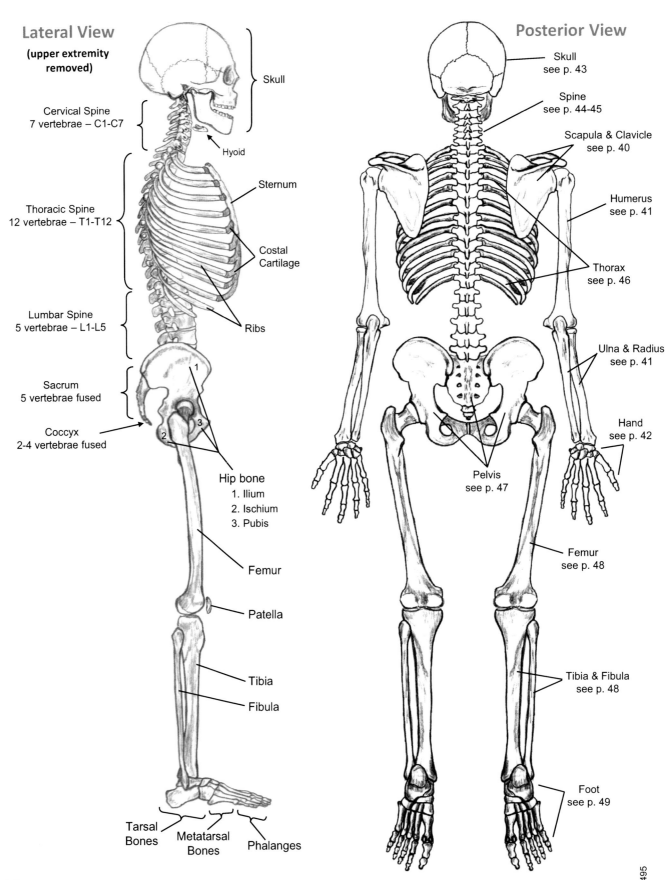

Lateral View
(upper extremity removed)

Skull

Cervical Spine
7 vertebrae – C1-C7

Hyoid

Sternum

Thoracic Spine
12 vertebrae – T1-T12

Costal
Cartilage

Lumbar Spine
5 vertebrae – L1-L5

Ribs

Sacrum
5 vertebrae fused

Coccyx
2-4 vertebrae fused

Hip bone
1. Ilium
2. Ischium
3. Pubis

Femur

Patella

Tibia

Fibula

Tarsal
Bones

Metatarsal
Bones

Phalanges

Posterior View

Skull
see p. 43

Spine
see p. 44-45

Scapula & Clavicle
see p. 40

Humerus
see p. 41

Thorax
see p. 46

Ulna & Radius
see p. 41

Hand
see p. 42

Pelvis
see p. 47

Femur
see p. 48

Tibia & Fibula
see p. 48

Foot
see p. 49

62495

Comparison of Bone and Joint Names

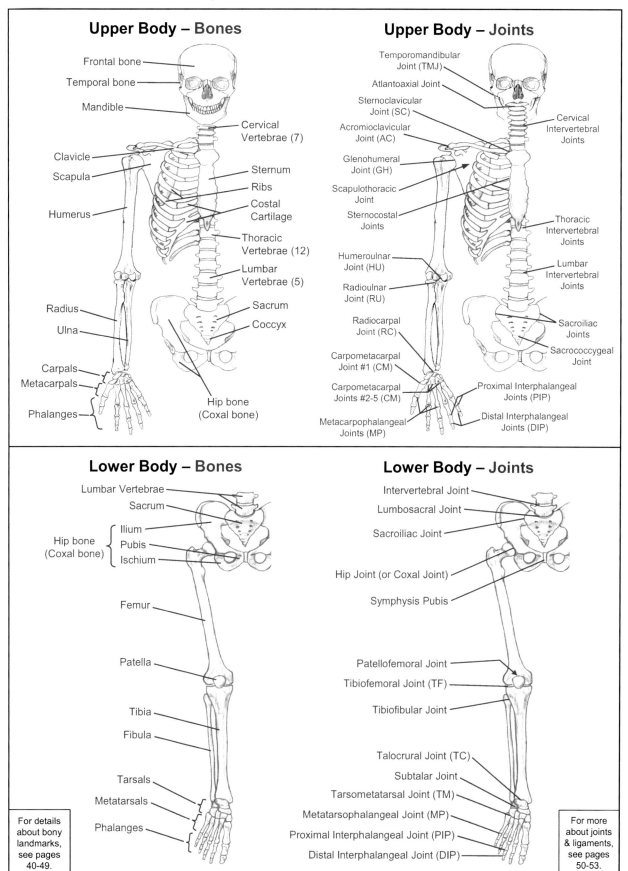

Upper Body – Bones

- Frontal bone
- Temporal bone
- Mandible
- Cervical Vertebrae (7)
- Clavicle
- Scapula
- Sternum
- Ribs
- Costal Cartilage
- Humerus
- Thoracic Vertebrae (12)
- Lumbar Vertebrae (5)
- Radius
- Sacrum
- Coccyx
- Ulna
- Carpals
- Metacarpals
- Hip bone (Coxal bone)
- Phalanges

Upper Body – Joints

- Temporomandibular Joint (TMJ)
- Atlantoaxial Joint
- Sternoclavicular Joint (SC)
- Acromioclavicular Joint (AC)
- Cervical Intervertebral Joints
- Glenohumeral Joint (GH)
- Scapulothoracic Joint
- Sternocostal Joints
- Thoracic Intervertebral Joints
- Humeroulnar Joint (HU)
- Lumbar Intervertebral Joints
- Radioulnar Joint (RU)
- Radiocarpal Joint (RC)
- Sacroiliac Joints
- Sacrococcygeal Joint
- Carpometacarpal Joint #1 (CM)
- Carpometacarpal Joints #2-5 (CM)
- Proximal Interphalangeal Joints (PIP)
- Metacarpophalangeal Joints (MP)
- Distal Interphalangeal Joints (DIP)

Lower Body – Bones

- Lumbar Vertebrae
- Sacrum
- Hip bone (Coxal bone)
  - Ilium
  - Pubis
  - Ischium
- Femur
- Patella
- Tibia
- Fibula
- Tarsals
- Metatarsals
- Phalanges

For details about bony landmarks, see pages 40-49.

Lower Body – Joints

- Intervertebral Joint
- Lumbosacral Joint
- Sacroiliac Joint
- Hip Joint (or Coxal Joint)
- Symphysis Pubis
- Patellofemoral Joint
- Tibiofemoral Joint (TF)
- Tibiofibular Joint
- Talocrural Joint (TC)
- Subtalar Joint
- Tarsometatarsal Joint (TM)
- Metatarsophalangeal Joint (MP)
- Proximal Interphalangeal Joint (PIP)
- Distal Interphalangeal Joint (DIP)

For more about joints & ligaments, see pages 50-53.

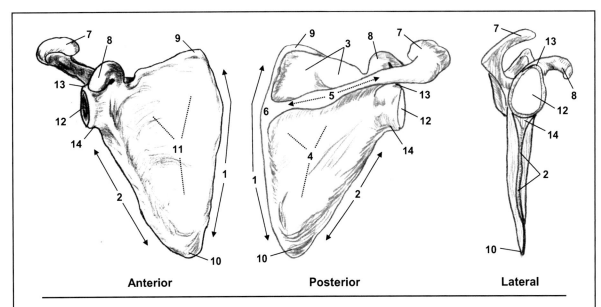

Anterior   **Posterior**   **Lateral**

Right Scapula

1. Medial (vertebral) border
2. Lateral (axillary) border
3. Supraspinous fossa
4. Infraspinous fossa
5. Spine

6. Root of spine
7. Acromion
8. Coracoid process
9. Superior angle
10. Inferior angle

11. Subscapular fossa
12. Glenoid fossa (Glenoid cavity)
13. Supraglenoid tubercle
14. Infraglenoid tubercle

Scapula

Anterior View   **Superior View**

Shoulder Girdle (= Scapula + Clavicle)

A. Scapula

3. Supraspinous fossa
5. Spine of scapula
6. Root of spine
7. Acromion
8. Coracoid process
9. Superior angle
10. Inferior angle

B. Clavicle

15. Sternal (medial) end
16. Acromial (lateral) end

Joints

J1. Sternoclavicular joint (SC)
J2. Acromioclavicular joint (AC)

Shoulder Girdle

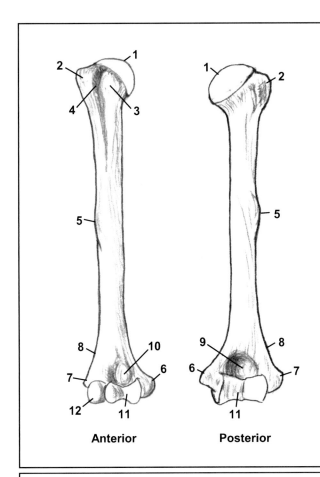

Anterior   **Posterior**

Right Humerus

1. Head
2. Greater tubercle
3. Lesser tubercle
4. Intertubercular groove (Bicipital groove)
5. Deltoid tuberosity
6. Medial epicondyle
7. Lateral epicondyle
8. Lateral supracondylar ridge
9. Olecranon fossa
10. Coronoid fossa
11. Trochlea
12. Capitulum

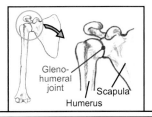

Gleno-humeral joint
Scapula
Humerus

Upper Arm

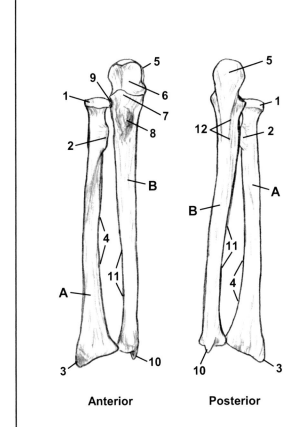

Anterior   **Posterior**

Right Radius & Ulna

A. Radius
1. Head of radius
2. Radial tuberosity
3. Styloid process
4. Interosseus border

B. Ulna
5. Olecranon process
6. Trochlear notch
7. Coronoid process
8. Ulnar tuberosity
9. Radial notch
10. Styloid process
11. Interosseus border
12. Supinator crest

Interosseus membrane

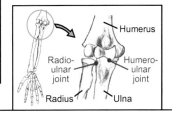

Humerus
Radio-ulnar joint
Humero-ulnar joint
Radius
Ulna

Forearm

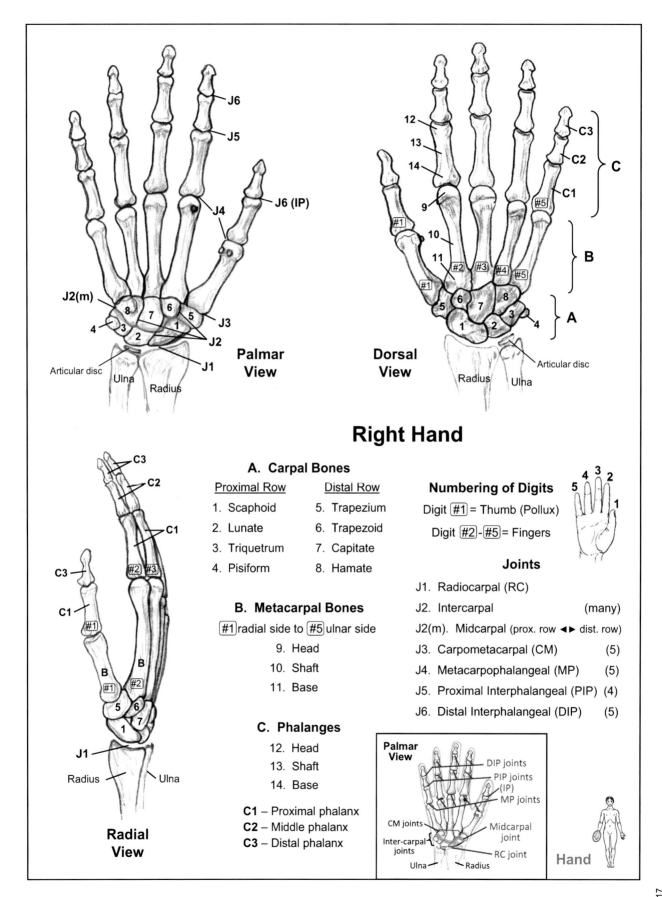

J6
J5
J6 (IP)
J4
J2(m)
J3
J2
J1
Palmar View
8 7 6 5
4 3 2 1
Articular disc
Ulna
Radius

12
13
14
9
10
11
#1
#2
#3
#4
#5
#1
#5
C3
C2
C1
C
B
A
5 6 7 8
1 2 3 4
Dorsal View
Radius
Ulna
Articular disc

Right Hand

Radial View
C3
C2
C1
C3
C1
#1
#2 #3
B
B
#1
#2
5 6 7
1
J1
Radius
Ulna

A. Carpal Bones

Proximal Row	Distal Row
1. Scaphoid	5. Trapezium
2. Lunate	6. Trapezoid
3. Triquetrum	7. Capitate
4. Pisiform	8. Hamate

B. Metacarpal Bones

#1 radial side to #5 ulnar side

9. Head
10. Shaft
11. Base

C. Phalanges

12. Head
13. Shaft
14. Base

C1 – Proximal phalanx
C2 – Middle phalanx
C3 – Distal phalanx

Numbering of Digits

Digit #1 = Thumb (Pollux)

Digit #2 - #5 = Fingers

5 4 3 2 1

Joints

J1. Radiocarpal (RC)
J2. Intercarpal   (many)
J2(m). Midcarpal (prox. row ◄► dist. row)
J3. Carpometacarpal (CM)   (5)
J4. Metacarpophalangeal (MP)   (5)
J5. Proximal Interphalangeal (PIP) (4)
J6. Distal Interphalangeal (DIP)   (5)

Palmar View
DIP joints
PIP joints
(IP)
MP joints
CM joints
Midcarpal joint
Inter-carpal joints
RC joint
Ulna   Radius

Hand

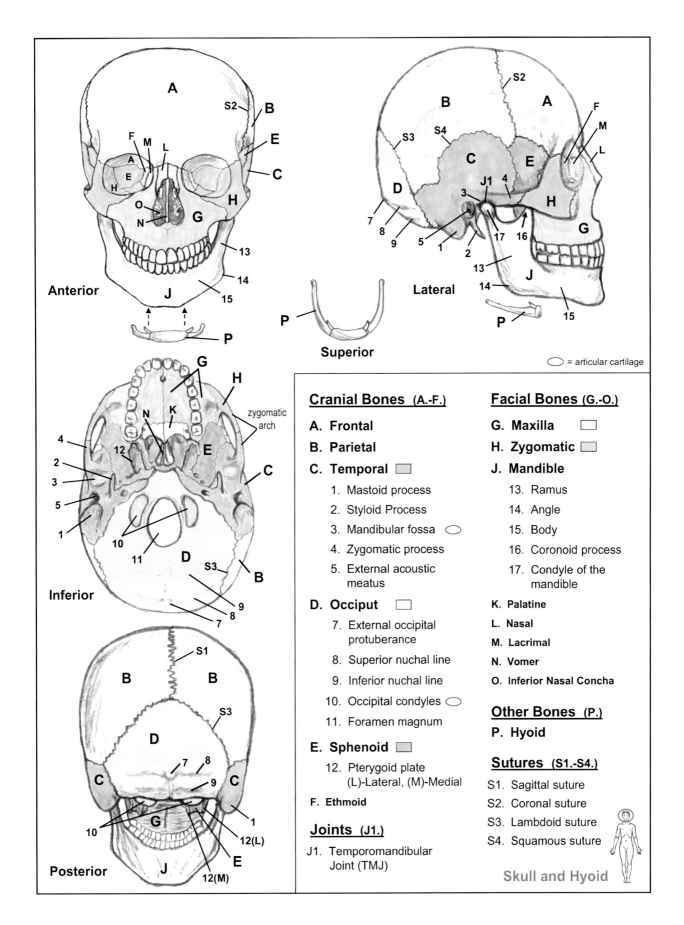

Anterior

Lateral

Superior

Inferior

Posterior

◯ = articular cartilage

Cranial Bones (A.-F.)

A. Frontal

B. Parietal

C. Temporal ▦

  1. Mastoid process

  2. Styloid Process

  3. Mandibular fossa ◯

  4. Zygomatic process

  5. External acoustic
     meatus

D. Occiput ▢

  7. External occipital
     protuberance

  8. Superior nuchal line

  9. Inferior nuchal line

  10. Occipital condyles ◯

  11. Foramen magnum

E. Sphenoid ▦

  12. Pterygoid plate
     (L)-Lateral, (M)-Medial

F. Ethmoid

Joints (J1.)

J1. Temporomandibular
    Joint (TMJ)

Facial Bones (G.-O.)

G. Maxilla ▢

H. Zygomatic ▦

J. Mandible

  13. Ramus

  14. Angle

  15. Body

  16. Coronoid process

  17. Condyle of the
     mandible

K. Palatine

L. Nasal

M. Lacrimal

N. Vomer

O. Inferior Nasal Concha

Other Bones (P.)

P. Hyoid

Sutures (S1.-S4.)

S1. Sagittal suture

S2. Coronal suture

S3. Lambdoid suture

S4. Squamous suture

Skull and Hyoid

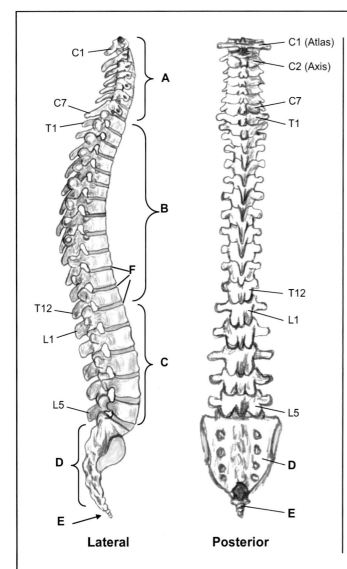

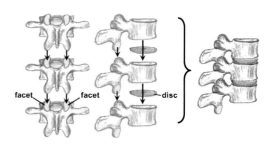

Intervertebral Joints
(3 articulations per joint: 1 disc + 2 facet joints)

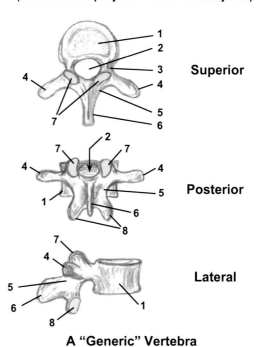

A "Generic" Vertebra

◯ = articular cartilage

Vertebral Column

A. Cervical Spine
7 vertebrae: C1-C7
Lordotic curve (secondary curve)

B. Thoracic Spine
12 vertebrae: T1-T12 – ribs attach
Kyphotic curve (primary curve)

C. Lumbar Spine
5 vertebrae: L1-L5
Lordotic curve (secondary curve)

D. Sacrum
5 vertebrae: S1-S5 (fused)
Kyphotic curve (primary curve)

E. Coccyx
2 - 4 vertebrae (fused)

F. Intervertebral Discs (23)

**Landmarks Common to All
Vertebrae (except C1)**

(see page 45 for landmarks
unique to each spinal section)

1. Body
2. Vertebral foramen
   (spinal cord passes through it)
3. Pedicle
4. Transverse process (TVP)
5. Lamina
6. Spinous process (SP)
7. Superior facet (articular process)
8. Inferior facet (articular process)

Spine

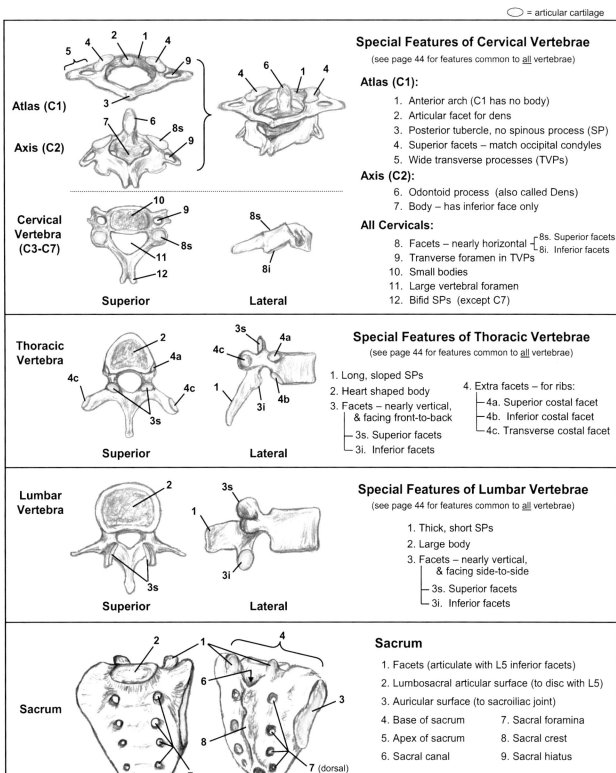

= articular cartilage

Special Features of Cervical Vertebrae
(see page 44 for features common to all vertebrae)

Atlas (C1):
1. Anterior arch (C1 has no body)
2. Articular facet for dens
3. Posterior tubercle, no spinous process (SP)
4. Superior facets – match occipital condyles
5. Wide transverse processes (TVPs)

Axis (C2):
6. Odontoid process (also called Dens)
7. Body – has inferior face only

All Cervicals:
8. Facets – nearly horizontal ⎰ 8s. Superior facets
   ⎱ 8i. Inferior facets
9. Tranverse foramen in TVPs
10. Small bodies
11. Large vertebral foramen
12. Bifid SPs (except C7)

Atlas (C1)
Axis (C2)

Cervical Vertebra (C3-C7)
Superior   Lateral

Special Features of Thoracic Vertebrae
(see page 44 for features common to all vertebrae)

1. Long, sloped SPs
2. Heart shaped body
3. Facets – nearly vertical, & facing front-to-back
   — 3s. Superior facets
   — 3i. Inferior facets
4. Extra facets – for ribs:
   — 4a. Superior costal facet
   — 4b. Inferior costal facet
   — 4c. Transverse costal facet

Thoracic Vertebra
Superior   Lateral

Special Features of Lumbar Vertebrae
(see page 44 for features common to all vertebrae)

1. Thick, short SPs
2. Large body
3. Facets – nearly vertical, & facing side-to-side
   — 3s. Superior facets
   — 3i. Inferior facets

Lumbar Vertebra
Superior   Lateral

Sacrum
1. Facets (articulate with L5 inferior facets)
2. Lumbosacral articular surface (to disc with L5)
3. Auricular surface (to sacroiliac joint)
4. Base of sacrum   7. Sacral foramina
5. Apex of sacrum   8. Sacral crest
6. Sacral canal   9. Sacral hiatus

Coccyx
10. Coccygeal horns
11. Transverse processes

Sacrum
Coccyx
Anterior
(and slightly lateral)
Posterior
(and slightly lateral)

Vertebrae & Sacrum

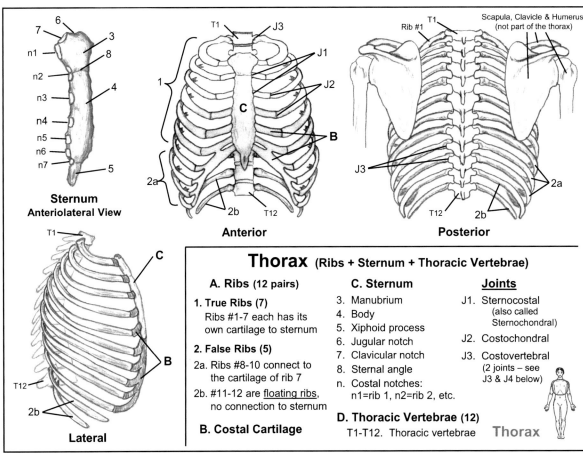

Sternum
Anteriolateral View

T1 — J3

Anterior

Rib #1 — T1

Scapula, Clavicle & Humerus
(not part of the thorax)

Posterior

Lateral

Thorax (Ribs + Sternum + Thoracic Vertebrae)

A. Ribs (12 pairs)

1. True Ribs (7)
Ribs #1-7 each has its own cartilage to sternum

2. False Ribs (5)
2a. Ribs #8-10 connect to the cartilage of rib 7
2b. #11-12 are _floating ribs_, no connection to sternum

B. Costal Cartilage

C. Sternum
3. Manubrium
4. Body
5. Xiphoid process
6. Jugular notch
7. Clavicular notch
8. Sternal angle
n. Costal notches: n1=rib 1, n2=rib 2, etc.

D. Thoracic Vertebrae (12)
T1-T12. Thoracic vertebrae

Joints
J1. Sternocostal (also called Sternochondral)
J2. Costochondral
J3. Costovertebral (2 joints – see J3 & J4 below)

Thorax

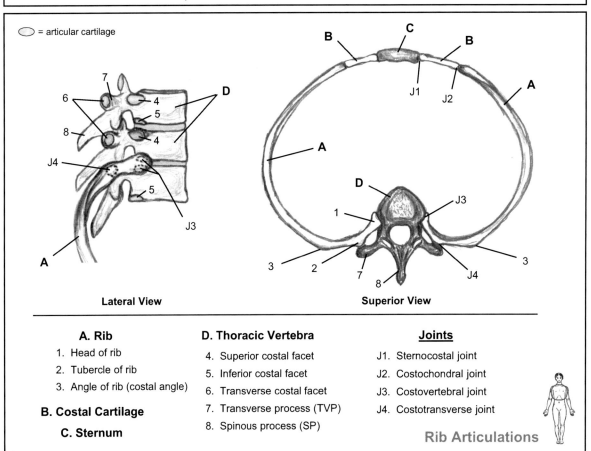

⬭ = articular cartilage

Lateral View

Superior View

A. Rib
1. Head of rib
2. Tubercle of rib
3. Angle of rib (costal angle)

B. Costal Cartilage

C. Sternum

D. Thoracic Vertebra
4. Superior costal facet
5. Inferior costal facet
6. Transverse costal facet
7. Transverse process (TVP)
8. Spinous process (SP)

Joints
J1. Sternocostal joint
J2. Costochondral joint
J3. Costovertebral joint
J4. Costotransverse joint

Rib Articulations

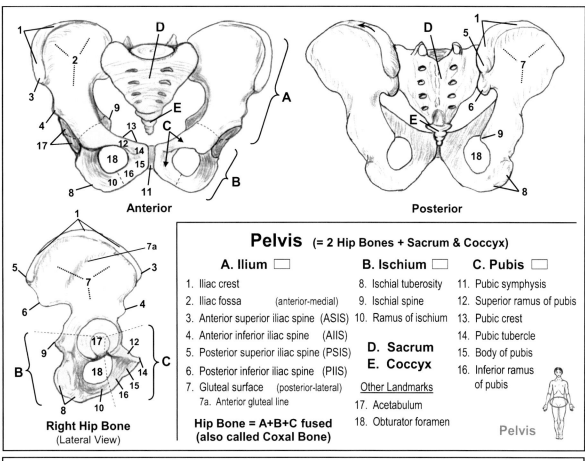

Anterior

Posterior

Pelvis (= 2 Hip Bones + Sacrum & Coccyx)

A. Ilium ☐   **B. Ischium** ☐   **C. Pubis** ☐

1. Iliac crest
2. Iliac fossa   (anterior-medial)
3. Anterior superior iliac spine (ASIS)
4. Anterior inferior iliac spine   (AIIS)
5. Posterior superior iliac spine (PSIS)
6. Posterior inferior iliac spine   (PIIS)
7. Gluteal surface   (posterior-lateral)
    7a. Anterior gluteal line

8. Ischial tuberosity
9. Ischial spine
10. Ramus of ischium

D. Sacrum
E. Coccyx

Other Landmarks
17. Acetabulum
18. Obturator foramen

11. Pubic symphysis
12. Superior ramus of pubis
13. Pubic crest
14. Pubic tubercle
15. Body of pubis
16. Inferior ramus of pubis

Hip Bone = A+B+C fused (also called Coxal Bone)

Right Hip Bone
(Lateral View)

Pelvis

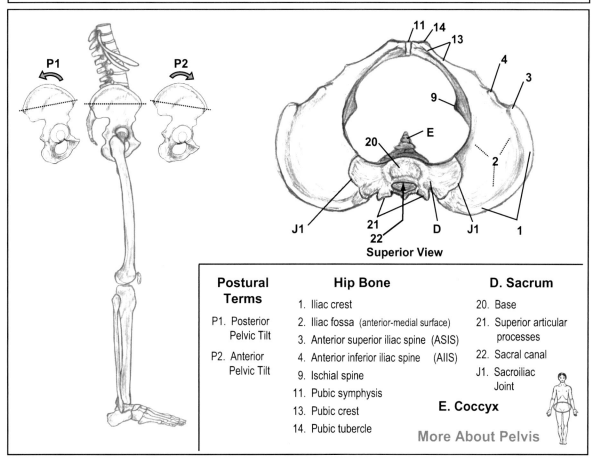

Superior View

Postural Terms

P1. Posterior Pelvic Tilt

P2. Anterior Pelvic Tilt

Hip Bone

1. Iliac crest
2. Iliac fossa (anterior-medial surface)
3. Anterior superior iliac spine (ASIS)
4. Anterior inferior iliac spine   (AIIS)
9. Ischial spine
11. Pubic symphysis
13. Pubic crest
14. Pubic tubercle

D. Sacrum

20. Base
21. Superior articular processes
22. Sacral canal
J1. Sacroiliac Joint

E. Coccyx

More About Pelvis

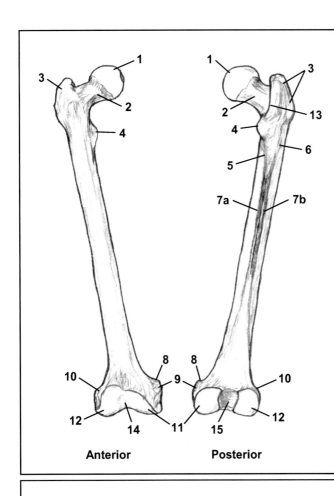

Right Femur

1. Head
2. Neck
3. Greater trochanter
4. Lesser trochanter
5. Pectineal line
6. Gluteal tuberosity
7. Linea aspera
   - 7a: Medial lip
   - 7b: Lateral lip
8. Adductor tubercle
9. Medial epicondyle
10. Lateral epicondyle
11. Medial condyle
12. Lateral condyle
13. Intertrochanteric crest
14. Patellar surface
15. Intercondylar fossa

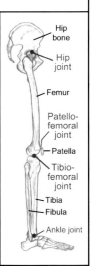

Thigh

Anterior   **Posterior**

Right Tibia & Fibula

A. Tibia

1. Medial condyle
2. Lateral condyle
3. Tibial tuberosity
4. Soleal line
5. Medial malleolus
6. Interosseus border
7. Proximal Medial Shaft
   (Pes anserinus attachment)
8. Superior articular surfaces
   (Tibial plateau)
9. Gerdy's Tubercle
   (Iliotibial tract attachment)

B. Fibula

10. Head
11. Lateral malleolus
12. Interosseus border

Joints

J1. Proximal Tibiofibular joint
J2. Distal Tibiofibular joint

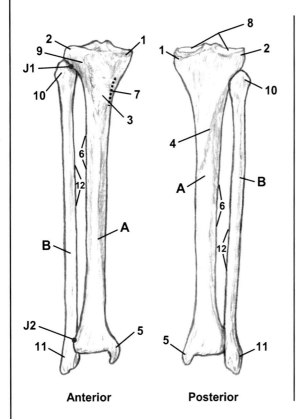

Anterior   **Posterior**

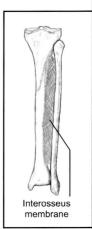

Interosseus membrane

Leg

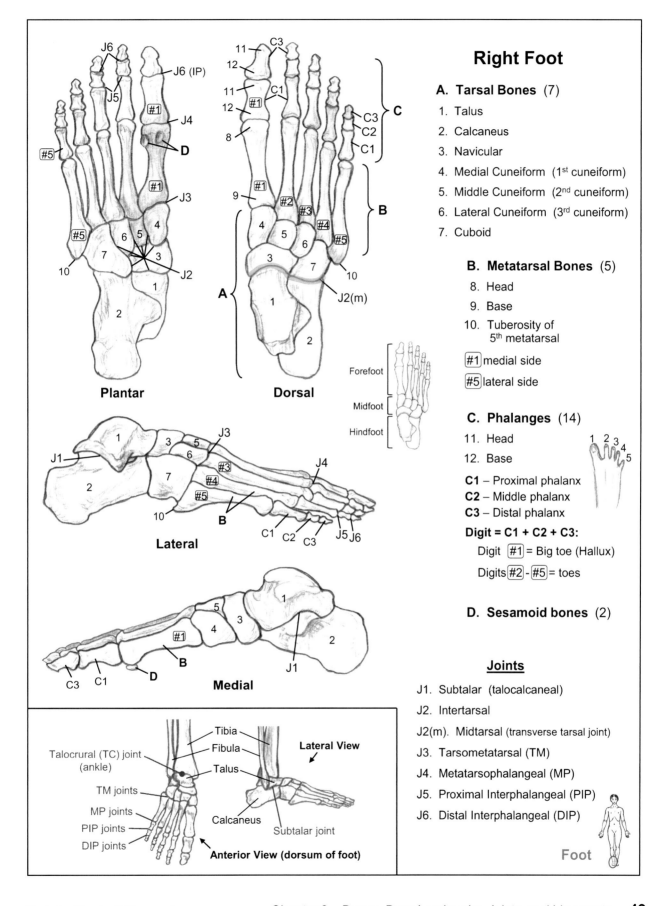

Right Foot

A. Tarsal Bones (7)

1. Talus
2. Calcaneus
3. Navicular
4. Medial Cuneiform (1st cuneiform)
5. Middle Cuneiform (2nd cuneiform)
6. Lateral Cuneiform (3rd cuneiform)
7. Cuboid

B. Metatarsal Bones (5)

8. Head
9. Base
10. Tuberosity of 5th metatarsal

#1 medial side
#5 lateral side

C. Phalanges (14)

11. Head
12. Base

C1 – Proximal phalanx
C2 – Middle phalanx
C3 – Distal phalanx

Digit = C1 + C2 + C3:

Digit #1 = Big toe (Hallux)
Digits #2 - #5 = toes

D. Sesamoid bones (2)

Joints

J1. Subtalar (talocalcaneal)
J2. Intertarsal
J2(m). Midtarsal (transverse tarsal joint)
J3. Tarsometatarsal (TM)
J4. Metatarsophalangeal (MP)
J5. Proximal Interphalangeal (PIP)
J6. Distal Interphalangeal (DIP)

Foot

Plantar

Dorsal

Forefoot
Midfoot
Hindfoot

Lateral

Medial

Tibia
Fibula
Talocrural (TC) joint (ankle)
Talus
TM joints
MP joints
PIP joints
DIP joints
Calcaneus
Subtalar joint
Lateral View
Anterior View (dorsum of foot)

Joints of the Body

JOINT NAME		JOINT TYPE	COMMENTS ("◄►" = articulation)

Shoulder Complex

Glenohumeral (GH) — Ball & socket — This is the true shoulder joint, humerus ◄► glenoid fossa
(GH allows the 6 B&S actions + horiz. abduction & horiz. adduction)

Sternoclavicular (SC) — Modif. ball&socket/gliding — ⎧ SC, AC, & ST joints move together, with 6 actions:
Acromioclavicular (AC) — Gliding — ⎨ elevation, depression, protraction, retraction,
Scapulothoracic (ST) — False (also called a functional joint) — ⎩ upward rotation, downward rotation

Elbow and Forearm

Humeroulnar (HU) — Hinge — The elbow joint
Radioulnar (Proximal) (RU) — Pivot — Radius pivots against ulna during supination & pronation
Radioulnar (Distal) — Pivot — Radius rotates around ulna during supination & pronation

Wrist, Hand, Fingers

Radiocarpal (RC) — Ellipsoid — Radius ◄► scaphoid + lunate + triquetrum
Intercarpal — Gliding — Articulations of carpal bones to other carpal bones
Midcarpal joint — Hinge — Proximal row of carpals ◄► Distal row of carpals
Carpometacarpal (CM) #1 — Saddle — Trapezium ◄► 1st metacarpal (allows thumb opposition)
Carpometacarpal (CM) #2-#5 — Gliding
Metacarpophalangeal (MP or MCP) — Condyloid — Knuckles between palm and fingers
Interphalangeal (IP, PIP, DIP) — Hinge — Fingers (#2-#5) have DIP & PIP, thumb (#1) has IP only

Face and Jaw

Temporomandibular (TMJ) — Condyloid/gliding/hinge — Complex joint with 6 actions: elevation, depression, +
protraction, retraction, R.&L. lateral deviation

Spine

Atlantooccipital (Occipitoatlantal) — Ellipsoid — 2 points of contact (at facets) = 1 ellipsoid joint
Atlantoaxial ⎰ Atlanto-odontoid — Pivot ⎱(together allow — C1/C2: anterior arch of atlas ◄► dens of axis
Joint ⎱ Atlantoaxial facets — Gliding ⎰ rotation only) — C1/C2: inferior facets C1 ◄► superior facets C2
Intervertebral ⎰ Facets — Gliding — (facets are also called zygapophyseal or apophyseal joints)
Joints ⎱ Disc — (amphiarthrotic) — Cartilaginous joint (not synovial)
Sacroiliac — Part gliding, part fibrous — Allows a small amount of gliding and rotation

Thorax

Sternocostal (rib 1) — (synarthrotic-fibrous) — Rib 1: manubrium of sternum ◄► costal cartilage
Sternocostal (ribs 2-7) — Gliding — Ribs 2-7: sternum ◄► costal cartilage
Costochondral — (synarthrotic-fibrous) — Ribs 1-10: "junctions" of rib ◄► costal cartilage
Costovertebral — Gliding — Head of rib ◄► costal facet(s) on vertebral body
Costotransverse — Gliding — Tubercle of rib ◄► costal facet on transverse process

Hip

Coxal (also called Acetabulofemoral Jt.) — Ball & socket — Head of femur ◄► Acetabulum of hip bone

Knee

Tibiofemoral (TF) — Modified hinge — The knee – "modified" because also rotates when flexed
Patellofemoral — Gliding — Posterior patella ◄► Patellar surface on distal femur
Tibiofibular (Proximal) — Gliding — Proximal lateral tibia ◄► Head of fibula
Tibiofibular (Distal) — (synarthrotic-fibrous) — Where tib./fib. connect to form upper lateral ankle joint

Ankle, Foot, Toes

Talocrural (TC) = the Ankle joint — Hinge — Distal tibia+fibula ◄► Talus (plantar flexion, dorsiflexion)
Subtalar (=Talocalcaneal joint) — Gliding/pivot — Inversion & eversion occur at the subtalar joint
Talocalcaneonavicular (TCN) — Gliding, rotation — ⎫
Transverse Tarsal (Midtarsal) — Gliding — ⎬ These create the springy arches of the foot
Tarsometatarsal (TM) — Gliding — ⎭
Metatarsophalangeal (MP or MTP) — Condyloid — Ball of foot
Interphalangeal (IP, PIP, DIP) — Hinge — Toes (#2-#5) have DIP & PIP, big toe (#1) has IP only

Synovial Joints (Diarthrotic) – Six Joint Types and Movements Available		
Ball & Socket: Flexion, extension, abduction, adduction, lateral rotation, medial rotation	**Hinge:** Flexion, extension	**Pivot:** Rotation
Ellipsoid/Condyloid: Flexion, extension, abduction, adduction	**Saddle:** Same actions as ellipsoid, + opposition	**Gliding:** Gliding

02051

Joints of the Body and Their Types

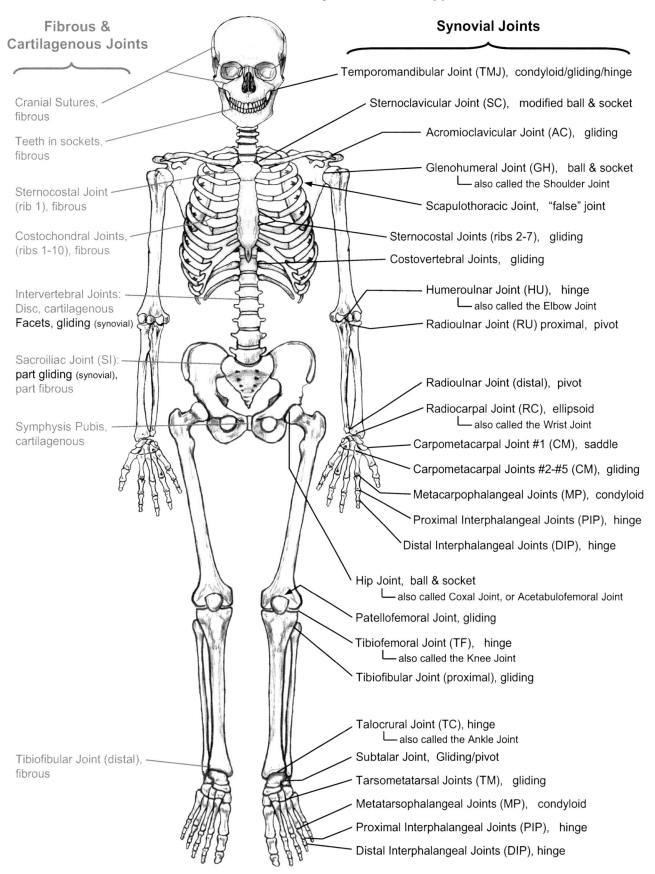

Fibrous & Cartilagenous Joints

Cranial Sutures, fibrous

Teeth in sockets, fibrous

Sternocostal Joint (rib 1), fibrous

Costochondral Joints, (ribs 1-10), fibrous

Intervertebral Joints: Disc, cartilagenous
Facets, gliding (synovial)

Sacroiliac Joint (SI): **part gliding** (synovial), part fibrous

Symphysis Pubis, cartilagenous

Tibiofibular Joint (distal), fibrous

Synovial Joints

Temporomandibular Joint (TMJ), condyloid/gliding/hinge

Sternoclavicular Joint (SC), modified ball & socket

Acromioclavicular Joint (AC), gliding

Glenohumeral Joint (GH), ball & socket
└─ also called the Shoulder Joint

Scapulothoracic Joint, "false" joint

Sternocostal Joints (ribs 2-7), gliding

Costovertebral Joints, gliding

Humeroulnar Joint (HU), hinge
└─ also called the Elbow Joint

Radioulnar Joint (RU) proximal, pivot

Radioulnar Joint (distal), pivot

Radiocarpal Joint (RC), ellipsoid
└─ also called the Wrist Joint

Carpometacarpal Joint #1 (CM), saddle

Carpometacarpal Joints #2-#5 (CM), gliding

Metacarpophalangeal Joints (MP), condyloid

Proximal Interphalangeal Joints (PIP), hinge

Distal Interphalangeal Joints (DIP), hinge

Hip Joint, ball & socket
└─ also called Coxal Joint, or Acetabulofemoral Joint

Patellofemoral Joint, gliding

Tibiofemoral Joint (TF), hinge
└─ also called the Knee Joint

Tibiofibular Joint (proximal), gliding

Talocrural Joint (TC), hinge
└─ also called the Ankle Joint

Subtalar Joint, Gliding/pivot

Tarsometatarsal Joints (TM), gliding

Metatarsophalangeal Joints (MP), condyloid

Proximal Interphalangeal Joints (PIP), hinge

Distal Interphalangeal Joints (DIP), hinge

Ligaments of the Joints of the Body

Note: This page lists the major ligaments. More ligaments, details, and illustrations are presented in Chapters 4 - 6.

Chapter 4 – Upper Extremity

Shoulder Complex

Shoulder Girdle: Sternoclavicular (SC) Joint

Sternoclavicular Ligs. (anterior & posterior)	Resist ant. & post. translation of clavicle; resist dislocation of clavicle from sternum.
Costoclavicular Lig.	Limits elevation of clavicle. Also limits protraction and retraction.
Interclavicular Lig.	Limits depression of clavicle

Shoulder Girdle: Acromioclavicular (AC) Joint

Acromioclavicular Lig.	Reinforce the AC joint capsule superiorly and inferiorly. Resists separation.
Coracoclavicular Lig. (trapezoid + conoid)	Prevent clavicle from raising superiorly away from the scapula.
Coracoacromial Lig.	Forms a roof over head of humerus, protecting rotator cuff tendons & SA bursa

Shoulder Joint: Glenohumeral (GH) Joint

Glenohumeral Capsular Ligs.	Limit external rotation, abduction, and anterior translation of the humeral head.
Coracohumeral Lig.	Resists inferior translation of humeral head. Limits external rotation.
Transverse Humeral Lig.	Holds biceps brachii tendon (long head) in the bicipital groove.

Elbow

Elbow: Humeroulnar, Humeroradial, and Radioulnar Joints

Radial (Lateral) Collateral Lig.	Resists varus forces. Resists extremes of flexion.
Ulnar (Medial) Collateral Lig.	Resists valgus forces. Different parts tighten during both flexion and extension.
Annular Lig.	Holds head of radius against radial notch of ulna (completes the RU pivot joint)

Wrist & Hand

Wrist: Radiocarpal Joint

Radial (Lateral) Collateral Lig.	Prevents too much ulnar deviation and resists varus forces
Ulnar (Medial) Collateral Lig.	Prevents too much radial deviation and resists valgus stress
Radiocarpal and Ulnocarpal Ligs.	Palmar ligaments limit wrist extension, dorsal ligaments limit wrist flexion

Hand: Carpal, Metacarpal, Phalangeal Joints

Intercarpal & Carpometacarpal Ligs.	Reinforce joints within the hand (on both palmar and dorsal sides)
MCP, PIP and DIP Collateral Ligs.	Resist varus and valgus stresses on the MCP, PIP and DIP joints. Go taut with flexion.
Palmar Interphalangeal Ligs. (plates)	Limit extension of fingers. Provide channel for tendons of finger flexor muscles

Chapter 5 – Axial Skeleton

Jaw

Temporomandibular Joint (TMJ)

Temporomandibular Lig. (lateral)	The main TMJ stabilizer. Limits downward, lateral, and posterior motion of the condyle.
Sphenomandibular Lig.	Limits anterior and downward motion, stabilizing during opening.
Stylomandibular Lig.	Assists in limiting anterior motion and lateral deviation

Cervical

Upper Cervical Complex: Atlanto-occipital (AO) Joint & Atlanto-axial (AA) Joint

Alar Ligs.	Taut in AO joint flexion. Limits rotation of head-and-atlas relative to dens of the axis.
Transverse Lig. of Atlas (part of Cruciate Lig.)	Completes the AO pivot joint; stops posterior displacement of dens (protect spinal cord)
Nuchal Lig. (Ligamentum Nuchae)	Limits excessive flexion of the neck & head (occiput to C7). Attachment site for muscles.

Spine

Intervertebral Joints (cervical/thoracic/lumbar)

Anterior Longitudinal Lig.	Resists too much extension of spine.
Posterior Longitudinal Lig.	Resists too much flexion of spine. Anterior boundary of spinal canal.
Ligamentum flavum	Connects adjacent lamina, stabilizing during flexion. Posterior boundary of spinal canal.
Interspinous & Supraspinous Ligs.	Resist too much flexion of spine.
Intertransverse Lig.	Limits lateral flexion to the opposite side.

Ribs

Sternocostal & Costovertebral Joints

Radiate Sternocostal Lig.	Attaches costal cartilage of rib to sternum (ribs 1 through 7)
Costotransverse Ligs. (3)	Attach neck of rib to transverse process of vertebra (3 Ligs: superior, lateral, inner)
Radiate Lig. of head of rib	Attaches head of rib to costal facets on the vertebral bodies

Pelvis

Lumbosacral Junction, Sacroiliac Joints, Sacrococcygeal Joint

Iliolumbar Lig.	Restrains movement at the lumbosacral junction (L5/S1). Helps stabilize SI joints.
Sacroiliac Ligs. (anterior & posterior)	Main stabilizers of sacroiliac (SI) joints. Limit rotation/gliding in SI joints.
Sacrotuberous Lig.	Limits forward rotation of the sacrum at SI joints (nutation)
Sacrospinous Lig.	Stabilizes sacrum vs. hip bone. Boundary between greater and lesser sciatic foramen.

Chapter 6 – Lower Extremity

Hip

Hip Joint (also called Coxal Joint or Acetabulofemoral Joint)

Iliofemoral Lig.	Limits extension and lateral rotation
Ischiofemoral Lig.	Limits extension and medial rotation
Pubofemoral Lig.	Limits extension and abduction

Knee

Tibiofemoral Joint

Anterior Cruciate Lig. (ACL)	Prevents anterior displacement of tibia on femur. Resists medial rotation.
Posterior Cruciate Lig. (PCL)	Prevents posterior displacement of tibia on femur. Resists extreme flexion of knee.
Medial (tibial) Collateral Lig. (MCL)	Medial stabilizer, resists valgus forces. Taut when knee is in full extension.
Lateral (fibular) Collateral Lig. (LCL)	Lateral stabilizer, resists varus forces. Taut when knee is in full extension.
Patellar Lig.	Connects patella to tibia, completing the pulley structure to extend the knee

Ankle

Talocrural Joint & Subtalar Joint

Tibiofibular Ligs. (anterior & post.)	Stabilize the distal tibiofibular joint (a fibrous synarthrotic joint)
Deltoid Lig.	Medial stabilizer, limits eversion, resists valgus forces on the ankle
Deltoid lig. has 4 parts:	1. Anterior tibiotalar, 2. Tibionavicular, 3. Tibiocalcaneal, 4. Posterior tibiotalar
Anterior Talofibular Lig. (ATFL)	Lateral stabilizer, limits inversion and plantarflexion, resists varus stress (most injured)
Calcaneofibular Lig.	Lateral stabilizer, limits inversion and dorsiflexion, resists varus stress
Posterior Talofibular Lig.	Lateral stabilizer, limits inversion and dorsiflexion, resists varus stress

Foot

Tarsal, Metatarsal and Phalangeal Joints (and arches of the foot)

Spring Lig. (Plantar calcaneonavicular lig.)	Supports medial longitudinal arch of foot, keeps head of talus from "falling down"
Long Plantar Lig.	Supports longitudinal arches of foot
Metatarsophalangeal, PIP, DIP Ligs.	Collateral ligs and Plantar ligs (plates) - similar to ligaments in the hand

Ligaments by Region (Overview)

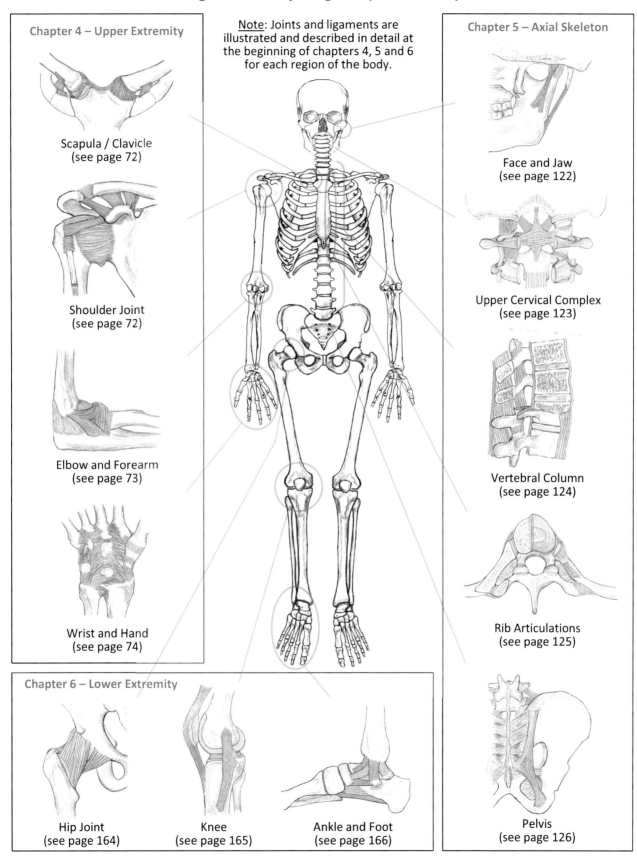

Note: Joints and ligaments are illustrated and described in detail at the beginning of chapters 4, 5 and 6 for each region of the body.

Chapter 4 – Upper Extremity

Scapula / Clavicle
(see page 72)

Shoulder Joint
(see page 72)

Elbow and Forearm
(see page 73)

Wrist and Hand
(see page 74)

Chapter 5 – Axial Skeleton

Face and Jaw
(see page 122)

Upper Cervical Complex
(see page 123)

Vertebral Column
(see page 124)

Rib Articulations
(see page 125)

Pelvis
(see page 126)

Chapter 6 – Lower Extremity

Hip Joint
(see page 164)

Knee
(see page 165)

Ankle and Foot
(see page 166)

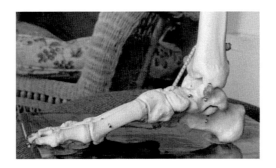

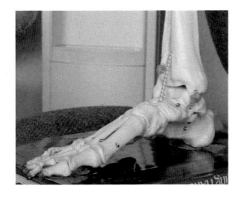

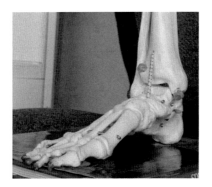

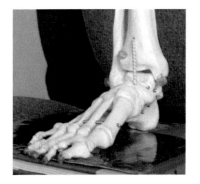

Chapter 3

Using the Brain-Friendly System to Optimize Your Learning

Introduction

Chapter 3 – Using the Brain-Friendly System to Optimize Your Learning provides an orientation before you begin learning all the muscles described in the following chapters (4, 5, and 6). You will learn how to use the tables and figures in Chapters 4 – 6 and how to get the most out of studying the muscles.

Because this book is for the study of kinesiology (i.e., movement of the body), the muscles are organized into groups based on the bones and joints they move as they contract. For example, all muscles whose primary action is to move the humerus around an axis at the shoulder joint are presented in "Muscle Group 2 – Movement of the Shoulder Joint". This arrangement makes it easier to recall the information when you are looking at the body from a movement perspective.

Thirteen **muscle groups** are presented in Chapters 4, 5 and 6 based on major body divisions:

Chap. 4	Muscles That Move the Upper Extremity
Group 1:	Movement of the Scapula/Clavicle
Group 2:	Movement of the Shoulder Joint
Group 3:	Movement of the Elbow, Forearm
Group 4:	Movement of the Wrist, Hand, Fingers
Group 5:	Movement of the Thumb
Chap. 5	**Muscles That Move the Axial Skeleton**
Group 6:	Movement of the Face and Jaw
Group 7:	Movement of the Neck and Head
Group 8:	Movement of the Spine
Group 9:	Movement of Thorax, Abdomen, Breathing
Chap. 6	**Muscles That Move the Lower Extremity**
Group 10:	Movement of the Hip Joint (Part 1)
Group 11:	Movement of the Hip Joint (Part 2)
Group 12:	Movement of the Knee (& Hip Joint, Part 3)
Group 13:	Movement of the Ankle, Foot and Toes

In addition, concise **bonus muscle groups** have been added at the end of each chapter (they do not use the full 8-page format described next).

At the end of:	Bonus Muscle Groups
Chapter 4	Intrinsic Muscles of the Hand
Chapter 5	Muscles of the Pelvic Floor
Chapter 6	Intrinsic Muscles of the Foot

8-Page Format

A consistent **8-page format** is used to present each group of muscles. The repetitive format supports the brain-friendly philosophy of this book. A diagram of this 8-page format is shown on the next page. The following organization is used:

General Information –
The first three pages include a list of the muscles in the group, a description of the joints and actions involved, a list of the associated bones and bony landmarks, and overview drawings showing all the muscles and their attachments in place on the skeleton. Please see pages 58-59 for details.

The "A" Table and Figure –
The 4th and 5th pages provide text and drawings about the structure and function of the muscles in the group (see pages 60-61 for more information).

> Table (A) – Origins, Insertions, Actions
> A table presenting the descriptive information for the muscles.

> Figure (A) – Muscle Attachments
> Bone drawings with red and blue areas showing origins and insertions of the muscles.

The "B" Table and Figure –
The 6th and 7th pages allow further analysis of muscle actions, show innervation, and give full size illustrations of the muscles (see pages 62-63).

> Table (B) – Synergists & Antagonists
> A special table to study and compare muscle **actions.** This table also includes the **innervation** for each muscle.

> Figure (B) – Muscle Pictures
> Illustrations of the muscles, to encourage looking at muscle shapes and fiber directions while analyzing actions.

Note-Taking Page (or Bonus Muscle Group) –
The final (8th) page for a group has small pictures of the muscles with blank areas for writing notes. (Note that this 8th page is sometimes used to show a bonus muscle group).

43216

8-Page **Format For Each** <u>**Group**</u> **of Muscles**

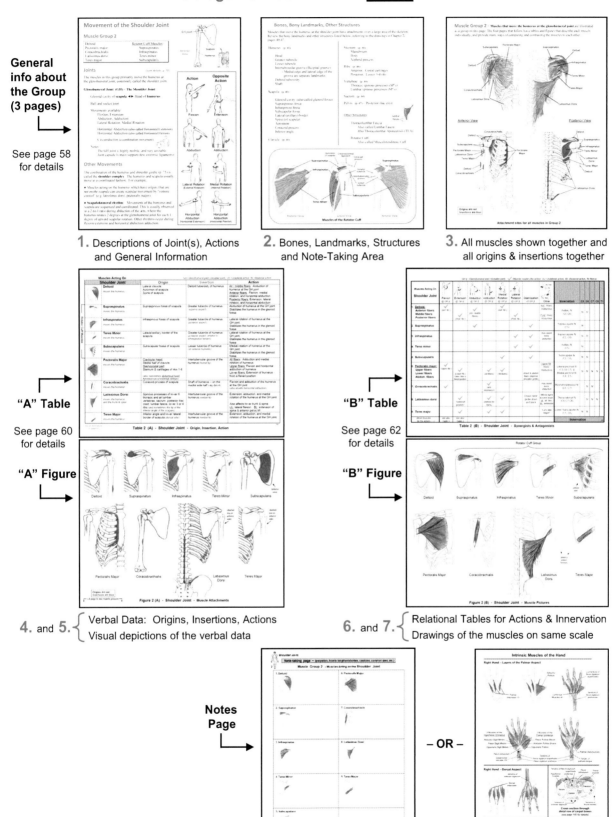

General info about the Group (3 pages)

See page 58 for details

1. Descriptions of Joint(s), Actions and General Information

2. Bones, Landmarks, Structures and Note-Taking Area

3. All muscles shown together and all origins & insertions together

"A" Table

See page 60 for details

"B" Table

See page 62 for details

"A" Figure

"B" Figure

4. and 5. { Verbal Data: Origins, Insertions, Actions / Visual depictions of the verbal data

6. and 7. { Relational Tables for Actions & Innervation / Drawings of the muscles on same scale

Notes Page

– OR –

8. Page for writing notes about muscles

The **Notes** page is sometimes replaced with a **Bonus Muscle Group** like this.

How to Use the General Information Pages

Each group of muscles in chapters 4, 5, and 6 begins with three pages of general information. This overview of the group includes summaries of the joint(s) involved, the actions that are possible, and the bones, landmarks and other structures that are muscle attachments or are significantly involved in some other way. The General Information pages have the following components:

- A list of the muscles in the group

- Descriptions of the joint(s) moved by the muscles

- Movements available at those joints

- Action drawings

- Bony landmarks and other structures to preview before studying the individual muscles

- Overview drawings of the muscles and their attachments

Joints and Actions

(1st page of the 8-page format)

The main joint or joints that are moved by the muscle group are given first, and other joints that are secondarily involved are listed second. A special symbol ◄► is used to indicate the meeting point (articulation) of the bones that make up the joint. Also included are the type of joint, the movements available at the joint, and other pertinent information.

Action Pair Drawings

For each muscle group, illustrations show the actions available for the main joints or structures moved when the muscles contract. These illustrations are organized in pairs to show how different actions oppose each other (opposite actions are done by antagonist muscles). The precise point where the joint in question is moving around its axis is indicated with a symbol " ⊗ ", and the direction the body part is moving is indicated with an arrow. Examples of action pairs are shown in the figure to the right.

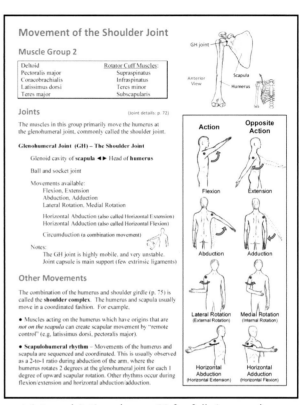

Joints and Actions (see p. 83 for full size page)

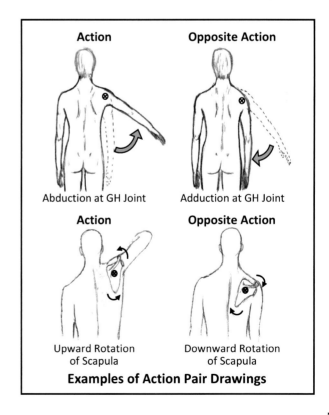

Examples of Action Pair Drawings

Bones, Bony Landmarks, Other Structures – Preview List

(2ⁿᵈ page of the 8-page format)

This page lists the bones, bony landmarks, and other body structures that are attachments for the muscles in the group. Also listed are other structures that are significantly involved with the use of the muscles. It is a good idea to <u>preview</u> the bony landmarks listed on this page before you begin studying the origins and insertions of the muscles (all bony landmark drawings are centralized in Chapter 2 of this book). Then, as you read and memorize each muscle, the names of landmarks will be familiar.

The bottom of this page often provides additional illustrations and information to highlight special features and terminology related to the muscle group. This may include special groupings within the group, cross-sections, or brief descriptions of smaller muscles that are not included in the main "**A**" and "**B**" tables for the muscle group.

Muscle Overview Drawings

(3ʳᵈ page of the 8-page format)

Overview drawings provide a "big picture" for the muscle group to give an overall sense of the group before going on to study the individual muscles. Two types of drawings are provided:

1. All muscles shown together in place on the skeleton.

2. Skeleton pictures with all origins in red and insertions in blue.

Use these drawings to look for patterns to help you understand how the muscles in the group work together. For example, Muscle Group 2 has muscles that move the humerus at the glenohumeral joint. You can see that all the insertions (shown in blue) are gathered on the humerus, while the origins (shown in red) are spread over a large area on many other bones of the body.

These illustrations are also useful to begin understanding which of the muscles in the group reside in different layers.

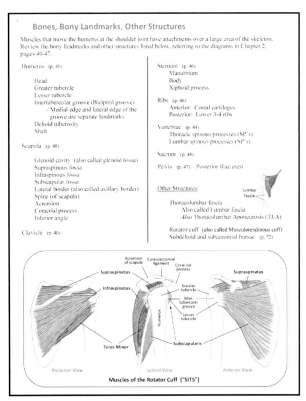

Bones, Bony Landmarks, etc. (see p. 84 for full size page)

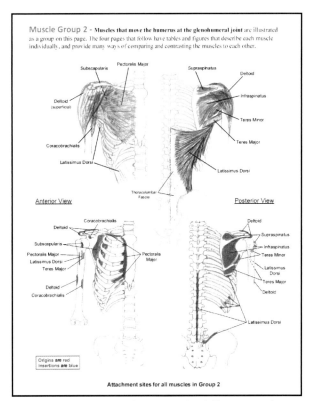

Overview Drawings (see p. 85 for full size page)

How to Use the Tables and Figures

Each group of muscles is presented in a consistent manner. Once you get used to this organization, you will find it easy to study and interrelate the information, as well as quickly look up individual muscles.

Each of the 13 groups of muscles is presented with two pairs of tables and figures: The "**A**" table and figure, and the "**B**" table and figure. All tables and figures for a given muscle group are enumerated with the group number, for example,

Muscle Group **1**: Table **1**(A),   Figure **1**(A),
                       Table **1**(B),   Figure **1**(B)
Muscle Group **2**: Table **2**(A),   Figure **2**(A),
                       Table **2**(B),   Figure **2**(B)
                               •
                               •
                               •
Muscle Group **13**: Table **13**(A), Figure **13**(A),
                       Table **13**(B), Figure **13**(B)

The "A" Table and Figure

(4ᵗʰ and 5ᵗʰ pages of the 8-page format)

An "A" Table and "A" Figure for a muscle group are shown on pages facing each other, so you can easily refer back and forth as you study them. The example on the following page shows Table 2 (A) and Figure 2 (A), which are from Muscle Group 2, the muscles that move the humerus at the shoulder joint (glenohumeral joint).

Table 2 (A) – Origin, Insertion, Action

The "**A**" **Table** contains verbal descriptions of the origins, insertions, and actions for each muscle. As you study the muscles, occasionally look up and down each column to compare and contrast which muscles have similar attachments and actions, and which muscles differ. By continually looking for word patterns as you learn the information, you will help anchor the words in your brain and make them easier to recall later.

As you read the **Origins** and **Insertions** for each muscle, look down to the facing page (Figure 2 (A)), and observe the red and blue spots drawn on the bones. This will help relate the words in the Table to an image of exactly what the words mean. It will be easier to do this if you have *previewed* the bony landmarks listed a few pages prior.

As you read the **Actions**, move your body, or that of a partner, to relate the words to actual movements. Also, remember all the actions named in the right hand column of this "A" table have been gathered, sorted out, and re-listed across the top of the "B" table for further study (see next section).

Note that sometimes portions of text in the tables are in smaller print and enclosed in parentheses. These parenthetical phrases add extra detail to the basic information in a table cell. The idea is to have a concise description of origin, insertion, and action that is sufficient for most readers, and then provide more details for those readers who require advanced information.

Figure 2 (A) – Muscle Attachments

The "**A**" **Figure** illustrates the places where the muscles attach to the bones. **Red** indicates **origin** and blue indicates **insertion**. Visualize lines of force (e.g., puppet strings, ropes,…) connecting the red area to the blue area and think about what happens when the blue point on the more moveable bone is pulled toward the red area on the more stable bone.

Relate the movement you visualize to the words in the **Action** column of Table 2 (A), keeping in mind any constraints imposed by the bone shapes, joint type, etc. (see "Real-time Factors that Affect a Muscle's Actions" on page 67).

Comparing O/I Pictures to Muscle Pictures

Note that you can lift the "A" Figure page to see pictures of the individual muscles to go with each of the origin/insertion bone drawings. The "**B**" **Figure – Muscle Pictures** page is always two pages after the "A" Figure, so the muscle pictures lie directly under the bone attachment drawings.

Example of an "A" Table and Figure

Each **row** gives all information for a single muscle. For example, row 2 gives Origin, Insertion & Action for the Supraspinatus muscle.

Each **column** gives a single feature for all muscles. For example, column 3 gives the Insertions for all the muscles.

Muscles Acting On Shoulder Joint		Origin	Insertion	Action
Deltoid *moves the humerus*		Lateral clavicle, Acromion of scapula, Spine of scapula	Deltoid tuberosity of humerus	All / middle fibers: Abduction of humerus at the GH joint. Anterior fibers: Flexion, medial rotation, and horizontal adduction. Posterior fibers: Extension, lateral rotation, and horizontal abduction
Supraspinatus *moves the humerus*		Supraspinous fossa of scapula	Greater tubercle of humerus (superior aspect)	Abduction of humerus at the GH joint, Stabilizes the humerus in the glenoid fossa
Infraspinatus *moves the humerus*		Infraspinous fossa of scapula	Greater tubercle of humerus (posterior aspect)	Lateral rotation of humerus at the GH joint, Stabilizes the humerus in the glenoid fossa
Teres Minor *moves the humerus*		Lateral/axillary border of the scapula	Greater tubercle of humerus (posterior aspect, inferior to infraspinatus tendon)	Lateral rotation of humerus at the GH joint, Stabilizes the humerus in the glenoid fossa
Subscapularis *moves the humerus*		Subscapular fossa of scapula	Lesser tubercle of humerus (on anterior humerus)	Medial rotation of humerus at the GH joint, Stabilizes the humerus in the glenoid fossa
Pectoralis Major *moves the humerus*		Clavicular head: Medial half of clavicle Sternocostal part: Sternum & cartilages of ribs 1-6 (also sometimes abdominal head: Aponeurosis of external oblique)	Intertubercular groove of the humerus (lateral lip)	All fibers: Adduction and medial rotation of humerus Upper fibers: Flexion and horizontal adduction of humerus Lower fibers: Extension of humerus - from a flexed position
Coracobrachialis *moves the humerus*		Coracoid process of scapula	Shaft of humerus -- on the medial side half way down	Flexion and adduction of the humerus at the GH joint (also assists horizontal adduction)
Latissimus Dorsi *moves the humerus and the trunk & spine*		Spinous processes of lower 6 thoracic and all lumbar vertebrae, sacrum, posterior iliac crest, lumbar fascia, lower 3 or 4 ribs (and sometimes the tip of the inferior angle of the scapula)	Intertubercular groove of humerus (medial lip)	Extension, adduction, and medial rotation of the humerus at the GH joint. Also affects lower trunk & spine: UL: lateral flexion, BL: extension of spine & anterior pelvic tilt
Teres Major *moves the humerus*		Inferior angle and lower lateral border of scapula (dorsal side)	Intertubercular groove of the humerus (medial lip)	Extension, adduction, and medial rotation of the humerus at the GH joint.

GH=Glenohumeral joint (shoulder joint), UL=Unilateral action, BL=Bilateral action

Rotator Cuff Muscles

(larger illustrations on page 83)

Table 2 (A) - Shoulder Joint - Origin, Insertion, Action

See page 86 for full size Table 2 (A)

Compare the words in the A Table above to the pictures in the A Figure below.

Origins: Shown in Red
Insertions: Shown in Blue
Actions: Visualize the blue being pulled toward the red

See page 87 for full size Figure 2 (A)

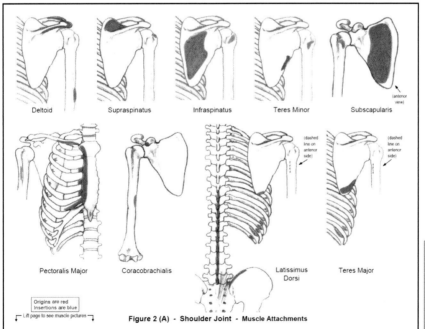

Deltoid   Supraspinatus   Infraspinatus   Teres Minor   Subscapularis (anterior view)

Pectoralis Major   Coracobrachialis   Latissimus Dorsi   Teres Major

(dashed line on anterior side)

Origins are red
Insertions are blue
Lift page to see muscle pictures

Figure 2 (A) - Shoulder Joint - Muscle Attachments

Lift this "A" Figure page to see the associated "B" Figure

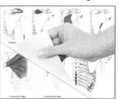

Each row of pictures is sized and oriented for easy comparison of muscle attachments.

A dashed line indicates a muscle attachment on the opposite side of the bone from the side you are viewing.

The "B" Table and Figure

(6ᵗʰ and 7ᵗʰ pages of the 8-page format)

The "**B**" Table and "**B**" Figure are on pages facing each other so you can easily refer back and forth as you study them. The example on the following page shows Table 2 (B) and Figure 2 (B), which are from Muscle Group 2, the muscles that move the humerus at the shoulder joint.

Table 2 (B) – Synergists & Antagonists

The **B Table** has muscle names listed down the left-hand side. Across the top are all actions that are possible for the joint(s) of that muscle group. This creates a grid format where each muscle is represented by a row and each action by a column.

	Action 1	Action 2	Action 3	Action 4	Action 5
Muscle 1		✓	✓		
Muscle 2					✓
Muscle 3	✓				✓
Muscle 4		✓			

Each **row** shows all the Actions
created by that Muscle

	Action 1	Action 2	Action 3	Action 4	Action 5
Muscle 1		✓	✓		
Muscle 2					✓
Muscle 3	✓				✓
Muscle 4		✓			

Each **column** shows all the Muscles
that create that Action

In the cells of this grid are ✓ marks or other symbols that indicate how the muscle (the row) is involved with the action (the column). The following table describes all symbols that are used in the cells.

The arrangement of the **B** table is particularly suitable for learning the relationships of muscles that work together to perform a given action (synergists), as well as which muscles oppose that action (antagonists).

Symbols used in the B Tables

Symbol	Meaning
✓	The muscle creates the action (agonist, prime mover)
✓ assist	The muscle assists the action but is not a prime mover
may assist	May assist, depending on strength requirements or relative bone angles
"__ fibers"	A muscle *portion* creates the action (e.g., "anterior fibers" or "upper fibers")
UL	Unilateral contraction creates the action (applies to axial skeleton, see p. 121)
BL	Bilateral contraction creates the action (applies to axial skeleton, see p. 121)
⌐ ¬ (empty cell)	(empty cell) The muscle *does not* contribute to the action

More Features of the B tables:

- Pairs of actions that are opposites are placed in adjacent columns. This allows looking down one column to see the synergists for an action, and then looking at the adjacent column to see the antagonists for the action.   (ref. page 31)

- The **B** table also has an area on the right hand side that gives the **Innervation** for each muscle. The names of the nerve(s) that supply each muscle are listed, and the spinal segments are indicated in table format.   (ref. page 24)

- The bottom row, with title "More muscles for the action --->", indicates when muscles in other muscle groups also contribute to the action indicated in a column. If so, the words "see also Group #" are in the cell.

Figure 2 (B) – Muscle Pictures

The **B Figure** contains pictures of the muscles for comparison. For example, Figure 2 (B) is located on a page facing Table 2 (B) so you can look back and forth to relate the actions in the table with muscle positions, shapes, and fiber directions.

Note that the **B** Figure is on a page directly under the **A** Figure two pages prior, so you can easily compare the muscle shape with the red and blue origins and insertions shown in the **A** Figure.

Example of a "B" Table and Figure

Each **row** shows ✓'s for the actions created by a single muscle. For example, row 2 indicates that the Supraspinatus muscle creates abduction and stabilizes the GH joint.

Each **column** shows ✓'s for all muscles that create an action. For example, Lateral Rotation at the GH joint is created by the Deltoid (posterior fibers), Infraspinatus, and Teres Minor muscles.

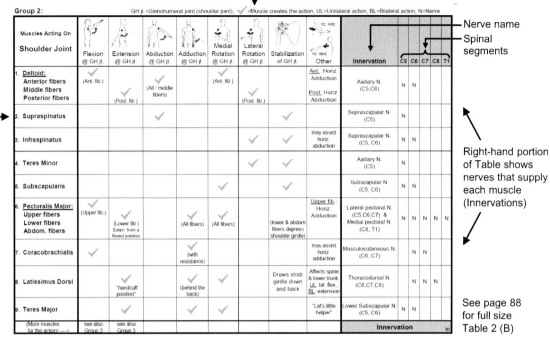

Group 2: GH jt =Glenohumeral joint (shoulder joint), ✓ =Muscle creates the action, UL=Unilateral action, BL=Bilateral action, N=Nerve

Muscles Acting On Shoulder Joint	Flexion @ GH jt.	Extension @ GH jt	Abduction @ GH jt.	Adduction @ GH jt.	Medial Rotation @ GH jt.	Lateral Rotation @ GH jt.	Stabilization of GH jt.	Other	Innervation	C5	C6	C7	C8	T1
1. **Deltoid:** Anterior fibers / Middle fibers / Posterior fibers	✓ (Ant. fib.)	✓ (Post. fib.)	✓ (All / middle fibers)		✓ (Ant. fib.)	✓ (Post. fib.)		Ant. Horiz. Adduction / Post. Horiz. Abduction	Axillary N. (C5,C6)	N	N			
2. Supraspinatus			✓			✓	✓		Suprascapular N. (C5)	N				
3. Infraspinatus					✓	✓		may assist horiz. abduction	Suprascapular N. (C5, C6)	N	N			
4. Teres Minor					✓	✓			Axillary N. (C5)	N				
5. Subscapularis					✓		✓		Subscapular N (C5, C6)	N	N			
6. **Pectoralis Major:** Upper fibers / Lower fibers / Abdom. fibers	✓ (Upper fib.)	✓ (Lower fib.) Exten. from a flexed position		✓ (All fibers)	✓ (All fibers)		(lower & abdom fibers depress shoulder girdle)	Upper fib.: Horiz. Adduction	Lateral pectoral N. (C5,C6,C7) & Medial pectoral N. (C8, T1)	N	N	N	N	N
7. Coracobrachialis	✓		✓ (with resistance)					may assist horiz. adduction	Musculocutaneous N. (C6, C7)		N	N		
8. Latissimus Dorsi		✓ "handcuff position"		✓ (behind the back)	✓		Draws shldr girdle down and back	Affects spine & lower trunk. UL: lat. flex , BL: extension	Thoracodorsal N. (C6,C7,C8)		N	N	N	
9. Teres Major		✓		✓	✓			"Lat's little helper"	Lower Subscapular N. (C5, C6)	N	N			
(More muscles for the action) --->	see also Group 3	see also Group 3							Innervation					

Table 2 (B) - Shoulder Joint - Synergists & Antagonists

Nerve name
Spinal segments

Right-hand portion of Table shows nerves that supply each muscle (Innervations)

See page 88 for full size Table 2 (B)

See page 89 for full size Figure 2 (B)

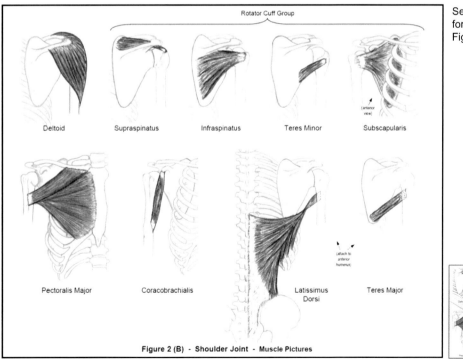

Rotator Cuff Group

Deltoid   Supraspinatus   Infraspinatus   Teres Minor   Subscapularis

Pectoralis Major   Coracobrachialis   Latissimus Dorsi   Teres Major

Figure 2 (B) - Shoulder Joint - Muscle Pictures

Lift previous page "A" Figure to see this "B" Figure

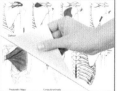

Each row of pictures is sized and oriented for easy comparison of muscles.

Dashed lines indicate that part of a muscle is on the <u>opposite</u> side of the bone from the side you are viewing.

An Example: Learning the Deltoid Muscle

This section demonstrates how to use the tables and figures to study the Deltoid muscle and compare and contrast it to other muscles in its group. The components of this example are taken from the section "Muscle Group 2 – Movement of the Shoulder Joint" on pages 86-89, in Chapter 4 – Muscles That Move the Upper Extremity.

The figure below shows the **Deltoid** muscle portions from Table 2(A), Figure 2(A), and Figure 2(B). This demonstrates how to tie together the information and optimize your study time by learning from both the verbal and visual directions.

As you *read* the words describing Origin and Insertion in the table, *visually* identify those landmarks on the bone picture on the facing page (they are labeled in the figure below). Next, to strengthen your understanding, start by looking at the bone picture and see if you can *name* the bony

locations that have red and blue marks. Then, read the words in the table and see if you were correct.

As you study other muscles in the table, you can further help your brain anchor the information by comparing and contrasting both words and pictures. For example, compare the origins of the deltoid with its neighboring muscles (see figure on page 65). Do this *verbally* by comparing the words in the Origin column of the table, and *visually* by comparing the red markings on the bone drawings. Do the same for the insertions. Now, view the muscle drawings in Figure 2(B) with clarity about where beneath the muscle fibers each muscle attaches to the bones.

Finally, if possible, move and touch your body or that of a partner. Experience touching the bones, landmarks and muscles. Demonstrate the actions the agonist muscles are creating (or resisting if playing the role of antagonist).

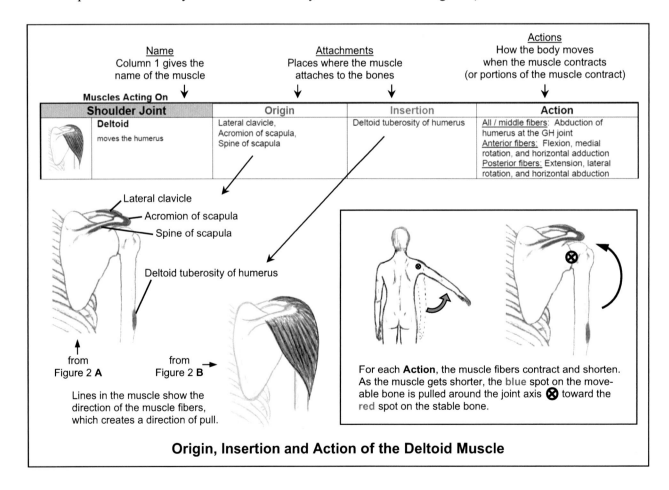

Origin, Insertion and Action of the Deltoid Muscle

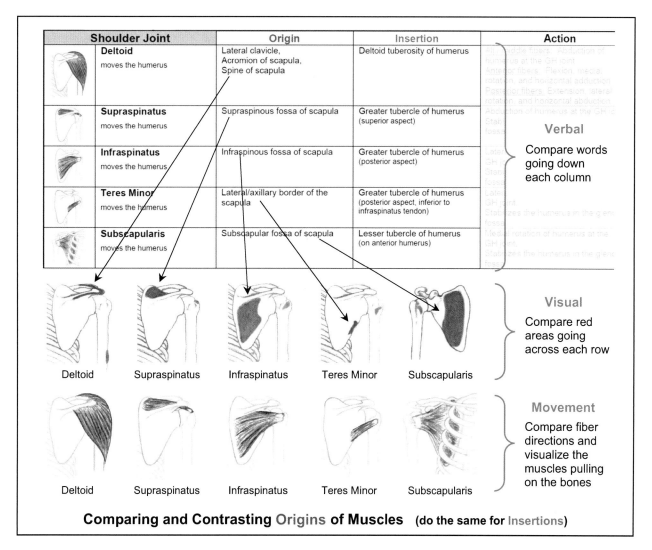

Shoulder Joint		Origin	Insertion	Action
Deltoid moves the humerus		Lateral clavicle, Acromion of scapula, Spine of scapula	Deltoid tuberosity of humerus	**Verbal** Compare words going down each column
Supraspinatus moves the humerus		Supraspinous fossa of scapula	Greater tubercle of humerus (superior aspect)	
Infraspinatus moves the humerus		Infraspinous fossa of scapula	Greater tubercle of humerus (posterior aspect)	
Teres Minor moves the humerus		Lateral/axillary border of the scapula	Greater tubercle of humerus (posterior aspect, inferior to infraspinatus tendon)	
Subscapularis moves the humerus		Subscapular fossa of scapula	Lesser tubercle of humerus (on anterior humerus)	

Deltoid   Supraspinatus   Infraspinatus   Teres Minor   Subscapularis

Visual

Compare red areas going across each row

Deltoid   Supraspinatus   Infraspinatus   Teres Minor   Subscapularis

Movement

Compare fiber directions and visualize the muscles pulling on the bones

Comparing and Contrasting Origins of Muscles (do the same for Insertions)

Once you have studied the physical attributes of the deltoid and compared and contrasted it with its neighbors, you can study its actions with the other muscles in the group using the "B" table.

- Scan across its row in the "B" table, observe its fiber direction(s) and think about the fibers shortening to create the actions marked with a green ✓.

- For each of its actions marked with a ✓, scan down the action column to learn other muscles that are synergists with the deltoid for that action.

- Also look at the adjacent column (that shows the opposite action) to learn antagonists for that deltoid action.

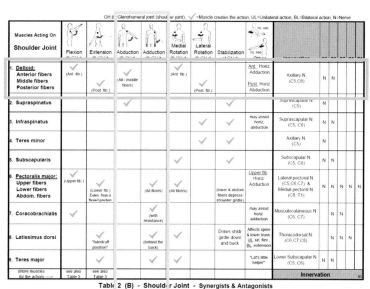

Table 2 (B) - Shoulder Joint - Synergists & Antagonists

Using the "B" Table to Study Actions

About Mastering the Muscles

As you study each group of muscles, you will be building a *foundation* of basic knowledge that will enable you to apply and communicate anatomical and movement information in a clear and efficient way. A few situations where this may be useful are:

- Assessing and working with clients
- Communicating with other health professionals (verbally and written)
- Reading books and magazine/journal articles
- Attending or teaching continuing education classes relevant to your specialty

In order to be fluent in the language of muscles and movement, you will need to learn a basic set of information about each muscle. Then, you will need to be able to communicate and apply that information in a variety of ways.

What to Learn About Each Muscle

Use the table below as a guide to what you need to know about each muscle to master it.

Items 1 through 6 describe the basic knowledge needed to "know" the muscle you are learning.

Items 7 and 8 list further knowledge that relates to physically using the muscle in daily life. These skills are developed by applying the basic facts about the muscle in different situations.

Note that this list is *not* about learning everything for one muscle before you move on to the next. Rather, the list is a framework to be filled in over time as you study and practice with all the muscles in a muscle group.

What to Learn About Each Muscle

Basic Knowledge	**Practical Applications**

1. Name and palpate the origin(s).	7. For the muscle's main action (or action<u>s</u>):
	• Passively shorten it
	• Passively lengthen it
	• Instruct client to actively shorten it (concentric contraction)
	• Instruct client to actively lengthen it (the antagonist is working)
	• Provide correct resistance to test strength of the muscle
	• Name one or more synergists
	   - (<u>must</u> indicate the *action* that is being "synergized")
	• Name one or more antagonists
	   - (<u>must</u> indicate the *action* that is being "antagonized")

2. Name and palpate the insertion(s).	
3. Trace the shape of the entire muscle on the body. • Palpate the muscle • Know where the tendon is vs. the muscle belly	
4. Know and touch the joint(s) the muscle acts on. • More than one joint may be involved	8. Know something about the muscle as it applies to the daily life of a person: • Activities and exercises that use this muscle - (as agonist, antagonist, and stabilizer) • Movements where the muscle contracts concentrically • Movements where the muscle contracts eccentrically • Problems or pathologies that may apply to this muscle
5. Indicate the fiber arrangement. • Show shape and fiber direction on a body • Describe it, draw a diagram showing it	
6. Name and demonstrate the actions of the muscle.	

Real-time Factors that Affect a Muscle's Actions

The table below provides a summary of the influences involved when a movement is created by the contraction of a muscle.

Factors Affecting How a Movement Occurs
The movement that occurs when a muscle contracts can be summarized as the sum of six factors: 1. Direction and arrangement of its fibers **+** 2. Locations of its attachment sites (and their positions relative to the joint axis) **+** 3. The mechanical capability and limitations of the joint(s) being moved **+** 4. Stuff in the way (muscle tissue, fascia, bones, ligaments, skin, fat, organs, etc.) **+** 5. What other muscles are doing at the same time (opposing, stabilizing, etc.) **+** 6. Which bones are most moveable at the moment (what is weight bearing, current direction of gravity, what is held in place by outside forces like a wall, table, another person, etc.)

How You Will Use the Information You've Learned

There are many ways that you will use your knowledge of a muscle. You may have to recall or communicate the information from any of three main directions: **verbal**, **visual**, or **kinesthetic**. The triangle in the figure illustrates this concept. In any given situation, you may need to recall your knowledge from one of the corners of the triangle. In addition, you may need to think **relationally**, i.e., for a muscle or action, be able to think of related muscles or actions.

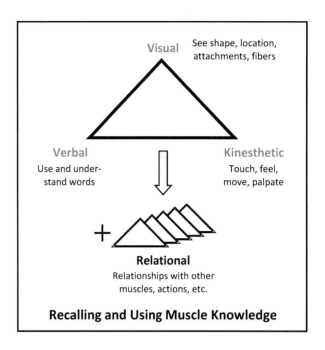

Recalling and Using Muscle Knowledge

You then need to be able to connect to the types of information represented by the other corners of the triangle as you pursue the requirements of the situation at hand. The table below gives a few examples.

Using the Types of Muscle Knowledge

Legs of △	If this happens:	Can you:
Verbal to Visual	You hear or read the name of a muscle.	Visualize where it is on the body and what it looks like.
Visual to Verbal to Kinesthetic	Your client points to a place on their body that hurts.	Recall the name of a muscle there, and have client perform an action to test it.
Kinesthetic to Verbal to Relational	Your client moves a body part and says it is "stiff" and they can't move it very far.	Name the joint and movement involved, and identify which muscles are shortening (agonists), and which muscles are lengthening (antagonists)

Generalizations

The list below gives some general rules of thumb to use while you are learning the muscles in Chapters 4, 5 and 6. Keeping these in mind will help you stay oriented, see useful patterns, and reduce the amount of rote memorization you have to do.

- Muscles on the anterior body usually create flexion (except at knee and below).

- Muscles on the posterior body usually create extension (except at knee and below).

- Muscles that have an oblique (diagonal) angle usually create or control rotations.

- Muscles that insert on the lateral side of limbs create abduction.

- Muscles that insert on the medial side of limbs create adduction.

- For muscles of the axial skeleton, an antagonist for a *unilateral* action is the same muscle on the other side of the body (see Chapter 5, page 121).

- Muscles are strongest at their resting or neutral position (see "mid-range" on pages 18-19). When moved into a substantially shortened state, the muscle has reduced pulling force. The muscle's power is also reduced when it is put in a markedly lengthened position.

Palpation Techniques

The list below provides some ideas to consider when you are palpating the body to identify, assess, or treat muscles.

- Steps to palpate a specific structure: Locate, isolate, engage, palpate, observe cautions

- Be aware of the tactile: Touch, pressure, texture.

- Find landmarks to locate the full length of the muscle.

- Try to feel different depths, being aware of changes in fiber direction and knowing that layers of fascia separate muscles that lie at different depths.

- Use movement (passive, active) to help locate muscles.

- Consider main movements vs. secondary (or assist) movements.

- Provide correct contact point and direction of resistance to engage or activate a muscle.

- Remember gravity is always there to provide resistance (position the body so the muscle has to work against gravity).

- To palpate on yourself, look for a way to "self-engage" the muscle – press against a table, wall, chair, or a place on your own body.

- A muscle is easier to feel upon initial muscle activation rather than full-out contraction – have your partner initiate the action and then release it repeatedly to help isolate the muscle.

Brain-Friendly Conventions Used in Chapters 4 - 6

- All illustrations of muscles and bones are shown on the **right side of the body**. This allows easy comparison of images within each group and from group to group. Once learned and well-organized in memory, the brain can easily "mirror-image" the information to the left side of the body in practice.

- Wherever possible, related illustrations are shown at the **same size and angle of view**. This helps the brain draw comparisons and contrasts without having to translate/flip/resize before observing the features to compare.

- For verbal learners: Note that in the A tables (described on page 60), **related words are lined up** so a visual scan down a column can reveal similarities and differences in the attachments and actions of the different muscles.

- When viewing the side-by-side muscle illustrations (the A Figures and B Figures described on pages 60-63), the origin/insertion pictures 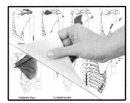 and the corresponding muscle pictures are sized and lined up so you can simply **lift the page** to directly study each muscle with its underlying attachments on the bones.

Chapter 4

Muscles That Move the Upper Extremity

Group 1 – Scapula / Clavicle

Trapezius
Levator scapula
Rhomboid major & minor
Serratus anterior
Pectoralis minor
Subclavius

p. 75-82

Group 2 – Shoulder Joint

Deltoid
Supraspinatus
Infraspinatus
Teres minor
Subscapularis
Pectoralis major
Coracobrachialis
Latissimus dorsi
Teres major

p. 83-90

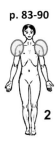

Group 3 – Elbow, Forearm

Biceps brachii
Brachialis
Brachioradialis
Pronator teres
Pronator quadratus
Triceps brachii
Anconeus
Supinator

p. 91-98

Group 4 – Wrist, Hand, Fingers

Flexor carpi radialis
Palmaris longus
Flexor carpi ulnaris
Flexor digitorum superficialis
Flexor digitorum profundus
Extensor carpi radialis longus
Extensor carpi radialis brevis
Extensor carpi ulnaris
Extensor digitorum
Extensor indicis

p. 99-106

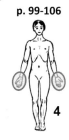

Group 5 – Thumb

Flexor pollicis longus
Flexor pollicis brevis
Opponens pollicis
Adductor pollicis
Abductor pollicis brevis
Abductor pollicis longus
Extensor pollicis longus
Extensor pollicis brevis

p. 107-113

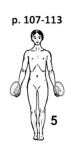

Bonus Group

Intrinsic Muscles
of the Hand

p. 114-115

Introduction

The **upper extremity** is the upper-body portion of the appendicular skeleton (p. 37). It is made up of the scapula and clavicle (shoulder girdle), upper arm, forearm, and hand. The sternoclavicular joint, where the medial end of the clavicle articulates with the sternum, is the *only* synovial joint connecting each upper extremity to the trunk.

This chapter describes the muscles that move the scapula on the torso, and move the various joints within the upper extremity. The muscles are separated into five functional groups, with some overlap of function between groups for muscles that cross multiple joints:

Group 1 – Movement of the shoulder girdle, which is the scapula and clavicle moving together on the torso

Group 2 – Movement of the humerus at the shoulder joint

Group 3 – Movement of the forearm, bending at the elbow and rotating on its lengthwise axis

Group 4 – Movement of the wrist, hand and fingers

Group 5 – Movement of the thumb

At the end of the chapter, a bonus muscle group presents the intrinsic muscles of the hand.

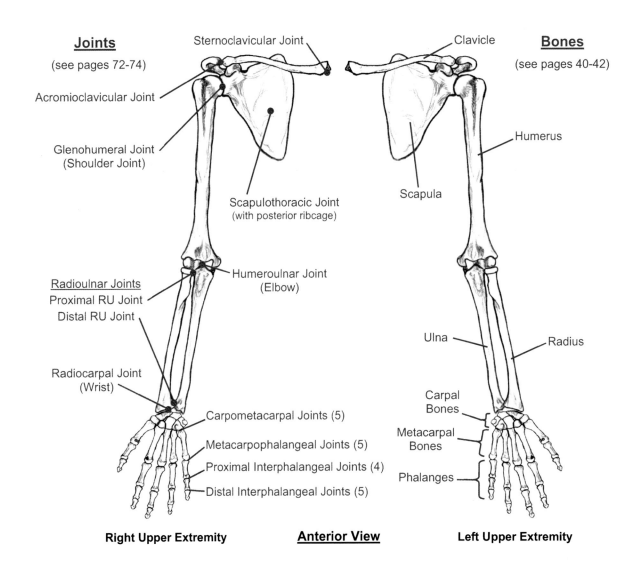

Joints
(see pages 72-74)

Sternoclavicular Joint

Acromioclavicular Joint

Glenohumeral Joint
(Shoulder Joint)

Scapulothoracic Joint
(with posterior ribcage)

Radioulnar Joints
Proximal RU Joint
Distal RU Joint

Humeroulnar Joint
(Elbow)

Radiocarpal Joint
(Wrist)

Carpometacarpal Joints (5)

Metacarpophalangeal Joints (5)

Proximal Interphalangeal Joints (4)

Distal Interphalangeal Joints (5)

Clavicle

Bones
(see pages 40-42)

Humerus

Scapula

Ulna

Radius

Carpal Bones

Metacarpal Bones

Phalanges

Right Upper Extremity   <u>**Anterior View**</u>   **Left Upper Extremity**

Overview of Muscles

The illustration below shows superficial muscles from groups 1-4 that can be seen from a lateral viewpoint. This gives an idea about the expanse of body regions that are involved with moving the upper extremity.

Note that only muscles that have superficial exposure can be seen. There are also many other muscles at deeper layers that are hidden beneath the superficial muscles.

Joint Details and Ligaments

The joints of the upper extremity begin proximally with the sternoclavicular joint, which is the only bony attachment of the upper extremity to the axial skeleton. Progressing distally, there are numerous joints at the shoulder, elbow, wrist, and hand.

The details and ligaments of these joints are described on the following three pages.

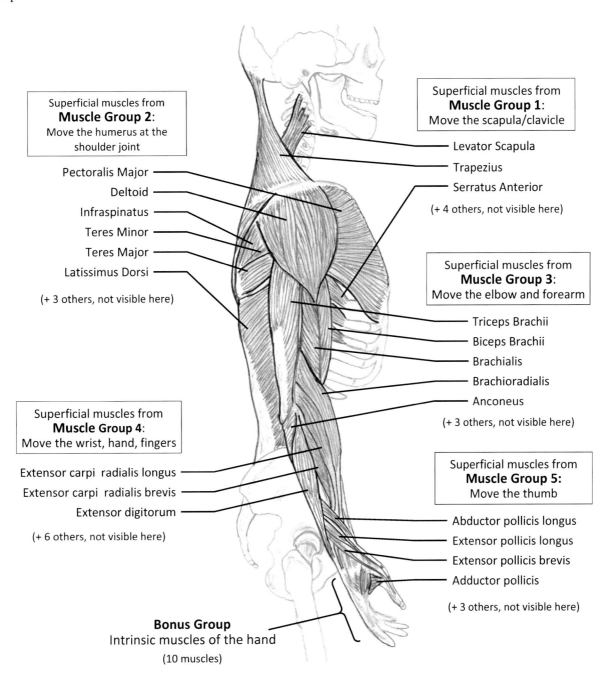

Superficial muscles from
Muscle Group 2:
Move the humerus at the shoulder joint

Pectoralis Major
Deltoid
Infraspinatus
Teres Minor
Teres Major
Latissimus Dorsi

(+ 3 others, not visible here)

Superficial muscles from
Muscle Group 1:
Move the scapula/clavicle

Levator Scapula
Trapezius
Serratus Anterior

(+ 4 others, not visible here)

Superficial muscles from
Muscle Group 3:
Move the elbow and forearm

Triceps Brachii
Biceps Brachii
Brachialis
Brachioradialis
Anconeus

(+ 3 others, not visible here)

Superficial muscles from
Muscle Group 4:
Move the wrist, hand, fingers

Extensor carpi radialis longus
Extensor carpi radialis brevis
Extensor digitorum

(+ 6 others, not visible here)

Superficial muscles from
Muscle Group 5:
Move the thumb

Abductor pollicis longus
Extensor pollicis longus
Extensor pollicis brevis
Adductor pollicis

(+ 3 others, not visible here)

Bonus Group
Intrinsic muscles of the hand
(10 muscles)

Shoulder Complex – Joints and Ligaments

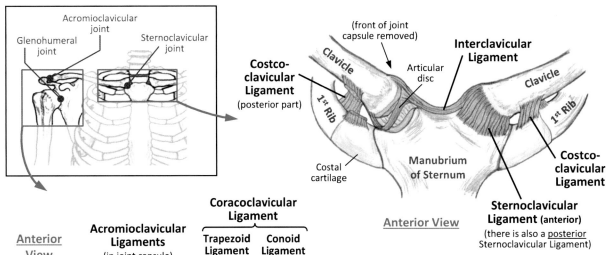

Anterior View

Costco-clavicular Ligament (posterior part)

Clavicle

(front of joint capsule removed)

Articular disc

Interclavicular Ligament

Clavicle

1st Rib

1st Rib

Costal cartilage

Manubrium of Sternum

Costco-clavicular Ligament

Sternoclavicular Ligament (anterior)

(there is also a posterior Sternoclavicular Ligament)

Acromioclavicular joint

Glenohumeral joint

Sternoclavicular joint

Anterior View

Acromioclavicular Ligaments (in joint capsule)

Coracoclavicular Ligament

Trapezoid Ligament **Conoid Ligament**

Clavicle

Acromion of scapula

Coracoacromial Ligament

Coracohumeral Ligament

Greater tubercle

Superior Transverse Scapular Lig.

Scapular notch

Coracoid process

Transverse Humeral Ligament

Biceps brachii tendon (in synovial sheath)

Bicipital groove (intertubercular groove)

Humerus

Axillary recess

Scapula

Glenohumeral Capsular Ligaments

Sternoclavicular (SC) Joint	
Ligament	**Function**
Sterno-clavicular Ligs.	Resist anterior/posterior translation of clavicle; resist dislocation of clavicle from sternum.
Costo-clavicular Ligs.	Anterior part limits retraction of clavicle, posterior part limits protraction. Both limit elevation.
Inter-clavicular Lig.	Limits depression of clavicle.

Acromioclavicular (AC) Joint	
Ligament	**Function**
Acromio-clavicular Ligs.	Reinforce the AC joint capsule superiorly and inferiorly, resisting separation.
Coraco-clavicular Ligs.	Has 2 parts: Trapezoid & Conoid. Prevent clavicle from raising superiorly away from the scapula.
Coraco-acromial Lig.	Forms a roof over head of humerus, protecting rotator cuff tendons & SA bursa. Blocks superior translation.

Glenohumeral (GH) Joint	
Ligament	**Function**
Gleno-humeral Capsular Ligs.	Limit external rotation, abduction, and anterior translation of the humeral head.
Coraco-humeral Lig.	Resists inferior translation of humeral head, esp. during adduction. Limits external rotation.
Transverse Humeral Lig.	Holds biceps brachii tendon (long head) in the bicipital groove.

Acromion of scapula

AC Joint

Clavicle

Subacromial bursa*

Supraspinatus tendon

Subdeltoid bursa*

*Together called the SASD (subacromial-subdeltoid bursa)

Joint capsule

Synovial membrane

Glenoid labrum

Supraspinatus muscle

Glenoid fossa of scapula

Scapula

Glenoid labrum

Synovial membrane

Joint capsule

Axillary pouch

Anterior View

Humerus

Humerus

Coronal Section Through Glenohumeral Joint

⬭ = articular cartilage

04396

Elbow and Forearm – Joints and Ligaments

Right Elbow

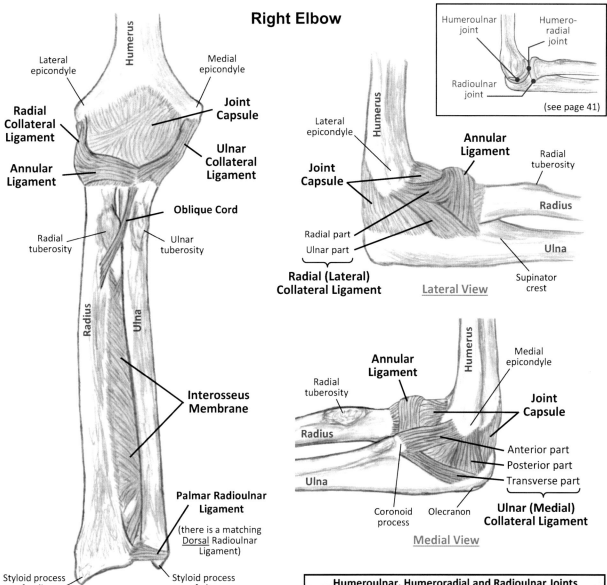

Lateral epicondyle

Humerus

Medial epicondyle

Radial Collateral Ligament

Annular Ligament

Joint Capsule

Ulnar Collateral Ligament

Oblique Cord

Radial tuberosity

Ulnar tuberosity

Radius

Ulna

Interosseus Membrane

Palmar Radioulnar Ligament

(there is a matching <u>Dorsal</u> Radioulnar Ligament)

Styloid process of radius

Styloid process of ulna

<u>Anterior View</u>

Humeroulnar joint

Humero-radial joint

Radioulnar joint

(see page 41)

Lateral epicondyle

Humerus

Annular Ligament

Radial tuberosity

Joint Capsule

Radial part

Ulnar part

Radius

Ulna

Supinator crest

Radial (Lateral) Collateral Ligament

<u>Lateral View</u>

Annular Ligament

Radial tuberosity

Humerus

Medial epicondyle

Radius

Joint Capsule

Anterior part

Posterior part

Transverse part

Ulna

Coronoid process

Olecranon

Ulnar (Medial) Collateral Ligament

<u>Medial View</u>

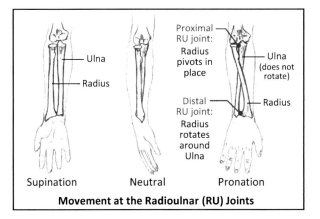

Ulna

Radius

Supination

Proximal RU joint: Radius pivots in place

Ulna (does not rotate)

Distal RU joint: Radius rotates around Ulna

Radius

Neutral

Pronation

Movement at the Radioulnar (RU) Joints

Humeroulnar, Humeroradial and Radioulnar Joints	
Ligament	**Function**
Radial (Lateral) Collateral Lig.	Resists medially applied/laterally driven (varus) forces. Resists extremes of flexion.
Ulnar (Medial) Collateral Lig.	Resists laterally applied/medially driven (valgus) forces. Anterior part tightens during extension, posterior tightens during flexion.
Annular Lig.	Holds head of radius against radial notch of ulna (radioulnar pivot joint). Resists radial distraction (hand pulled in a distal direction).
Interosseus Membrane	Binds the radius to the ulna. Transmits longitudinal compression forces between radius and ulna. Adds area for muscle attachments.
Distal Radio-ulnar Ligs.	Stabilize the distal radioulnar joint during pronation and supination (palmar and dorsal ligaments).

Wrist and Hand – Joints and Ligaments

| Metacarpal Bones: | 1 = to Thumb
2, 3, 4, 5 = to Fingers | Carpal Bones: | H = Hamate   C = Capitate   Tzd = Trapezoid   T = Trapezium
P = Pisiform   Tri = Triquetrum   L = Lunate   S = Scaphoid |

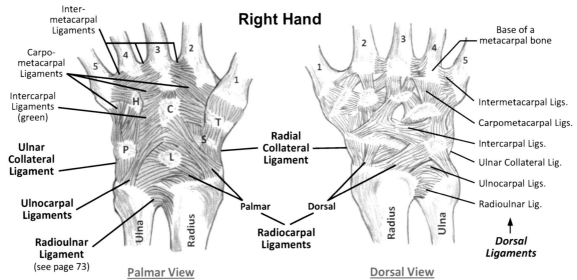

Right Hand

Inter-metacarpal Ligaments
Carpo-metacarpal Ligaments
Intercarpal Ligaments (green)
Ulnar Collateral Ligament
Ulnocarpal Ligaments
Radioulnar Ligament (see page 73)

Radial Collateral Ligament

Palmar   Dorsal
Radiocarpal Ligaments

Ulna   Radius

Palmar View
(flexor retinaculum removed, see p. 115)

Base of a metacarpal bone
Intermetacarpal Ligs.
Carpometacarpal Ligs.
Intercarpal Ligs.
Ulnar Collateral Lig.
Ulnocarpal Ligs.
Radioulnar Lig.

Radius   Ulna

Dorsal Ligaments

Dorsal View

Wrist: Radiocarpal Joint and Midcarpal Joint

Ligament	Function
Radial (Lateral) Collateral Lig.	Prevents too much ulnar deviation and resists varus forces (laterally-driven forces).
Ulnar (Medial) Collateral Lig.	Prevents too much radial deviation and resists valgus forces (medially-driven forces).
Radiocarpal Ligs.	Palmar: Limit wrist extension Dorsal: Limit wrist flexion
Ulnocarpal Ligs.	Palmar: Limit wrist extension Dorsal: Limit wrist flexion
Flexor Retinaculum (see page 115)	Holds down the tendons of the finger flexor muscles. Provides roof of the carpal tunnel.

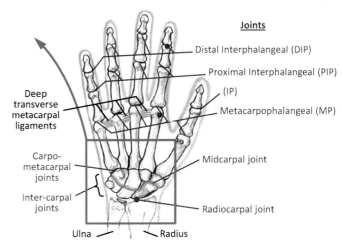

Joints
Distal Interphalangeal (DIP)
Proximal Interphalangeal (PIP)
(IP)
Metacarpophalangeal (MP)

Deep transverse metacarpal ligaments
Carpo-metacarpal joints
Inter-carpal joints

Midcarpal joint
Radiocarpal joint

Ulna   Radius

Right Hand (Palmar View)   (see page 42)

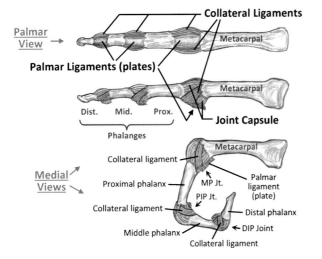

Palmar View →
Collateral Ligaments
Metacarpal
Palmar Ligaments (plates)
Metacarpal
Dist.   Mid.   Prox.
Phalanges
Joint Capsule

Medial Views
Collateral ligament
Metacarpal
Proximal phalanx
MP Jt.
Palmar ligament (plate)
PIP Jt.
Collateral ligament
Distal phalanx
Middle phalanx
DIP Joint
Collateral ligament

Hand: Carpal, Metacarpal and Phalangeal Joints

Ligament	Function
Intercarpal, Carpometacarpal, Intermetacarpal Ligs.	Palmar & Dorsal: Reinforce joints between carpal bones, and between carpals and bases of metacarpal bones #1 – #5.
Deep Transverse Metacarpal Ligs.	Connect the heads of metacarpal bones #2–#5, resisting lateral spreading between them.
MP, PIP and DIP Collateral Ligs.	Resist varus and valgus forces on the MP, PIP and DIP joints. Go taut with flexion of finger.
Palmar Interphalangeal Ligs. (plates)	Limit extension of fingers. Provide a channel for tendons of finger flexor muscles.

94407

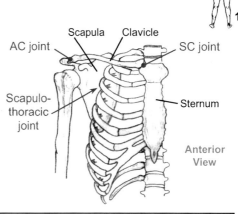

Movement of the Scapula/Clavicle

Muscle Group 1

Trapezius	Serratus anterior
Levator scapula	Pectoralis minor
Rhomboid major and minor	Subclavius

Joints

(Joint details: p. 72)

The scapula and clavicle combined are called the **shoulder girdle**. As the shoulder girdle moves, the scapula glides on the back and side of the ribcage. Three joints are involved with movement of the shoulder girdle.

Sternoclavicular Joint (SC)

Manubrium of **sternum** ◄► Medial end of **clavicle**
Modified ball and socket joint
(Complex joint - may also be classified in other ways, for example, some texts call it a saddle joint)

The SC joint is the <u>only</u> bony connection of the upper-body appendicular skeleton with the axial skeleton.

Acromioclavicular Joint (AC)

Acromion of **scapula** ◄► Lateral end of **clavicle**
Gliding joint

Scapulothoracic Joint (ST)

Anterior surface of **scapula** ◄► Posterior thoracic wall
False joint (the scapula suspended by muscles)
Also called a "functional joint" (i.e., no bone-to-bone articulation, but functions as a joint)

Movements Available

The scapula and clavicle move together, so all three joints (SC, AC, ST) are said to have the same movements, which are the actions of the scapula.

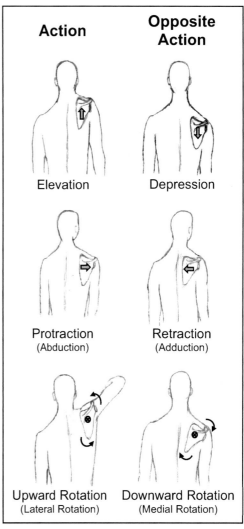

Action	Opposite Action
Elevation	Depression
Protraction (Abduction)	Retraction (Adduction)
Upward Rotation (Lateral Rotation)	Downward Rotation (Medial Rotation)

Scapular action pairs:
Elevation and Depression
Protraction and Retraction (also sometimes called Abduction and Adduction)
Upward Rotation – glenoid cavity goes <u>up</u> (also called Lateral Rotation – inferior angle moves laterally)
Downward Rotation – glenoid cavity goes <u>down</u> (also called Medial Rotation – inferior angle moves medially)

Note: As the scapula abducts, its lateral edge also slides *forward*, following the curve of the ribs. This is why moving the scapula away from the spine is usually called protraction (moving in the transverse plane).

Bones, Bony Landmarks, Other Structures

Muscles that move the Scapula/Clavicle have attachments on the upper trunk, spine, and head, and of course the scapula and clavicle. Review the bony landmarks and other structures listed below, referring to the drawings in Chapter 2, pages 40 and 43-46.

Scapula (p. 40)
    Acromion
    Coracoid process
    Superior angle
    Inferior angle
    Spine of scapula
    Root of spine
    Medial (vertebral) border
    Lateral (axillary) border
    Subscapular fossa

    Notes:
    - There are bony landmarks on both the
       posterior and anterior sides of the scapula

    - The <u>anterior</u> side of the scapula is also
       known as the <u>costal</u> side (root "costo"=rib)

Clavicle (p. 40)
    Medial end is called the sternal end
    Lateral end is called the acromial end

Sternum (p. 46)
    Manubrium

Occiput (p. 43)
    External occipital protuberance
    Superior nuchal line

Spine (p. 44)
    Cervical Vertebrae
       Spinous Processes (SP's)
       Transverse Processes (TVP's)

    Thoracic Vertebrae
       Spinous Processes (SP's)

Ribs (p. 46)
    Anterior and anteriolateral surfaces
    Costal cartilage

<u>Other Structures:</u>

Nuchal ligament
(also called the
Ligamentum Nuchae)

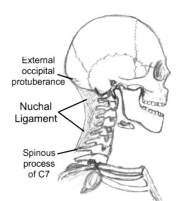

External occipital protuberance

Nuchal Ligament

Spinous process of C7

Notes

Muscle Group 1 - Muscles that move the shoulder girdle (scapula/clavicle) are illustrated as a group on this page. The next four pages have tables and figures that describe each muscle individually, and provide many ways of comparing and contrasting the muscles to each other.

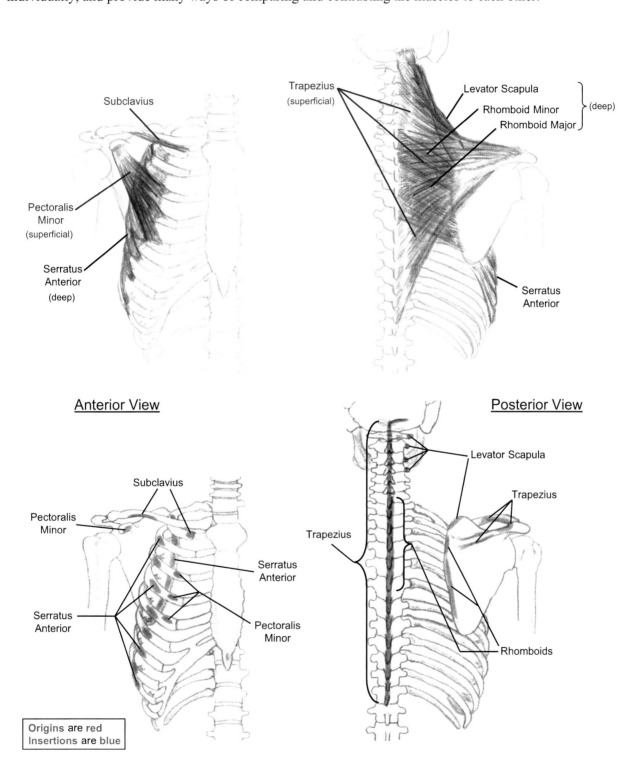

Attachment sites for all muscles in Group 1

Group 1: Muscles Acting On

TVP=Transverse process of vertebra, SP=Spinous process of vertebra

Scapula / Clavicle	Origin	Insertion	Action
Trapezius moves the scapula *(also moves the neck)* Has 3 parts: Upper fibers Middle fibers Lower fibers	Upper: Occiput, nuchal ligament, and SP of C7 Middle: SP's of T1-T4 Lower: SP's of T5-T12 *Overall description:* Occiput, nuchal ligament, and SP's of C7-T12 (Occipital attachment is the external occipital protuberance and medial 1/3 of superior nuchal line)	Upper: Lateral 1/3 of clavicle Middle: Acromion of scapula and spine of scapula (lateral superior portion) Lower: Spine of scapula (medial inferior portion) *Overall description:* Lateral clavicle, acromion and spine of scapula	Upper fibers: Elevation & upward rotation of the scapula Middle fibers: Retraction (adduction) Lower fibers: Depression & upward rotation All fibers: Stabilize and retract the scapula *(When the scapula is fixed:* The *upper* trapezius moves the head & neck -- See Muscle Group 7)
Levator Scapula moves the scapula *(also moves the neck)*	TVP's of C1-C4	Superior angle of the scapula (and upper medial border of scapula)	Elevation and downward rotation of the scapula. *(When scapula is fixed:* Moves the neck -- See Group 7)
Rhomboids move the scapula Rhomboid Minor Rhomboid Major	Minor: SP's of C7, T1 Major: SP's of T2-T5 *Overall description:* SP's of C7-T5 (deep to mid. trapezius)	Medial (vertebral) border of the scapula	Retraction (adduction) and elevation of the scapula. (Also assists downward rotation of the scapula)
Serratus Anterior moves the scapula	Ribs #1 - 8 or 9 (anterolateral surfaces)	Medial (vertebral) border of the scapula (on the anterior side)	Protraction (abduction) and upward rotation of the scapula. Stabilizes the scapula.
Pectoralis Minor moves the scapula	Anterior ribs #3-5 (deep to pec major)	Coracoid process of scapula	Anterior tilt (i.e., draws scapula forward, downward, and inward). Assists depression of scapula. *When scapula is fixed:* Assists in forced inhalation.
Subclavius stabilizes the clavicle	Rib #1 (medial portion at its junction with costal cartilage)	Inferior aspect of clavicle	Depresses the clavicle. Stabilizes the sternoclavicular joint.

Table 1 (A) - Scapula / Clavicle - Origin, Insertion, Action

(larger illustrations on page 81)

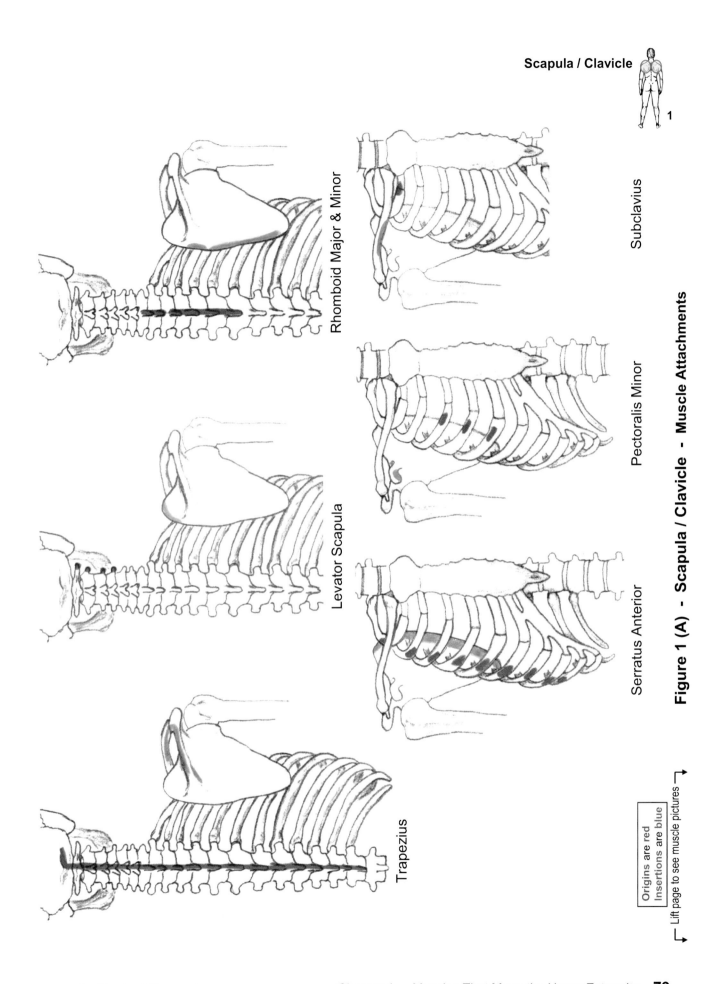

Rhomboid Major & Minor

Levator Scapula

Trapezius

Subclavius

Pectoralis Minor

Serratus Anterior

Figure 1 (A) - Scapula / Clavicle - Muscle Attachments

Origins are red
Insertions are blue

Lift page to see muscle pictures

Group 1:

All actions are the shoulder girdle (scapula+clavicle) moving as a unit, ⟩ =Muscle creates the action, N=Nerve

Muscles Acting On Scapula / Clavicle	Elevation	Depression	Protraction (abduction)	Retraction (adduction)	Upward Rotation	Downward Rotation	Stabilization of scapula	Other	Innervation	Cr. XI	C3	C4	C5	C6	C7	C8	T1
1. Trapezius:									Spinal Accessory N. (Cranial N. XI), and C3, C4								
Upper fibers	⟩ (upper fibers)				⟩ (upper fibers)			Upper fibers: See also Table 7 for reversed O/I actions		N	N	N					
Middle fibers				⟩ (middle fibers)			⟩ (All fibers)										
Lower fibers		⟩ (lower fibers)			⟩ (lower fibers)												
2. Levator Scapula	⟩					⟩		See also Table 7 for reversed O/I actions	Dorsal scapular N. (C5), and C3, C4		N	N	N				
3. Rhomboids: Rhomboid Major Rhomboid Minor	⟩			⟩		⟩ assist			Dorsal scapular N. (C5)				N				
4. Serratus Anterior			⟩		⟩		⟩	Reaching forward or "punching" motion	Long thoracic N. (C5-C7)				N	N	N		
5. Pectoralis Minor		⟩ assist (with anterior tilt)						Creates "Anterior tilt" = Draws scapula forward, down, and in	Medial pectoral N. (C8, T1)							N	N
6. Subclavius		⟩ assist (depresses clavicle)						Stabilizes sternoclavicular joint	Subclavian N. (C5, C6)				N	N			
(More muscles for the action) ---->									**Innervation**								

Table 1 (B) - Scapula / Clavicle - Synergists & Antagonists

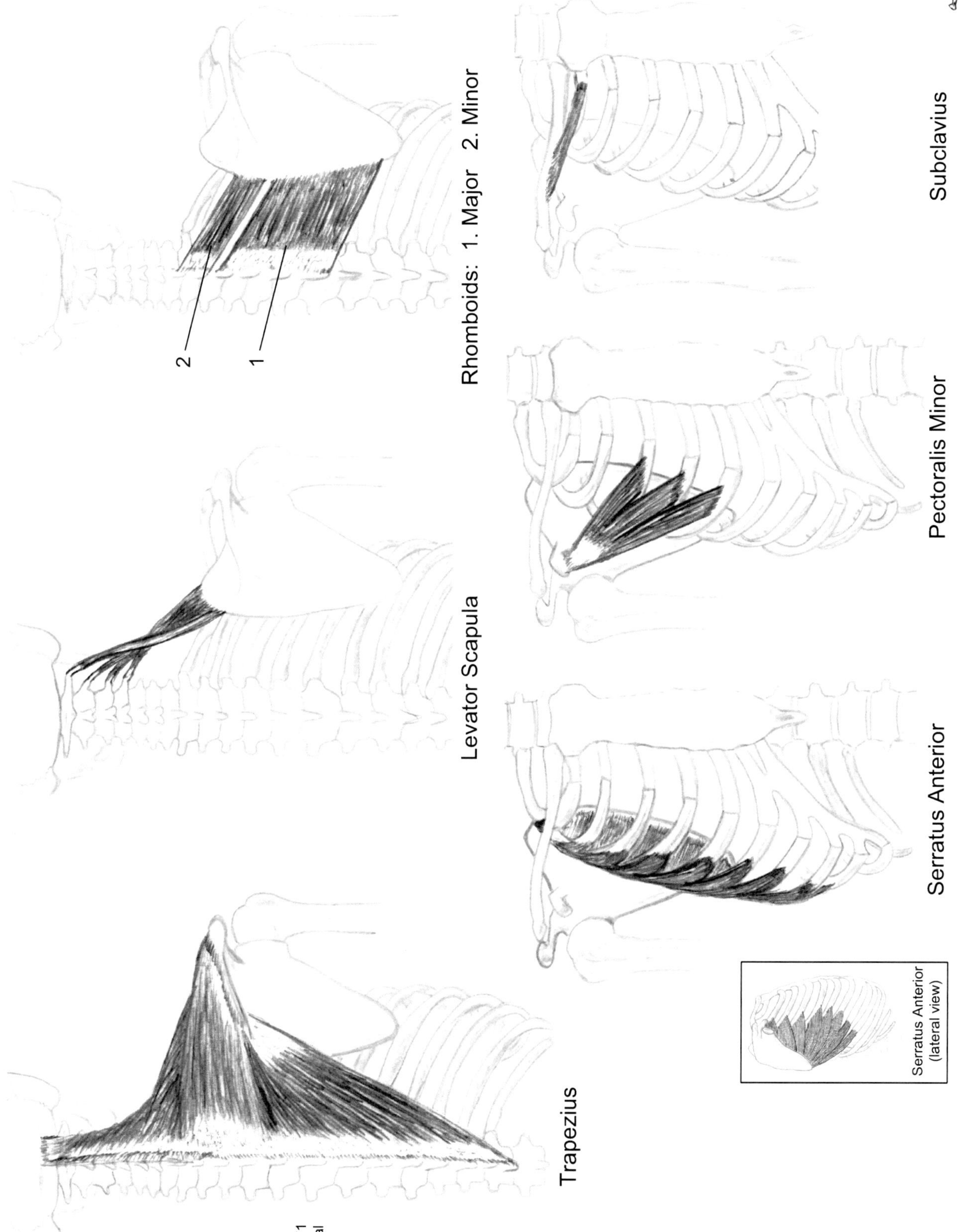

Rhomboids: 1. Major 2. Minor

2

1

Subclavius

Pectoralis Minor

Levator Scapula

Serratus Anterior

Serratus Anterior
(lateral view)

Trapezius

(see p. 71 for lateral view)

Figure 1 (B) - Scapula / Clavicle - Muscle Pictures

Note-taking page ~ (palpation, how to lengthen/shorten, cautions, common uses, etc.)

1

Muscle Group 1 - Muscles Acting on the **Scapula / Clavicle**

1. Trapezius

Upper fibers

Middle fibers

Lower fibers

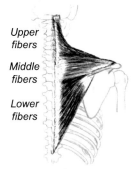

4. Serratus Anterior

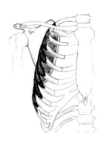

2. Levator Scapula

5. Pectoralis Minor

3. Rhomboid Major & Minor

6. Subclavius

Movement of the Shoulder Joint

Muscle Group 2

Deltoid	Rotator Cuff Muscles:
Pectoralis major	Supraspinatus
Coracobrachialis	Infraspinatus
Latissimus dorsi	Teres minor
Teres major	Subscapularis

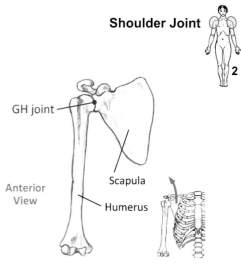

GH joint

Anterior View

Scapula

Humerus

Joints

(Joint details: p. 72)

The muscles in this group primarily move the humerus at the glenohumeral joint, commonly called the shoulder joint.

Glenohumeral Joint (GH) – The Shoulder Joint

Glenoid cavity of **scapula** ◄► Head of **humerus**

Ball and socket joint

Movements available:
Flexion, Extension
Abduction, Adduction
Lateral Rotation, Medial Rotation

Horizontal Abduction (also called Horizontal Extension)
Horizontal Adduction (also called Horizontal Flexion)

Circumduction (a combination movement)

Notes:
The GH joint is highly mobile, and very unstable. Joint capsule is main support (few extrinsic ligaments), but the rotator cuff muscles provide dynamic stability.

Other Movements

The combination of the humerus and shoulder girdle (p. 75) is called the **shoulder complex**. The humerus and scapula usually move in a coordinated fashion. For example,

• Muscles acting on the humerus which have origins that are *not on the scapula* can create scapular movement by "remote control" (e.g, latissimus dorsi, pectoralis major).

• **Scapulohumeral rhythm** – Movements of the humerus and scapula are sequenced and coordinated. This is usually observed as a 2-to-1 ratio during abduction of the arm, where the humerus rotates 2 degrees at the glenohumeral joint for each 1 degree of upward scapular rotation. Other rhythms occur during flexion/extension and horizontal abduction/adduction.

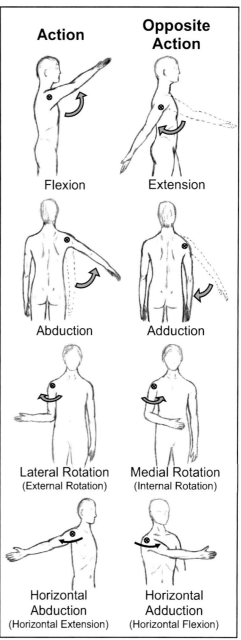

Action — **Opposite Action**

Flexion — Extension

Abduction — Adduction

Lateral Rotation (External Rotation) — Medial Rotation (Internal Rotation)

Horizontal Abduction (Horizontal Extension) — Horizontal Adduction (Horizontal Flexion)

Bones, Bony Landmarks, Other Structures

Muscles that move the humerus at the shoulder joint have attachments over a large area of the skeleton. Review the bony landmarks and other structures listed below, referring to the diagrams in Chapter 2, pages 40-47.

Humerus (p. 41)

    Head
    Greater tubercle
    Lesser tubercle
    Intertubercular groove (Bicipital groove)
       - Medial edge and lateral edge of the
         groove are separate landmarks
    Deltoid tuberosity
    Shaft

Scapula (p. 40)

    Glenoid cavity (also called glenoid fossa)
    Supraspinous fossa
    Infraspinous fossa
    Subscapular fossa
    Lateral border (also called axillary border)
    Spine (of scapula)
    Acromion
    Coracoid process
    Inferior angle

Clavicle (p. 40)

Sternum (p. 46)
    Manubrium
    Body
    Xiphoid process

Ribs (p. 46)
    Anterior: Costal cartilages
    Posterior: Lower 3-4 ribs

Vertebrae (p. 44)
    Thoracic spinous processes (SP's)
    Lumbar spinous processes (SP's)

Sacrum (p. 44)

Pelvis (p. 47) – Posterior iliac crest

Other Structures:

    Thoracolumbar fascia
       Also called Lumbar fascia
       Also Thoracolumbar Aponeurosis (TLA)

    Rotator cuff (also called Musculotendinous cuff)
    Subdeltoid and subacromial bursae (p. 72)

Lumbar fascia

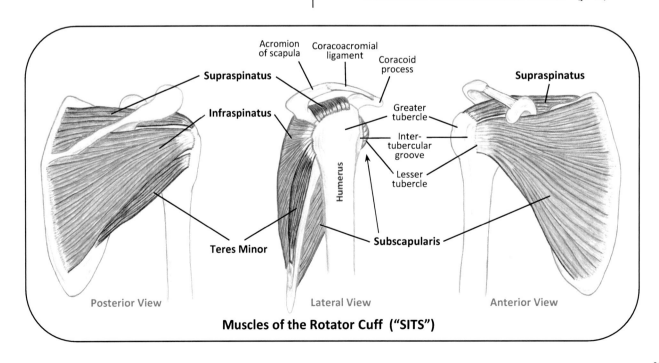

Muscles of the Rotator Cuff ("SITS")

Posterior View   Lateral View   Anterior View

Muscle Group 2 - **Muscles that move the humerus at the glenohumeral joint** are illustrated as a group on this page. The four pages that follow have tables and figures that describe each muscle individually, and provide many ways of comparing and contrasting the muscles to each other.

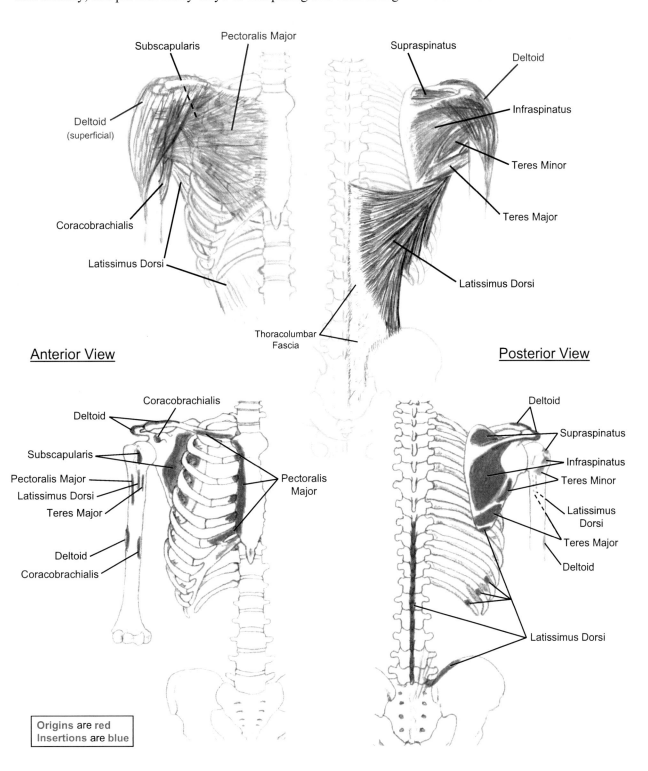

Attachment sites for all muscles in Group 2

Shoulder Joint

Group 2: Muscles Acting On

GH=Glenohumeral joint (shoulder joint), UL=Unilateral action, BL=Bilateral action

Shoulder Joint	Origin	Insertion	Action
Deltoid moves the humerus	Lateral clavicle, Acromion of scapula, Spine of scapula	Deltoid tuberosity of humerus	All / middle fibers: Abduction of humerus at the GH joint Anterior fibers: Flexion, medial rotation, and horizontal adduction Posterior fibers: Extension, lateral rotation, and horizontal abduction
Supraspinatus moves the humerus	Supraspinous fossa of scapula	Greater tubercle of humerus (superior aspect)	Abduction of humerus at the GH joint, Stabilizes the humerus in the glenoid fossa
Infraspinatus moves the humerus	Infraspinous fossa of scapula	Greater tubercle of humerus (posterior aspect)	Lateral rotation of humerus at the GH joint, Stabilizes the humerus in the glenoid fossa
Teres Minor moves the humerus	Lateral/axillary border of the scapula	Greater tubercle of humerus (posterior aspect, inferior to infraspinatus tendon)	Lateral rotation of humerus at the GH joint, Stabilizes the humerus in the glenoid fossa
Subscapularis moves the humerus	Subscapular fossa of scapula	Lesser tubercle of humerus (on anterior humerus)	Medial rotation of humerus at the GH joint, Stabilizes the humerus in the glenoid fossa
Pectoralis Major moves the humerus	Clavicular head: Medial half of clavicle Sternocostal part: Sternum & cartilages of ribs 1-6 (also sometimes abdominal head: Aponeurosis of external oblique)	Intertubercular groove of the humerus (lateral lip)	All fibers: Adduction and medial rotation of humerus Upper fibers: Flexion and horizontal adduction of humerus Lower fibers: Extension of humerus - from a flexed position
Coracobrachialis moves the humerus	Coracoid process of scapula	Shaft of humerus -- on the medial side half way down	Flexion and adduction of the humerus at the GH joint (also assists horizontal adduction)
Latissimus Dorsi moves the humerus and the trunk & spine	Spinous processes of lower 6 thoracic and all lumbar vertebrae, sacrum, posterior iliac crest, lumbar fascia, lower 3 or 4 ribs (and sometimes the tip of the inferior angle of the scapula).	Intertubercular groove of the humerus (medial lip)	Extension, adduction, and medial rotation of the humerus at the GH joint. Also affects lower trunk & spine: UL: lateral flexion, BL: extension of spine & anterior pelvic tilt
Teres Major moves the humerus	Inferior angle and lower lateral border of scapula (dorsal side)	Intertubercular groove of the humerus (medial lip)	Extension, adduction, and medial rotation of the humerus at the GH joint.

Rotator Cuff Muscles

(larger illustrations on page 89)

Table 2 (A) - Shoulder Joint - Origin, Insertion, Action

Mastering Muscles & Movement

34063

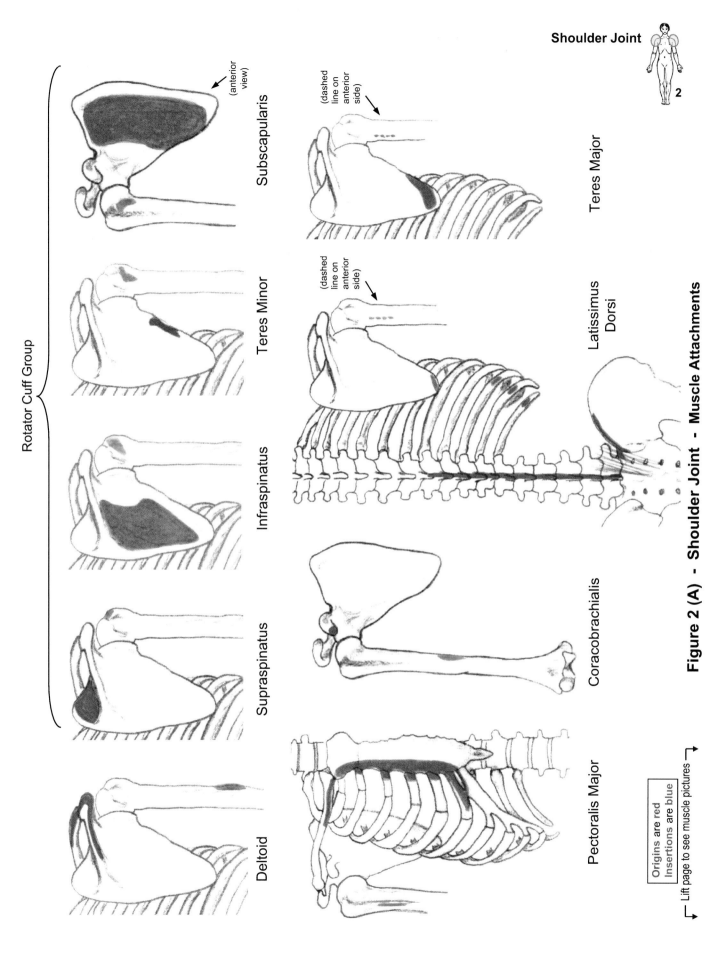

Subscapularis (anterior view)

Teres Major (dashed line on anterior side)

Rotator Cuff Group

Teres Minor

Latissimus Dorsi (dashed line on anterior side)

Infraspinatus

Supraspinatus

Coracobrachialis

Deltoid

Pectoralis Major

Origins are red
Insertions are blue

Lift page to see muscle pictures

Figure 2 (A) - Shoulder Joint - Muscle Attachments

Group 2:

GH jt.=Glenohumeral joint (shoulder joint), ⌄=Muscle creates the action, UL=Unilateral action, BL=Bilateral action, N=Nerve

Muscles Acting On **Shoulder Joint**	Flexion @ GH jt.	Extension @ GH jt.	Abduction @ GH jt.	Adduction @ GH jt.	Medial Rotation @ GH jt.	Lateral Rotation @ GH jt.	Stabilization of GH jt.	Other	Innervation	C5	C6	C7	C8	T1
1. Deltoid: Anterior fibers, Middle fibers, Posterior fibers	⌄ (Ant. fib.)	⌄ (Post. fib.)	⌄ (All / middle fibers)		⌄ (Ant. fib.)	⌄ (Post. fib.)		**Ant:** Horiz. Adduction / **Post:** Horiz. Abduction	Axillary N. (C5,C6)	N	N			
2. Supraspinatus			⌄				⌄		Suprascapular N. (C5)	N				
3. Infraspinatus						⌄	⌄	may assist horiz. abduction	Suprascapular N. (C5, C6)	N	N			
4. Teres Minor						⌄	⌄		Axillary N. (C5)	N				
5. Subscapularis					⌄		⌄		Subscapular N. (C5, C6)	N	N			
6. Pectoralis Major: Upper fibers, Lower fibers, Abdom. fibers	⌄ (Upper fib.)	⌄ (Lower fib.) Exten. from a flexed position		⌄ (All fibers)	⌄ (All fibers)		(lower & abdom fibers depress shoulder girdle)	<u>Upper fib.</u>: Horiz. Adduction	Lateral pectoral N. (C5,C6,C7) & Medial pectoral N. (C8, T1)	N	N	N	N	N
7. Coracobrachialis	⌄			⌄ (with resistance)				may assist horiz. adduction	Musculocutaneous N. (C6, C7)		N	N		
8. Latissimus Dorsi		⌄ "handcuff position"		⌄ (behind the back)	⌄		Draws shldr girdle down and back	Affects spine & lower trunk: <u>UL</u>: lat. flex., <u>BL</u>: extension	Thoracodorsal N. (C6,C7,C8)		N	N	N	
9. Teres Major		⌄		⌄	⌄			"Lat's little helper"	Lower Subscapular N. (C5, C6)	N	N			
(More muscles for the action) --->	see also Group 3	see also Group 3							**Innervation**					

Table 2 (B) - Shoulder Joint - Synergists & Antagonists

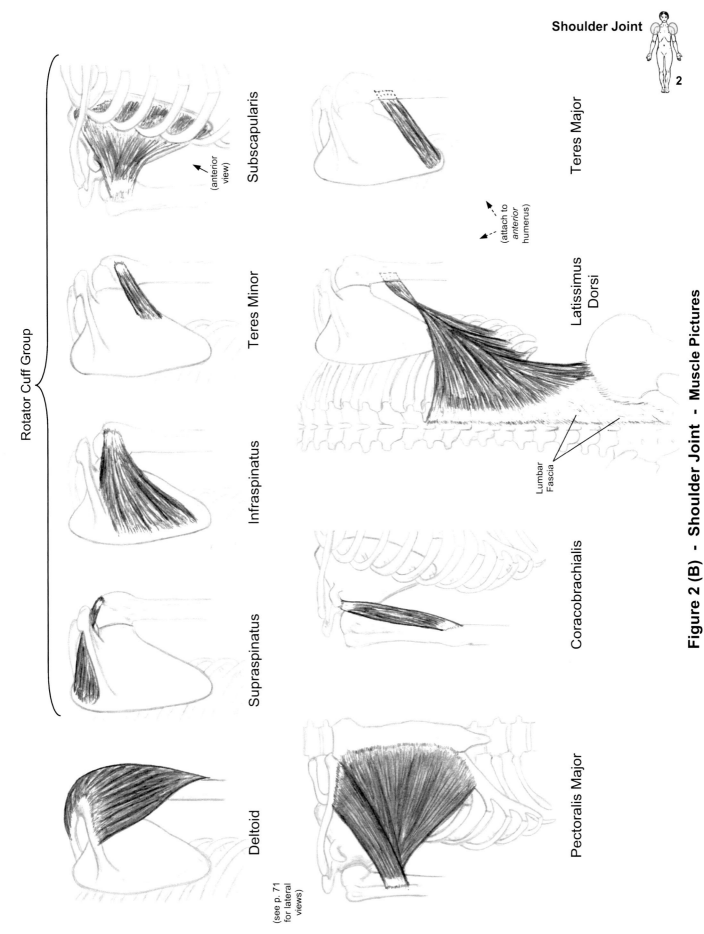

Rotator Cuff Group

Subscapularis

(anterior view)

Teres Minor

Infraspinatus

Supraspinatus

Deltoid

(see p. 71 for lateral views)

Teres Major

Latissimus Dorsi

(attach to anterior humerus)

Lumbar Fascia

Coracobrachialis

Pectoralis Major

Figure 2 (B) - Shoulder Joint - Muscle Pictures

Note-taking page ~ (palpation, how to lengthen/shorten, cautions, common uses, etc.)

2

Muscle Group 2 - Muscles Acting on the Shoulder Joint

1. Deltoid

6. Pectoralis Major

2. Supraspinatus

7. Coracobrachialis

3. Infraspinatus

8. Latissimus Dorsi

4. Teres Minor

9. Teres Major

5. Subscapularis

Movement of the Elbow and Forearm

Muscle Group 3

Biceps brachii	Pronator quadratus
Brachialis	Triceps brachii
Brachioradialis	Anconeus
Pronator teres	Supinator

Joints

(Joint details: p. 73)

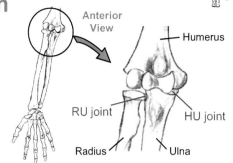

The muscles in this group primarily move the forearm at the humeroulnar joint and the radioulnar joints. In addition, some muscles that move the elbow also move the shoulder joint described in the previous section.

Humeroulnar Joint (HU) – The Elbow Joint

Trochlea of **humerus** ◄► Trochlear notch of **ulna**
Hinge Joint
Movements available: Flexion, Extension

Radioulnar Joint (RU) (proximal)

Head of **radius** ◄► Radial notch of **ulna**
Pivot joint: The radius pivots in place against the ulna
Movements available: Supination, Pronation

Supination and pronation of the forearm occur with lateral and medial rotation at this pivot joint. Moving is coupled with rotation at the *distal* radioulnar joint.

Glenohumeral Joint (GH)

(covered in previous section – Group 2: Shoulder Joint)

Other Joints

During actions of the elbow and forearm, the following joints move along with the main joints listed above.

Distal Radioulnar Joint
    Distal radius ◄► Head of ulna (distal end of ulna)
    Pivot joint: The radius rotates around the ulna
    Movements: Supination & Pronation (with proximal RU)

Radiohumeral Joint (also called the humeroradial joint)
    Head of radius ◄► Capitulum of humerus
    During supination & pronation: Movement = rotations
    With elbow joint: Movement = flexion, extension

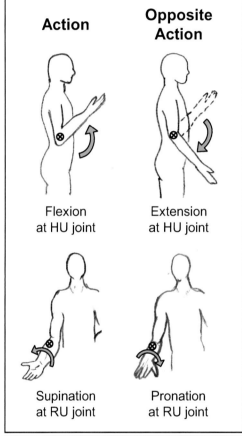

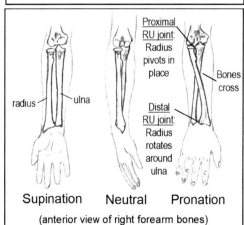

(anterior view of right forearm bones)

Bones, Bony Landmarks, Other Structures

Muscles that move the elbow and forearm have attachments on the scapula and the long bones of the upper extremity. Review the bony landmarks and other structures listed below, referring to the drawings in Chapter 2, pages 40-41.

Humerus (p. 41)

    Intertubercular groove (Bicipital groove)
    Epicondyles (lateral and medial)
    Supracondylar ridge (lateral)
    Trochlea
    Olecranon fossa
    Shaft (locations on it)

Scapula (p. 40)

    Supraglenoid tubercle
    Infraglenoid tubercle
    Coracoid process

Radius (p. 41)

    Head
    Radial tuberosity
    Styloid process
    Shaft (locations on it like mid lateral, etc.)

Ulna (p. 41)

    Olecranon process
    Coronoid process
    Ulnar tuberosity
    Trochlear notch
    Radial notch
    Supinator crest
    Shaft (locations on it like distal anterior, etc.)

Other Structures
    Bicipital aponeurosis   (p. 92)
    Intermuscular septum   "

Notes:

Note that biceps brachii is a multi-joint muscle, and it is an excellent example for exploring the concepts of force-length relationship and active/passive insufficiency (page 33).

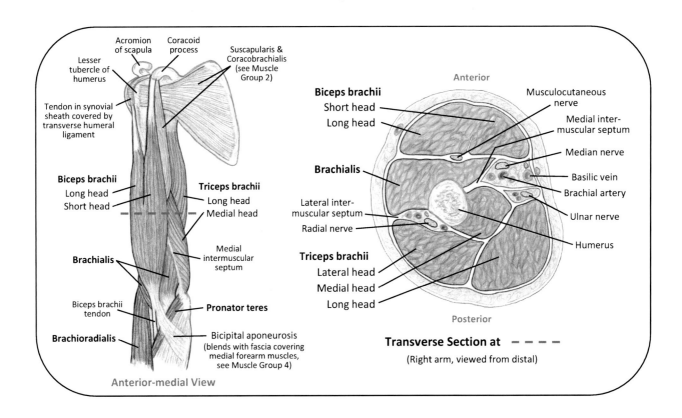

Anterior-medial View

Transverse Section at – – – –

(Right arm, viewed from distal)

Muscle Group 3 - **Muscles that move the elbow and forearm** (and sometimes the shoulder joint) are illustrated as a group on this page. The next four pages have tables and figures that describe each muscle individually, and provide ways of comparing and contrasting the muscles to each other.

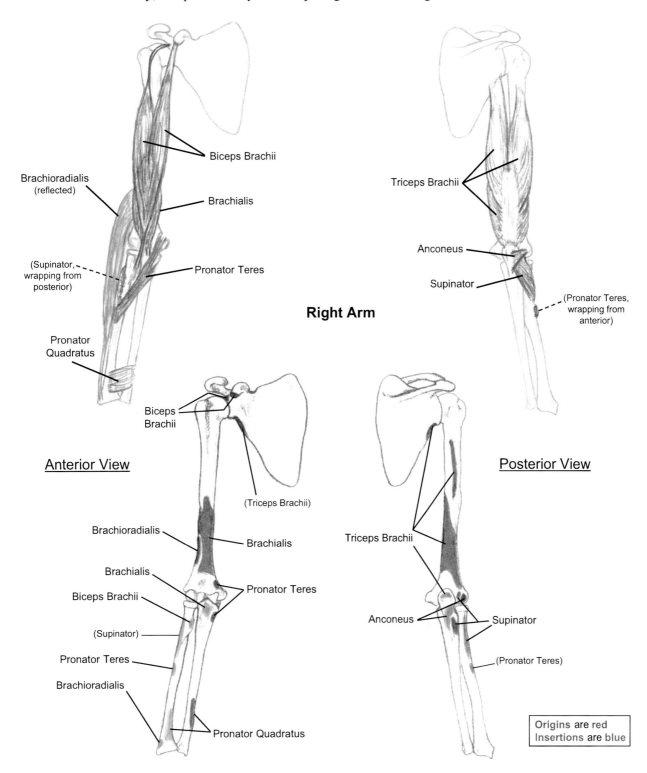

Biceps Brachii

Brachioradialis (reflected)

Brachialis

(Supinator, wrapping from posterior)

Pronator Teres

Pronator Quadratus

Right Arm

Triceps Brachii

Anconeus

Supinator

(Pronator Teres, wrapping from anterior)

Biceps Brachii

<u>Anterior View</u>

(Triceps Brachii)

Brachioradialis

Brachialis

Brachialis

Biceps Brachii

Pronator Teres

(Supinator)

Pronator Teres

Brachioradialis

Pronator Quadratus

<u>Posterior View</u>

Triceps Brachii

Anconeus

Supinator

(Pronator Teres)

Origins are red
Insertions are blue

Attachment sites for all muscles in Group 3

Joints: HU=Humeroulnar (elbow, hinge), RU=Radioulnar (pivot), GH=Glenohumeral (shoulder)

Group 3: Muscles Acting On
Elbow, Forearm

Muscle	Origin	Insertion	Action
Biceps Brachii — moves the elbow and forearm and shoulder joint	Long head: Supraglenoid tubercle of scapula (via the bicipital groove) Short head: Coracoid process of scapula	Radial tuberosity of radius (There is also a *non-bony* attachment, the bicipital aponeurosis - see p. 92)	Flexion at the elbow (HU joint), Supination at the radioulnar joints, Flexion at the GH joint (Short head: Assists horizontal adduction)
Brachialis — moves the elbow	Anterior humerus (distal half of anterior surface)	Ulnar tuberosity (and coronoid process of ulna)	Flexion at the elbow (HU joint)
Brachioradialis — moves the elbow	Lateral supracondylar ridge of humerus	Styloid process of radius	Flexion at the elbow (HU joint), especially when forearm is in a neutral/handshake position (Also assists: pronation from a supinated position to neutral, and supination from a pronated position to neutral)
Pronator Teres — moves the forearm and elbow	Medial epicondyle of humerus, Coronoid process of ulna	Mid lateral shaft of radius	Pronation at the radioulnar joints, Assists flexion at the elbow
Pronator Quadratus — moves the forearm	Distal anterior ulna	Distal anterior radius	Pronation at the radioulnar joints
Triceps Brachii — moves the elbow and shoulder joint	Long head: Infraglenoid tubercle of scapula Lateral head: Proximal posterior humerus Medial head: Distal half of posterior humerus	Olecranon process of ulna	All heads: Extension at the elbow (HU jt.), Long head: Extension at the GH joint, Assists adduction at the GH joint
Anconeus — moves the elbow	Lateral epicondyle of humerus (posterior aspect)	Olecranon process and proximal posterior ulna	Assists extension at the elbow (HU joint) (Also helps stabilize the elbow during pronation and supination at RU joints)
Supinator — moves the forearm	Lateral epicondyle of humerus, and supinator crest of ulna (proximal posterior ulna)	Proximal lateral shaft of radius (& wraps around to cover part of anterior and posterior surfaces)	Supination at the radioulnar joints

(larger illustrations on page 97)

Table 3 (A) - Elbow, Forearm - Origin, Insertion, Action

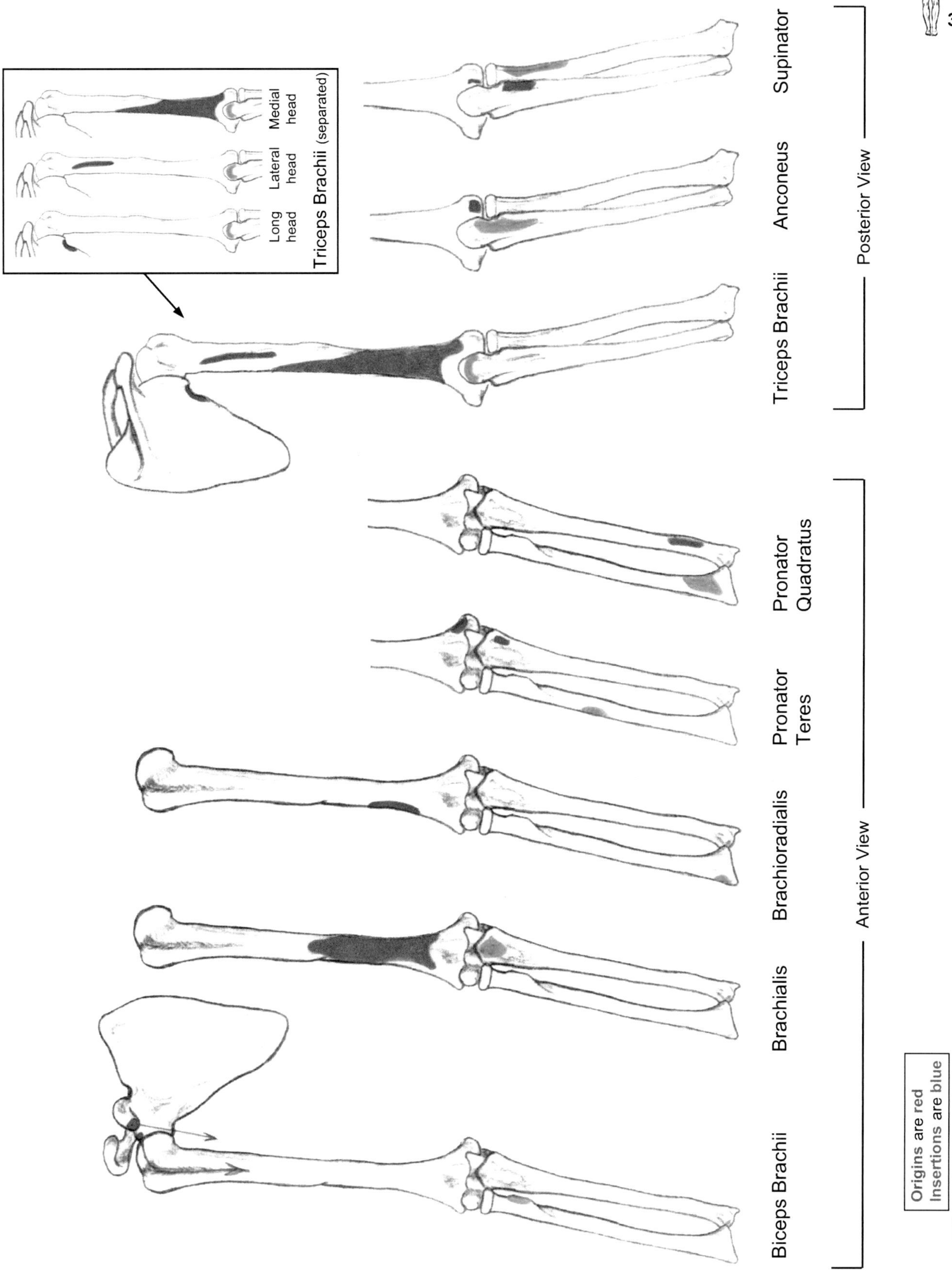

Figure 3 (A) - Elbow, Forearm - Muscle Attachments

Supinator

Anconeus

Posterior View

Triceps Brachii

Medial head
Lateral head
Long head

Triceps Brachii (separated)

Pronator Quadratus

Pronator Teres

Brachioradialis

Anterior View

Brachialis

Biceps Brachii

Origins are red
Insertions are blue

Lift page to see muscle pictures

3

Joints: HU jt.=Humeroulnar joint (elbow, hinge), RU jt.=Radioulnar joint (pivot), GH jt.=Glenohumeral joint (shoulder), ✓ =Muscle creates the action, N=Nerve

Group 3:

Muscles Acting On Elbow, Forearm	Flexion @ elbow	Extension @ elbow	Pronation @ RU jt.	Supination @ RU jt.	Flexion @ GH jt.	Extension @ GH jt.	Other	Innervation	C5	C6	C7	C8	T1
1. Biceps Brachii: Long head / Short head	✓			✓	✓		May assist abduction @ GH joint when externally rotated; <u>Short head</u>: Assists horizontal adduction	Musculocutaneous N. (C5, C6)	N	N			
2. Brachialis	✓						(the "true" flexor)	Musculocutaneous N. (C5, C6)	N	N			
3. Brachioradialis	✓ (in neutral / handshake position)		assist (moving from supinated position to neutral)	assist (moving from pronated position to neutral)				Radial N. (C5, C6)	N	N			
4. Pronator Teres	assist		✓					Median N. (C6, C7)		N	N		
5. Pronator Quadratus			✓					Median N. (C8, T1)				N	N
6. Triceps Brachii: Long head / Lateral head / Medial head						✓ (long head)	Long head assists adduction @ GH jt.	Radial N. (C7, C8)			N	N	
7. Anconeus		assist					Helps stabilize elbow during RU jt. rotations	Radial N. (C7, C8, T1)			N	N	N
8. Supinator				✓				Radial N. (C6)		N			
(More muscles for the action) --->	see also Group 4				see also Group 2	see also Group 2		**Innervation**					

Table 3 (B) - Elbow, Forearm - Synergists & Antagonists

B3

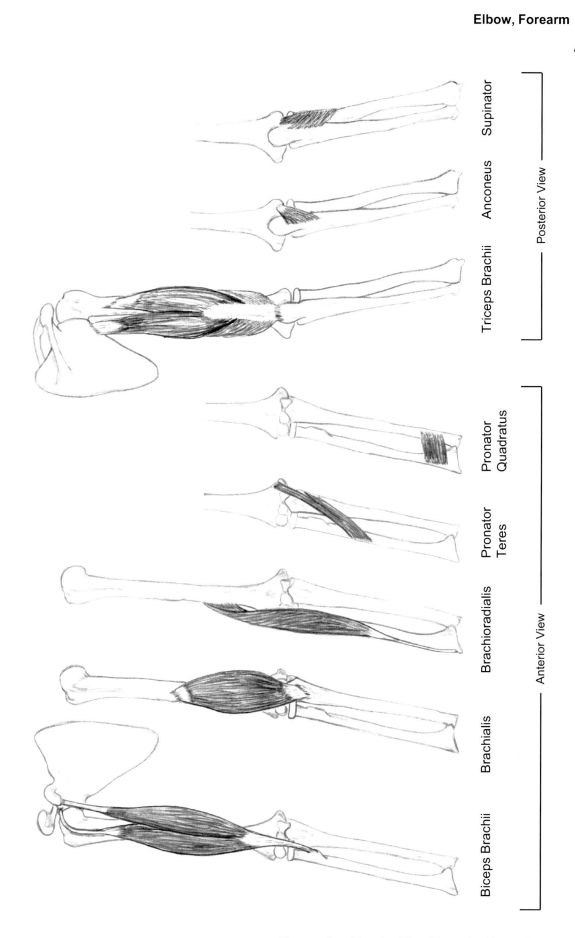

Supinator

Anconeus

Triceps Brachii

Posterior View

Pronator Quadratus

Pronator Teres

Brachioradialis

Anterior View

Brachialis

Biceps Brachii

Figure 3 (B) - Elbow, Forearm - Muscle Pictures

Note-taking page ~ (palpation, how to lengthen/shorten, cautions, common uses, etc.)

Muscle Group 3 - Muscles Acting on the Elbow, Forearm

1. Biceps Brachii

2. Brachialis

3. Brachloradialis

4. Pronator Teres

5. Pronator Quadratus

6. Triceps Brachii

7. Anconeus

8. Supinator

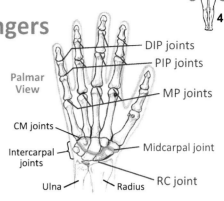

Movement of the Wrist, Hand and Fingers

Muscle Group 4

Flexors:	Extensors:
Flexor carpi radialis	Extensor carpi radialis longus
Palmaris longus	Extensor carpi radialis brevis
Flexor carpi ulnaris	Extensor carpi ulnaris
Flexor digitorum superficialis	Extensor digitorum
Flexor digitorum profundus	Extensor indicis

Joints

(Joint details: p. 74)

The muscles in this group move the wrist, or combinations of the wrist, hand, and fingers if they span multiple joints. Also, many of these muscles cross the elbow joint, but most have only minimal action there because they attach very close to the joint. (Note that joints specific to the *thumb* (digit #1) are *not* listed here -- the thumb is covered in the next muscle group - Group 5).

Radiocarpal Joint (RC) – The Wrist Joint
Distal end of **radius** ◄► Proximal row of **carpals**
Ellipsoid joint
Movements: Flexion, Extension, Abduction, Adduction
(Abduction= Radial deviation, Adduction= Ulnar deviation)
(Carpal bones involved: Scaphoid, lunate, triquetrum (not pisiform)

Intercarpal Joints (all articulations between carpal bones)
Any **carpal** surface ◄► Any **carpal** surface
Gliding joints (movement = gliding)
Midcarpal Joint: Between proximal and distal rows of carpal bones
(moves as part of wrist flexion and extension)

Carpometacarpal Joints #2 - #5 (CM or CMC)
Distal **carpals** ◄► Bases of **metacarpals** #2-5
Gliding joints (very limited movement)
(Carpal bones involved: Trapezoid, capitate, hamate (not trapezium)

Metacarpophalangeal Joints #2 - #5 (MP or MCP)
Heads of **metacarpal** bones ◄► Bases of proximal **phalanges**
Condyloid joints
Movements: Flexion, Extension, Abduction, Adduction
(Abduction=spreading the fingers, Adduction=closing the fingers)

Interphalangeal Joints #2 - #5
Joints between the **phalanges** of the fingers (PIP & DIP, see below)
Hinge joints
Movements: Flexion, Extension

Proximal Interphalangeal Joints (PIP)
Head of proximal phalanx ◄► Base of middle phalanx

Distal Interphalangeal Joints (DIP)
Head of middle phalanx ◄► Base of distal phalanx

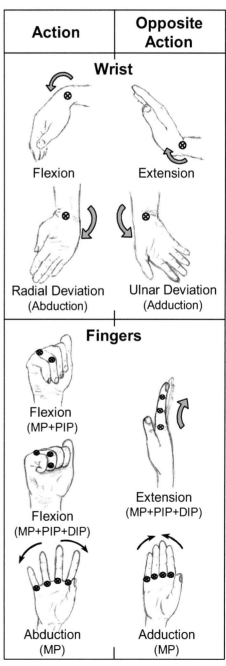

Action	Opposite Action
Wrist	
Flexion	Extension
Radial Deviation (Abduction)	Ulnar Deviation (Adduction)
Fingers	
Flexion (MP+PIP)	
Flexion (MP+PIP+DIP)	Extension (MP+PIP+DIP)
Abduction (MP)	Adduction (MP)

4

Bones, Bony Landmarks, Other Structures

Muscles that move the wrist, hand, and fingers have attachments near the elbow and on the bones of the forearm, hand, and fingers. There are also attachments to the interosseus membrane. Review the bony landmarks and other structures listed below, referring to the drawings in Chapter 2, pages 41-42.

Humerus (p. 41)
  Lateral and medial epicondyles
  Lateral supracondylar ridge

Radius (p. 41)
  Shaft (locations on it)

Ulna (p. 41)
  Coronoid process
  Shaft (locations on it)

Carpal Bones (p. 42)

	Proximal Row	Distal Row
Radial side:	Scaphoid	Trapezium
| :	Lunate	Trapezoid
| :	Triquetrum	Capitate
Ulnar side:	Pisiform	Hamate

Metacarpal Bones (p. 42)
  Base of MC bone, head of MC bone
  #1 on radial side to #5 on ulnar side

Phalanges of Hand (p. 42)
  Proximal, middle, and distal phalanges
  Base of phalanx, head of phalanx
  #1   = Pollux   = Thumb (2 phalanges)
  #2-#5 = Digits   = Fingers (3 phalanges)

Other Structures:
Interosseus membrane-	(p. 73)
Common flexor tendon	(p. 101)
Common extensor tendon	"
Palmar aponeurosis	(p. 115)
Flexor retinaculum	"
Extensor retinaculum	"
Tendon sheaths (synovial sheaths)	"
Carpal tunnel	(p. 100)

Notes:

The finger flexors and extensors are multi-joint muscles, and they are excellent examples for exploring the effects of the force-length relationship and active/passive insufficiency (page 33).

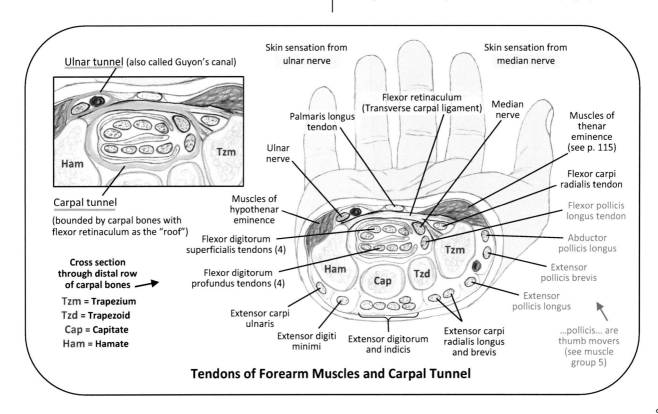

Tendons of Forearm Muscles and Carpal Tunnel

64930

Muscle Group 4 - **Muscles that move the wrist, hand and fingers** (and sometimes the elbow)

are illustrated as a group on this page. The following four pages have tables and figures that describe each muscle individually, and provide many ways of comparing and contrasting the muscles to each other.

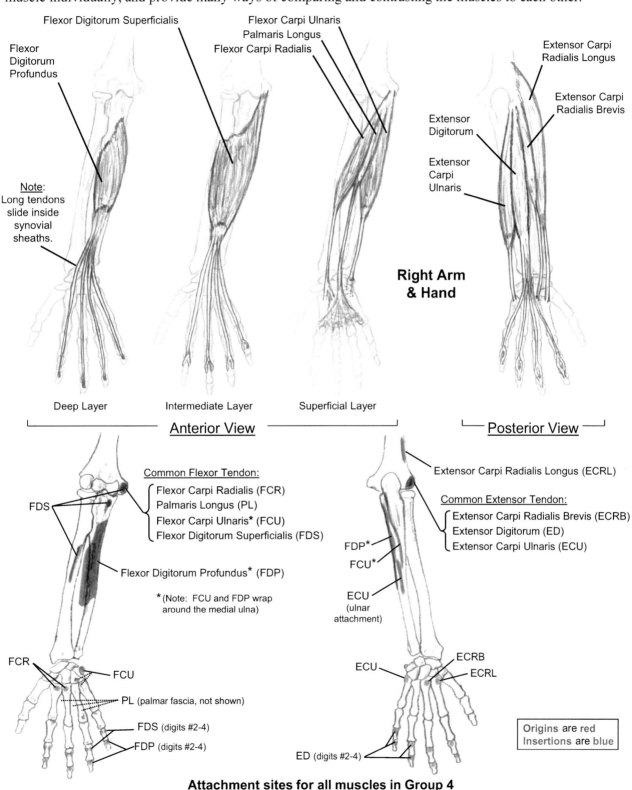

Flexor Digitorum Superficialis

Flexor Carpi Ulnaris
Palmaris Longus
Flexor Carpi Radialis

Flexor
Digitorum
Profundus

Extensor Carpi
Radialis Longus

Extensor Carpi
Radialis Brevis

Extensor
Digitorum

Extensor
Carpi
Ulnaris

Note:
Long tendons
slide inside
synovial
sheaths.

**Right Arm
& Hand**

Deep Layer   Intermediate Layer   Superficial Layer

Anterior View   Posterior View

Common Flexor Tendon:
Flexor Carpi Radialis (FCR)
Palmaris Longus (PL)
Flexor Carpi Ulnaris* (FCU)
Flexor Digitorum Superficialis (FDS)

FDS

Flexor Digitorum Profundus* (FDP)

*(Note: FCU and FDP wrap
around the medial ulna)

FCR

FCU

PL (palmar fascia, not shown)

FDS (digits #2-4)
FDP (digits #2-4)

Extensor Carpi Radialis Longus (ECRL)

Common Extensor Tendon:
Extensor Carpi Radialis Brevis (ECRB)
Extensor Digitorum (ED)
Extensor Carpi Ulnaris (ECU)

FDP*
FCU*

ECU
(ulnar
attachment)

ECU

ECRB
ECRL

ED (digits #2-4)

Origins are red
Insertions are blue

Attachment sites for all muscles in Group 4

Group 4: Muscles Acting On — Joints: RC=Radiocarpal (wrist), MP=Metacarpophalangeal (knuckles), PIP & DIP=Proximal & Distal Interphalangeal (fingers)

Wrist, Hand, Fingers	Origin	Insertion	Action
Flexor Carpi Radialis — moves the wrist	Medial epicondyle of the humerus	Bases of metacarpals #2 & #3 (palmar side)	Flexion at the wrist (RC joint), Radial Deviation (abduction) at the wrist (Also may assist flexion at the elbow, and pronation of the forearm)
Palmaris Longus — moves the palm and wrist	Medial epicondyle of the humerus	Palmar aponeurosis/ fascia	Flexion at the wrist, Assists cupping the hand by tensing the palmar fascia (Also may assist flexion at the elbow)
Flexor Carpi Ulnaris — moves the wrist	Medial epicondyle of the humerus, Proximal *posterior* ulna	Pisiform (also by ligaments to hamate & 5th metacarpal)	Flexion at the wrist, Ulnar Deviation (adduction) at the wrist (Also may assist flexion at the elbow)
Flexor Digitorum Superficialis — moves the fingers and wrist	Medial epicondyle of the humerus, Coronoid process of ulna, Anterior shaft of radius	Sides of middle phalanges of digits #2 - 5 (palmar side, the tendon splits)	Flexion of fingers at the PIP and MP joints, Flexion at the wrist (Also may assist flexion at the elbow)
Flexor Digitorum Profundus — moves the fingers and wrist	Proximal half of the anterior and medial ulna (wraps around) (and interosseous membrane)	Bases of distal phalanges of digits #2 - 5 (palmar side)	Flexion of fingers at the DIP, PIP, and MP joints (closing hand into a full fist), Assists flexion at the wrist
Extensor Carpi Radialis Longus — moves the wrist	Lateral supracondylar ridge of the humerus	Base of metacarpal #2 (dorsal side)	Extension at the wrist, Radial Deviation (abduction) at wrist, Assists flexion at the elbow (when forearm is in neutral/handshake position)
Extensor Carpi Radialis Brevis — moves the wrist	Lateral epicondyle of the humerus	Base of metacarpal #3 (dorsal side)	Extension at the wrist, Radial Deviation (abduction) at the wrist
Extensor Carpi Ulnaris — moves the wrist	Lateral epicondyle of the humerus, Posterior middle shaft of ulna	Base of metacarpal #5 (ulnar side)	Extension at the wrist, Ulnar Deviation (adduction) at the wrist
Extensor Digitorum *(including extensor digiti minimi)* — moves the fingers and wrist	Lateral epicondyle of the humerus	Bases of middle & distal phalanges #2-5 (dorsal side)	Extension of the fingers at the DIP, PIP, MP joints, Extension at the wrist (Also assists abduction of the fingers)
Extensor Indicis — moves the index finger and wrist	Distal posterior ulna (and interosseus membrane)	Merges with the extensor digitorum tendon near the base of the index finger	Extension of the index finger, Assists extension at the wrist

(larger illustrations on page 105)

Table 4 (A) - Wrist, Hand, Fingers - Origin, Insertion, Action

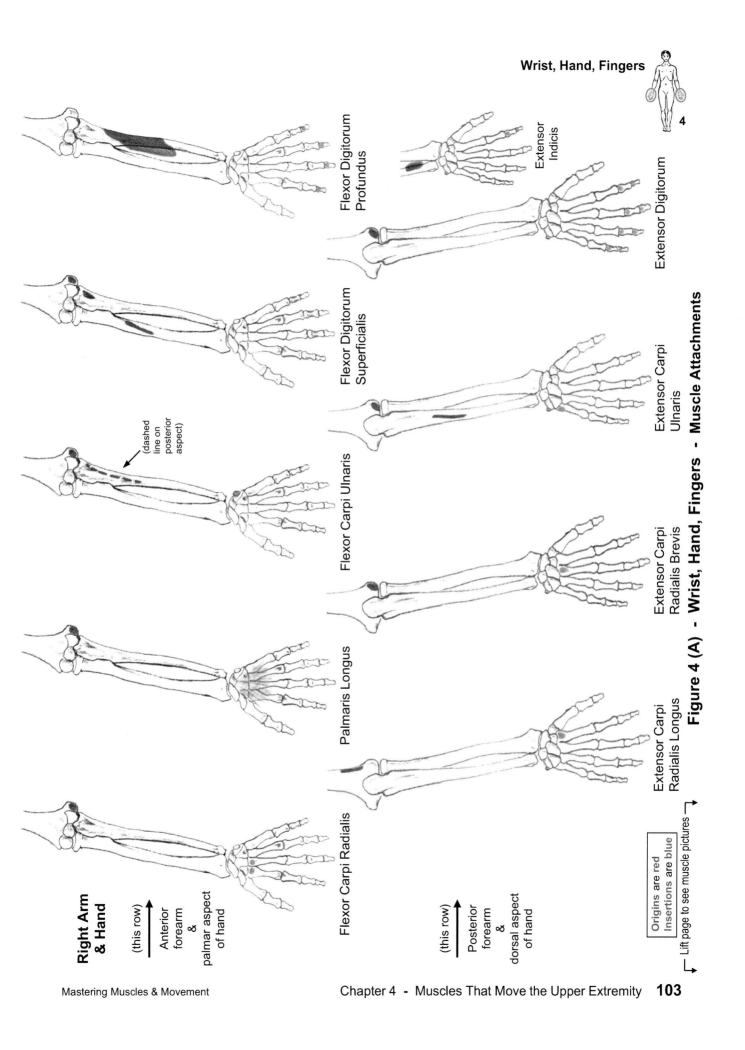

4

Flexor Digitorum
Profundus

Extensor
Indicis

Extensor Digitorum

Flexor Digitorum
Superficialis

Extensor Carpi
Ulnaris

(dashed
line on
posterior
aspect)

Flexor Carpi Ulnaris

Extensor Carpi
Radialis Brevis

Palmaris Longus

Extensor Carpi
Radialis Longus

**Right Arm
& Hand**

(this row)

Anterior
forearm
&
palmar aspect
of hand

Flexor Carpi Radialis

(this row)

Posterior
forearm
&
dorsal aspect
of hand

Origins are red
Insertions are blue

Lift page to see muscle pictures

Figure 4 (A) - Wrist, Hand, Fingers - Muscle Attachments

Joints: MP=Metacarpophalangeal, PIP & DIP=Proximal & Distal Interphalangeal, ⟍ =Muscle creates action, N=Nerve

Group 4:

Muscles Acting On Wrist, Hand, Fingers	Flexion @ wrist	Extension @ wrist	Abduction/ Radial Deviation	Adduction/ Ulnar Deviation	Flexion of fingers	Extension of fingers	Flexion @ elbow	Other	Innervation	C6	C7	C8	T1
1. Flexor Carpi Radialis	⟍		⟍				may assist	may assist pronation	Median N. (C6, C7)	N	N		
2. Palmaris Longus	⟍						may assist	Assists cupping the hand	Median N. (C6, C7)	N	N		
3. Flexor Carpi Ulnaris	⟍			⟍			may assist		Ulnar N. (C8, T1)			N	N
4. Flexor Digitorum Superficialis	⟍				PIP joints (+ MP)		may assist		Median N. (C7,C8,T1)		N	N	N
5. Flexor Digitorum Profundus	assist				DIP joints (+ PIP, MP)			Closes hand into full fist	Median N. (C8, T1) to digits 2 and 3, Ulnar N. (C8, T1) to digits 4 and 5			N	N
6. Extensor Carpi Radialis Longus		⟍	⟍				assist (in neutral/ handshake position)		Radial N. (C6, C7)	N	N		
7. Extensor Carpi Radialis Brevis		⟍	⟍						Radial N. (C6, C7)	N	N		
8. Extensor Carpi Ulnaris		⟍		⟍					Radial N. (C6,C7,C8)	N	N	N	
9. Extensor Digitorum (including Extensor Digiti Minimi)		⟍				DIP, PIP (+ MP) ⟍		works with lumbricals & interossei	Radial N. (C6,C7,C8)	N	N	N	
10. Extensor Indicis		assist ⟍				(index finger)	see also Group 3		Radial N. (C7,C8)		N	N	
(More muscles for the action) ---->	see also Group 5	see also Group 5							**Innervation**				

B3

Table 4 (B) - Wrist, Hand, Fingers - Synergists & Antagonists

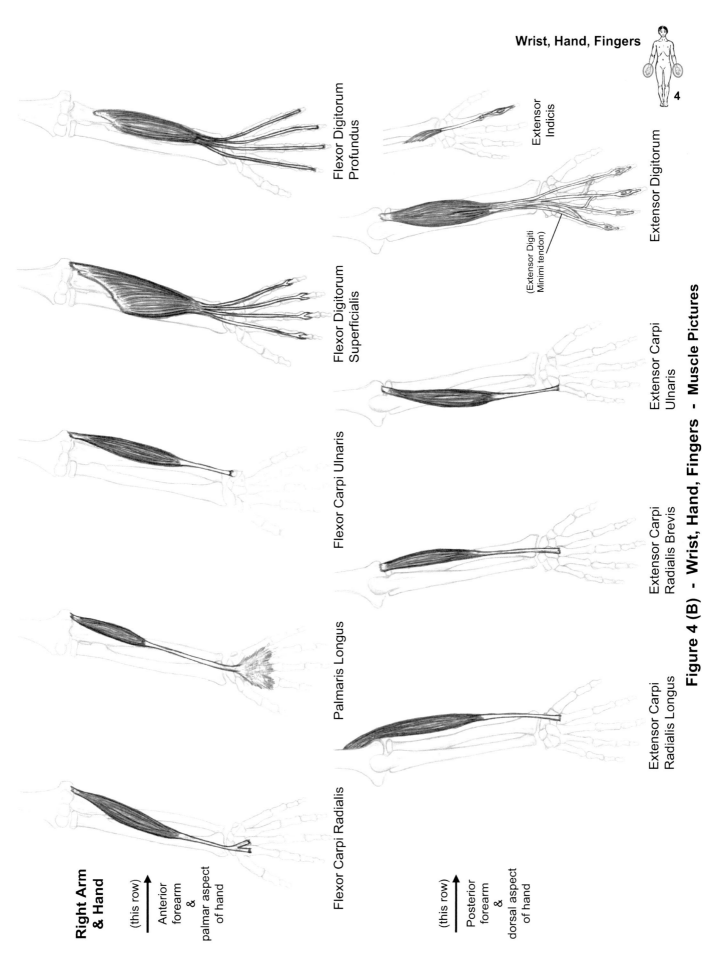

Flexor Digitorum Profundus

Extensor Indicis

Extensor Digitorum

(Extensor Digiti Minimi tendon)

Flexor Digitorum Superficialis

Extensor Carpi Ulnaris

Flexor Carpi Ulnaris

Extensor Carpi Radialis Brevis

Palmaris Longus

Extensor Carpi Radialis Longus

Flexor Carpi Radialis

Right Arm & Hand

(this row)

Anterior forearm & palmar aspect of hand

(this row)

Posterior forearm & dorsal aspect of hand

Figure 4 (B) - Wrist, Hand, Fingers - Muscle Pictures

Note-taking page ~ (palpation, how to lengthen/shorten, cautions, common uses, etc.)

4

Muscle Group 4 - Muscles Acting on the Wrist, Hand, Fingers

1. Flexor Carpi Radialis

6. Extensor Carpi Radialis Longus

2. Palmaris Longus

7. Extensor Carpi Radialis Brevis

3. Flexor Carpi Ulnaris

8. Extensor Carpi Ulnaris

4. Flexor Digitorum Superficialis

9. Extensor Digitorum

5. Flexor Digitorum Profundus

10. Extensor Indicis

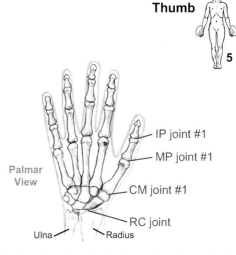

Movement of the Thumb

Muscle Group 5

Flexor pollicis longus	Abductor pollicis brevis
Flexor pollicis brevis	Abductor pollicis longus
Opponens pollicis	Extensor pollicis longus
Adductor pollicis	Extensor pollicis brevis

Joints

(Joint details: p. 74)

The muscles in this group move the thumb and the wrist. The anatomical word for thumb is *pollux*, hence "pollicis" in all the muscle names. The distinctive movements of the thumb are possible because of the special-shaped saddle joint at the carpometacarpal joint, which is at the base of the 1st metacarpal bone (near the wrist – *not* at base of thumb).

> Thumb movements are not the same as the fingers.
> Visualize the thumb as a finger rotated 90 degrees.

Carpometacarpal Joint #1 (CM or CMC)

Distal **carpal** (trapezium) ◄► Base of 1st **metacarpal**
Saddle joint
Movements available:
    Flexion, Extension
    Abduction, Adduction
    Opposition, (reverse movement is called Reposition)

Metacarpophalangeal Joint #1 (MP or MCP)

Head of **metacarpal** bone ◄► Base of proximal **phalange**
Condyloid joint
Movements available: Flexion, Extension
                    Abduction, Adduction (very limited)

Interphalangeal Joint #1 (IP)

Head of proximal **phalange** ◄► Base of distal **phalange**
Hinge joint
Movements available: Flexion, Extension

The thumb has only two phalanges (fingers have three),
so it has only an IP joint rather than DIP and PIP.

Radiocarpal Joint (RC) – Wrist

(covered in previous section: Group 4 – Wrist, Hand, Fingers)

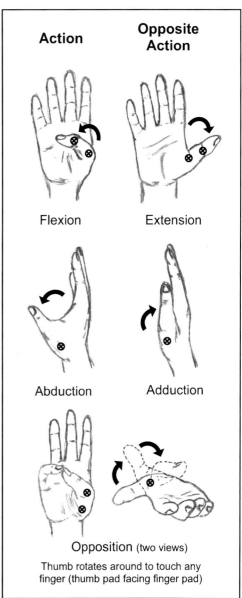

Action	Opposite Action
Flexion	Extension
Abduction	Adduction

Opposition (two views)
Thumb rotates around to touch any
finger (thumb pad facing finger pad)

Bones, Bony Landmarks, Other Structures

Muscles that move the thumb have attachments on the radius and ulna and their interosseus membrane, and on the thumb and radial side of the hand and wrist. Review the bony landmarks and other structures listed below, referring to the drawings in Chapter 2, pages 41-42.

Radius   (p. 41)
Ulna   (p. 41)

Radial side of wrist/hand   (p. 42):
    Carpals bones: Trapezium, scaphoid
    Metacarpal bone #1

Center line of wrist/hand   (p. 42):
    Carpals bone: Capitate
    Metacarpal bone #3

Distal and proximal phalanges, digit #1 (thumb)   (p. 42)

<u>Other Structures</u>

    Interosseus membrane between radius and ulna   (p. 73)

    Flexor retinaculum   (p. 100, 115)

    Carpal tunnel – tendon of flexor
        pollicis longus is in it   (p. 100)

    Anatomical "snuffbox" – located between
        the tendons of EPL and EPB muscles

<u>Terminology</u>
    Palmar aspect of the hand
    Dorsum of the hand
    Thenar eminence
    Hypothenar eminence

1st Dorsal interosseus m.   Extensor pollicis longus (EPL)
Adductor pollicis
Extensor pollicis brevis (EPB)   Abductor pollicis longus
Anatomical snuffbox

Anatomical Snuffbox

Intrinsic Muscles of the Hand

Muscles that begin and end within the hand itself are called **intrinsic muscles** of the hand. The Group 5 tables include intrinsic muscles of the hand that move the *thumb*. There are other intrinsic muscles that move the fingers and shape the palm. Detailed drawings showing *all* intrinsic muscles of the hand are presented as a Bonus Group on page 114-115. Here are some features and terminology that apply to the intrinsic muscles of the hand:

- Thenar muscles are named "_____ pollicis _____"

- Hypothenar muscles are named "_____ digiti minimi"

- Muscles of the mid-hand or palm – Dorsal interossei, palmar interossei, lumbricals

- Muscles in the web between the index finger and thumb – Adductor pollicis and 1st dorsal interosseus

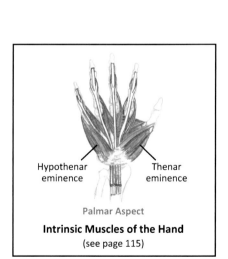

Hypothenar eminence   Thenar eminence

Palmar Aspect

Intrinsic Muscles of the Hand
(see page 115)

Thumb

5

Muscle Group 5 - **Muscles that move the thumb** (and wrist) are illustrated as a group on
this page. The next four pages have tables and figures that describe each muscle individually, and
provide many ways of comparing and contrasting the muscles to each other.

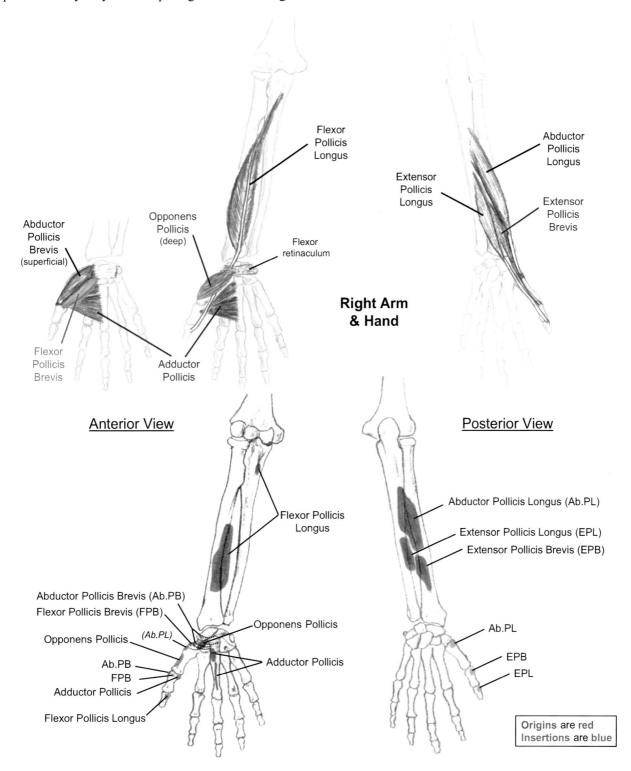

Attachment sites for all muscles in Group 5

Group 5: Muscles Acting On

RC=Radiocarpal (wrist), CM=Carpometacarpal, MP=Metacarpophalangeal, IP=Interphalangeal

Thumb	Origin	Insertion	Action
Flexor Pollicis Longus moves the thumb	Anterior shaft of radius, and interosseus membrane (also by a slip to coronoid process of ulna)	Base of distal phalanx of thumb (palmar side)	Flexion of the thumb (distal phalanx at the IP joint) (Also assists flexion of the thumb at the MP and CM joints, and may assist flexion at the wrist)
Flexor Pollicis Brevis moves the thumb	Flexor retinaculum and carpal bones (Superficial head to flexor retinaculum & trapezium, Deep head to trapezoid and capitate)	Base of proximal phalanx of thumb (palmar side)	Flexion of the thumb (at the MP and CM joints)
Opponens Pollicis moves the thumb	Trapezium and flexor retinaculum	Metacarpal #1 (whole length of radial side)	Opposition of thumb to the fingers (Opposition = abduction + flexion + rotation at the 1st CM joint (saddle joint). The finger pads face the thumb pad.)
Adductor Pollicis moves the thumb	Shaft of 3rd metacarpal bone, and capitate bone (palmar side) (+ bases of metacarpals 2 & 3)	Base of proximal phalanx of thumb (ulnar side)	Adduction of the thumb (also assists flexion of the thumb at the MP joint)
Abductor Pollicis Brevis moves the thumb	Flexor retinaculum, trapezium and scaphoid	Base of proximal phalanx of thumb (radial side)	Abduction of the thumb
Abductor Pollicis Longus moves the thumb and the wrist	Posterior ulna and radius, and interosseus membrane	Base of metacarpal #1 (radial side)	Abduction and extension of the thumb (at the CM joint), and Radial deviation (abduction) at the wrist
Extensor Pollicis Longus moves the thumb	Middle posterior ulna, and interosseus membrane	Base of distal phalanx of thumb (dorsal side)	Extension of the thumb (at the IP, MP & CM joints) (Also assists extension and radial deviation at the wrist)
Extensor Pollicis Brevis moves the thumb	Distal posterior radius, and interosseus membrane	Base of proximal phalanx of thumb (dorsal side)	Extension of the thumb (at the MP & CM joints) (Also assists radial deviation at the wrist)

— Intrinsic Hand Muscles —

(larger illustrations on page 113)

Table 5 (A) - Thumb - Origin, Insertion, Action

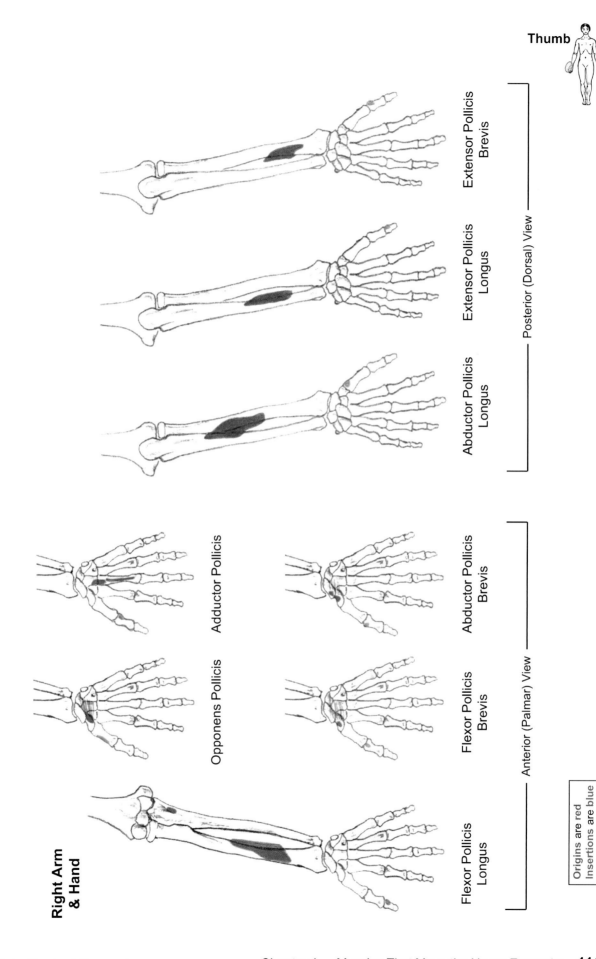

Thumb

5

Right Arm & Hand

Flexor Pollicis Longus

Opponens Pollicis

Adductor Pollicis

— Anterior (Palmar) View —

Flexor Pollicis Brevis

Abductor Pollicis Brevis

Abductor Pollicis Longus

Extensor Pollicis Longus

Extensor Pollicis Brevis

— Posterior (Dorsal) View —

Origins are red
Insertions are blue

Lift page to see muscle pictures

Figure 5 (A) - Thumb - Muscle Attachments

Group 5: Joints: RC=Radiocarpal (wrist, ellipsoid), CM=Carpometacarpal #1 (thumb, saddle), MP=Metacarpophalangeal #1, ⟍=Muscle creates the action, N=Nerve

Muscles Acting On **Thumb**	Flexion of thumb	Extension of thumb	Adduction of thumb	Abduction of thumb	Opposition of thumb	Radial Deviation @ wrist	Flexion @ wrist	Extension @ wrist	Innervation	C6	C7	C8	T1
1. Flexor Pollicis Longus	⟍								Median N. (C8, T1)			N	N
2. Flexor Pollicis Brevis	⟍						may assist		Sup. Head: Median N. Deep Head: Ulnar N. (C8, T1)			N	N
3. Opponens Pollicis					⟍ (abduct + flex + rotate at CM jt.)				Median N. (C8, T1)			N	N
4. Adductor Pollicis			⟍ (at CM jt.)						Ulnar N. (C8, T1)			N	N
5. Abductor Pollicis Brevis		⟍ (at CM jt.)		⟍ (at CM jt.)					Median N. (C8, T1)			N	N
6. Abductor Pollicis Longus				⟍		⟍			Radial N. (C7, C8)		N	N	
7. Extensor Pollicis Longus		⟍				⟍ assist		⟍ assist	Radial N. (C6, C7, C8)	N	N	N	
8. Extensor Pollicis Brevis		⟍ (at MP & CM jts)				⟍ assist			Radial N. (C7, C8)		N	N	
(More muscles for the action) ---->						see also Group 4	see also Group 4	see also Group 4	**Innervation**				

└─ Intrinsic Hand Muscles ─┘

Table 5 (B) - Thumb - Synergists & Antagonists

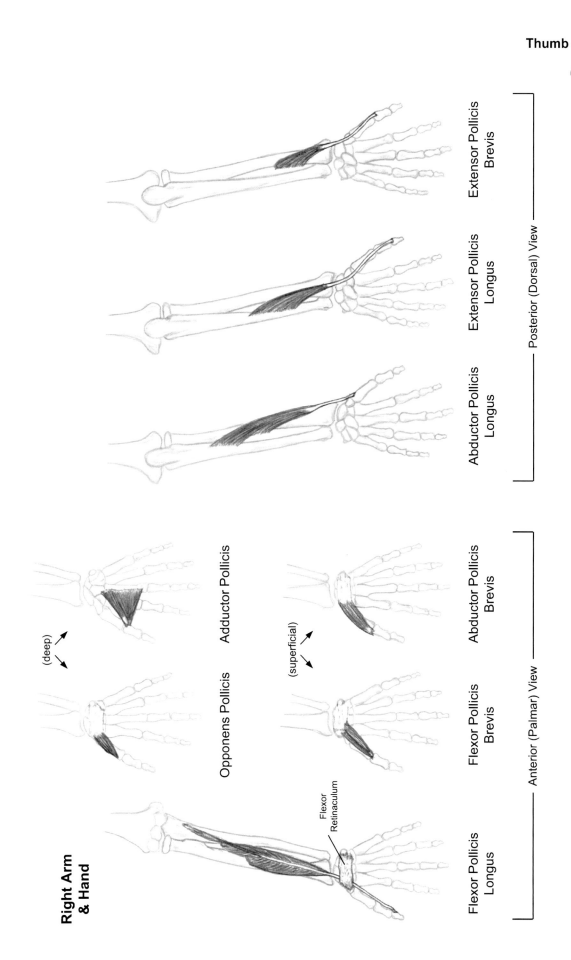

Thumb 5

Right Arm & Hand

Extensor Pollicis Brevis

Extensor Pollicis Longus

Abductor Pollicis Longus

Posterior (Dorsal) View

Adductor Pollicis

Opponens Pollicis

(deep)

Abductor Pollicis Brevis

Flexor Pollicis Brevis

(superficial)

Flexor Retinaculum

Flexor Pollicis Longus

Anterior (Palmar) View

Figure 5 (B) - Thumb - Muscle Pictures

Intrinsic Muscles of the Hand – Palmar Aspect

Joints: CM=Carpometacarpal, MP=Metacarpophalangeal (knuckles), IP=Interphalangeal (fingers)

Muscle	Origin	Insertion	Action	Innervation
Muscles of the Palm (move the fingers or thumb)				
Palmar Interossei (3) Deep Layer	Shafts of metacarpal bones #2, #4 and #5 (each muscle arises from the middle finger side of the metacarpal bone)	Bases of the proximal phalanges of fingers #2, #4 and #5 (and the dorsal digital expansions of fingers #2, #4 and #5)	Adduction of fingers #2, #4 and #5, Assist flexion of fingers #2, #4 and #5 at the MP joints, Assist extension of fingers #2, #4 and #5 at the IP joints	Ulnar N. (C8, T1)
Adductor Pollicis Intermediate Layer	Shaft of 3rd metacarpal bone, & capitate bone (palmar side) (+ bases of 2nd and 3rd metacarpal bones)	Base of proximal phalanx of thumb (ulnar side)	Adduction of the thumb (also assists flexion of the thumb at the MP joint)	Ulnar N. (C8, T1)
Lumbrical Muscles (4) Superficial Layer	The four tendons of the flexor digitorum profundus muscle	The four tendons of the extensor digitorum mm. (attach via radial side of the dorsal digital exansions)	Flexion of fingers #2-5 at the MP joints, and Extension of fingers #2-5 at the IP joints	Digits #2 and #3: Median N. Digits #4 and #5: Ulnar N.
Muscles of the Hypothenar Eminence (move the little finger, digit #5)				
Opponens Digiti Minimi Deep Layer	Hook of hamate and flexor retinaculum	Shaft of 5th metacarpal bone (ulnar side)	Opposition of the little finger (move its finger pad around to face the thumb)	Ulnar N. (C8, T1)
Flexor Digiti Minimi Intermediate Layer	Hook of hamate and flexor retinaculum	Proximal phalanx of little finger (base of phalanx on the palmar side)	Flexion of the little finger	Ulnar N. (C8, T1)
Abductor Digiti Minimi Superficial & Ulnar Layer	Pisiform and tendon of the flexor carpi ulnaris	Proximal phalanx of little finger (base of phalanx on the ulnar side)	Abduction of the little finger	Ulnar N. (C8, T1)
Muscles of the Thenar Eminence (move the thumb, digit #1)				
Opponens Pollicis Deep Layer	Trapezium and flexor retinaculum	Metacarpal #1 (whole length of radial side)	Opposition of thumb to the fingers (Opposition = abduction + flexion + rotation at the 1st CM joint (saddle joint). The finger pads face the thumb pad.)	Median N. (C8, T1)
Flexor Pollicis Brevis Intermediate Layer	Flexor retinaculum and carpal bones (Superficial head to flexor retinaculum & trapezium, Deep head to trapezoid and capitate)	Base of proximal phalanx of thumb (radial side)	Flexion of the thumb (at the MP and CM joints)	Sup. Head: Median N. Deep Head: Ulnar N. (C8, T1)
Abductor Pollicis Brevis Superficial Layer	Flexor retinaculum, trapezium and scaphoid	Base of proximal phalanx of thumb (radial side)	Abduction of the thumb	Median N. (C8, T1)

Intrinsic Muscles of the Hand – Dorsal Aspect

Muscle	Origin	Insertion	Action	Innervation
Dorsal Layer #1				
Dorsal Interossei (4)	Shafts of metacarpal bones #1-5 (each muscle arises from the sides of two adjacent metacarpal bones)	Bases of the proximal phalanges of fingers #2-4 (and the dorsal digital expansions of fingers #2-4)	Abduction of fingers #2-4, Assist flexion of fingers #2-4 at the MP joints, Assist extension of fingers #2-4 at the IP joints	Ulnar N. (C8, T1)

A2

Intrinsic Muscles of the Hand

Right Hand – Layers of the Palmar Aspect

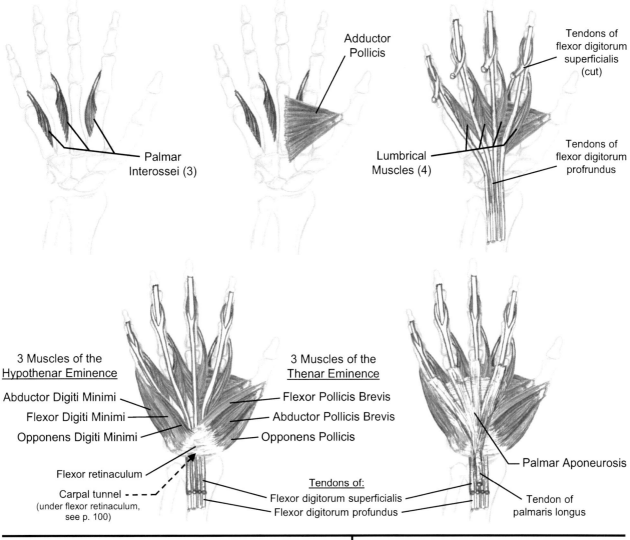

Adductor Pollicis

Palmar Interossei (3)

Tendons of flexor digitorum superficialis (cut)

Lumbrical Muscles (4)

Tendons of flexor digitorum profrundus

3 Muscles of the <u>Hypothenar Eminence</u>

Abductor Digiti Minimi

Flexor Digiti Minimi

Opponens Digiti Minimi

Flexor retinaculum

Carpal tunnel
(under flexor retinaculum, see p. 100)

3 Muscles of the <u>Thenar Eminence</u>

Flexor Pollicis Brevis

Abductor Pollicis Brevis

Opponens Pollicis

Tendons of:
Flexor digitorum superficialis
Flexor digitorum profundus

Palmar Aponeurosis

Tendon of palmaris longus

Right Hand – Dorsal Aspect

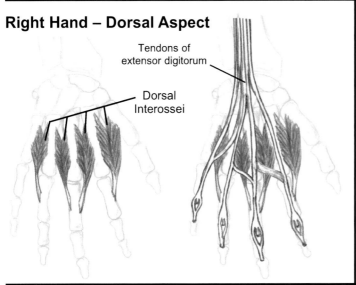

Tendons of extensor digitorum

Dorsal Interossei

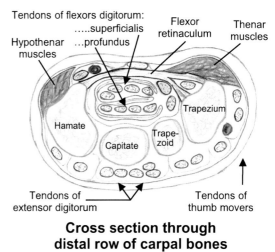

Tendons of flexors digitorum:
.....superficialis
...profundus

Hypothenar muscles

Flexor retinaculum

Thenar muscles

Trapezium

Hamate

Trape-zoid

Capitate

Tendons of extensor digitorum

Tendons of thumb movers

**Cross section through
distal row of carpal bones**
(see page 100 for details)

Thumb

Note-taking page ~ (palpation, how to lengthen/shorten, cautions, common uses, etc.)

5

Muscle Group 5 - **Muscles Acting on the Thumb**

1. Flexor Pollicis Longus

(palmar)

5. Abductor Pollicis Longus

(dorsal)

2. Flexor Pollicis Brevis

(palmar)

6. Abductor Pollicis Brevis

(palmar)

3. Opponens Pollicis

(palmar)

7. Extensor Pollicis Longus

(dorsal)

4. Adductor Pollicis

(palmar)

8. Extensor Pollicis Brevis

(dorsal)

Chapter 5

Muscles That Move the Axial Skeleton

Group 6 – Face, Jaw

Masseter
Temporalis
Lateral pterygoid
Medial pterygoid
Occipitofrontalis
Platysma
Suprahyoids group
    Geniohyoid, Mylohyoid,
    Stylohyoid, Digastric
Infrahyoids group
    Sternohyoid, Sternothyroid,
    Omohyoid, Thyrohyoid
Muscles of facial expression

p. 127-134

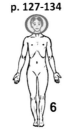

6

Group 7 – Neck, Head

Sternocleidomastoid
Scalenes group
Longus capitis & longus colli
Suboccipital group
    Rectus capitis posterior major
    Rectus capitis posterior minor
    Oblique capitis superior
    Oblique capitis inferior
Splenius capitis
Splenius cervicis
Semispinalis capitis
Levator scapula*
Trapezius, upper fibers*
    *(revisited for reversed O/I actions)

p. 135-142

7

Group 8 – Spine

Spinalis
Longissimus
Iliocostalis
Semispinalis
Multifidus
Rotatores
Quadratus lumborum
Interspinales & Intertransversarii

p. 143-150

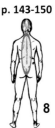

8

Group 9 – Thorax, Abdomen, Breathing

Rectus abdominis
External oblique
Internal oblique
Transverse abdominis
Diaphragm
External intercostals
Internal intercostals
Serratus posterior superior
Serratus posterior inferior
Levator costae
Transversus thoracis

p. 151-157

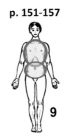

9

Bonus Group

p. 158-159

Muscles of the
Pelvic Floor and Perineum

Introduction

The **axial skeleton** comprises the center or "core" of the body, and includes the spine, skull, mandible, hyoid, sternum, and ribs. The axial skeleton articulates with the appendicular skeleton at the sternoclavicular joints for the upper extremities, and at the sacroiliac joints for the lower extremities (see page 37).

The major functional divisions of the axial skeleton are the head, neck, back, thorax, abdomen, and pelvis. The thorax is made up of the thoracic spine, ribs, and sternum, and contains the heart and lungs. The abdominopelvic region is the area from the bottom of the ribs down to the pelvic floor, and it contains digestive, blood processing, reproductive, and elimination organs. The respiratory diaphragm muscle creates a boundary between the thorax and abdomen (see page 153).

The spine (also called the vertebral column) is made up of 24 vertebrae, the sacrum, and the coccyx. Viewed from the side, it has four normal front-to-back curves that allow it to absorb shocks and move more freely - two kyphotic (primary) curves and two lordotic (secondary) curves. A healthy spine has no lateral curves.

At birth, the entire spine has a kyphotic curvature (hence the name *primary* curve). The cervical and lumbar lordotic curves develop *secondary* to the child raising the head to crawl and standing erect to walk.

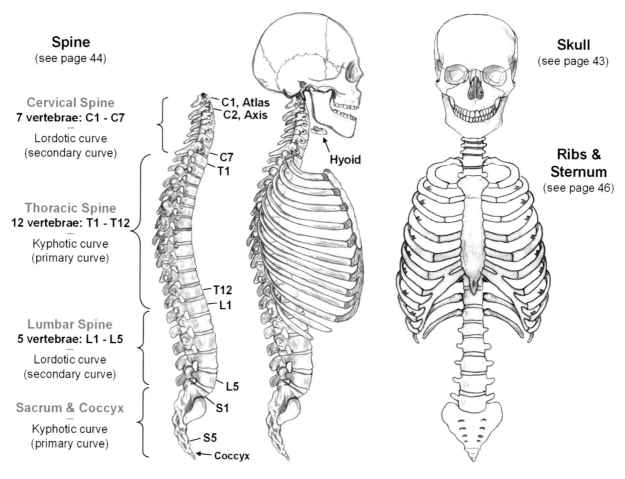

Spine
(see page 44)

Cervical Spine
7 vertebrae: C1 - C7

Lordotic curve
(secondary curve)

Thoracic Spine
12 vertebrae: T1 - T12

Kyphotic curve
(primary curve)

Lumbar Spine
5 vertebrae: L1 - L5

Lordotic curve
(secondary curve)

Sacrum & Coccyx

Kyphotic curve
(primary curve)

C1, Atlas
C2, Axis

C7
T1

T12
L1

L5

S1

S5
Coccyx

Hyoid

Skull
(see page 43)

Ribs & Sternum
(see page 46)

The Axial Skeleton: Spine, Skull, Mandible, Hyoid, Ribs, and Sternum

Bony Landmarks of a Typical Vertebra

The figure to the right shows a basic set of features that are common to all vertebrae except C1. The three types of vertebrae (cervical, thoracic, and lumbar) also have special features that distinguish them from each other (see Chapter 2, page 45).

The common landmarks are:

- Body
- Transverse process – TVP (2)
- Spinous process – SP
- Pedicle (2)
- Facets (a pair above, a pair below)
  The *articular process* is the bony protrusion, the *facet* is the smooth cartilage surface.
- Lamina (2)
- Vertebral foramen

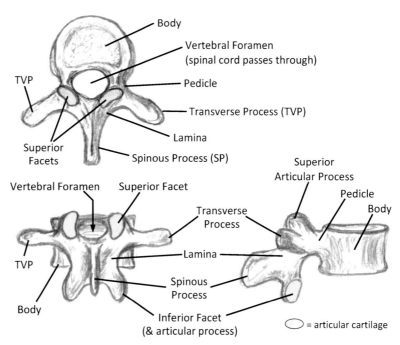

Bony Landmarks of a Typical Vertebra

How Vertebrae "Stack Up" to Make Up the Spine

An **intervertebral joint** between two vertebrae is really three joints – one at the body and two at the facets. The inferior facets of each vertebra match up with the superior facets of vertebra below. The **facet joints** (also called zygapophyseal joints) are synovial joints and their type is gliding. The body of each vertebra sits on the body of the vertebra below it and has an intervertebral disc firmly attached between. This **interbody joint** with its disc is an amphiarthrotic/cartilaginous joint.

The pedicle portions of the vertebrae above and below match up to form the **intervertebral foramen** where the nerve roots emerge. The vertebral bodies in the lower spine are large and stable because they must support more weight than the vertebrae near the top of the spine. Conversely, the vertebral foramen (the holes that create the channel for the spinal cord, called the **spinal canal**) are large near the top of the spine because the spinal cord is thicker.

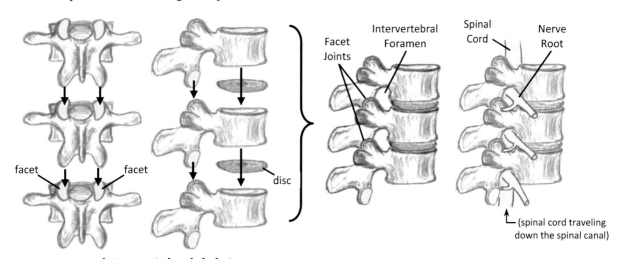

Intervertebral Joints (3 articulations per joint: 1 disc + 2 facet joints)

Kinesiology Concepts Specific to the Axial Body

Some additional kinesiology concepts are required when studying the muscles and actions of the *axial skeleton* vs. the actions of the limbs (the appendicular skeleton). This is because pairs of muscles on either side of the spine act on the spine from opposite directions.

Naming of Actions for Lateral and Rotational Movements

For limbs, described in Chapter 4:Upper Extremity and Chapter 6:Lower Extremity, movements that are lateral and rotational are named to describe whether the bones move *away from* the midline or *toward* the midline. Side-to-side limb movements are called abduction and adduction, and rotational movements are called lateral rotation and medial rotation (or external rotation and internal rotation).

For the axial skeleton the bones are *centered on* the midline, so the terminology that is used for the limbs does not make sense. Side-to-side movements in the frontal plane are defined as **right and left lateral flexion** (instead of abduction and adduction as used for limbs), and rotational movements in the transverse plane are defined as **right and left rotation** (instead of medial and lateral rotation as used for limbs). The figure below shows examples of this change in nomenclature.

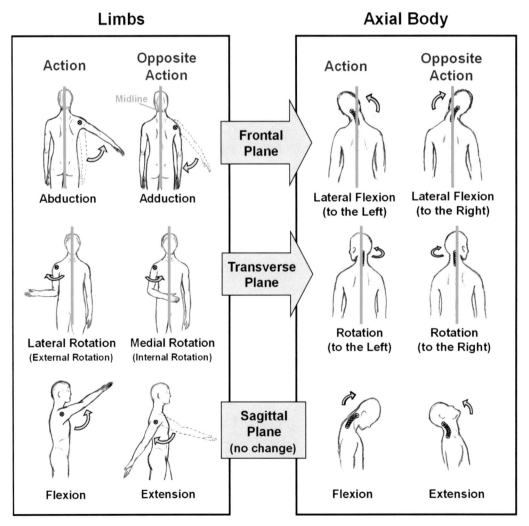

Changes in the Naming of Actions for the Axial Body

Muscle acting unilaterally
on left side
pulls neck to left

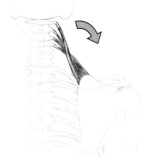

Muscle acting unilaterally
on right side
pulls neck to right

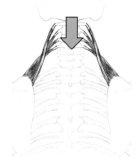

Muscle acting bilaterally
pulls neck to the rear

Unilateral vs. Bilateral Use of Muscles

There are two of each muscle – one on each side of the spine. **Unilateral action** of a muscle is when that muscle contracts and shortens on only one side of the spine. **Bilateral action** of a muscle occurs when that muscle contracts on both sides of the spine at the same time.

Unilateral muscle concentric contractions generally create lateral flexion and/or rotational movements, i.e., movements in the frontal and transverse planes. Bilateral muscle contractions generally create flexion or extension of the spine, i.e., movements in the sagittal plane. Also, notice that for unilateral muscle contractions, an antagonist to a given action is the *same* muscle on the *other* side of the spine.

Note: Unilateral and bilateral actions are indicated separately in the **B** Tables with a UL or BL (see page 62).

Rotational Actions to the "Same Side" vs. to the "Opposite Side"

The direction of a rotational movement is defined by the direction, right or left, the anterior surface of the body moves. For example, a left rotation of the head and neck means the person's face looks to the left. Rotational actions are created by unilateral muscle contractions.

If a muscle that is located on the *left* side of the spine contracts, and it causes the body to rotate to the *left*, then it is called a rotation **to the same side**. Conversely, if a muscle on the *right* side causes rotation to the *left* side, then it is creating a rotation **to the opposite side**.

Note that this concept only applies to rotational movements. Lateral flexion movements are always created by muscles pulling "to the same side".

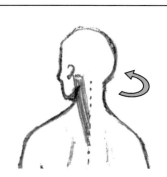

Rotation of the head/neck to
the **same** side.

The muscle is on the **left**
side of the spine, and the
rotation goes to the **left**.

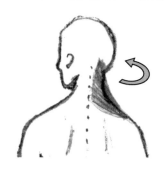

Rotation of the head/neck to
the **opposite** side.

The muscle is on the **right**
side of the spine, and the
rotation goes to the **left**.

Face and Jaw – Joint and Ligaments

Right Temporomandibular Joint

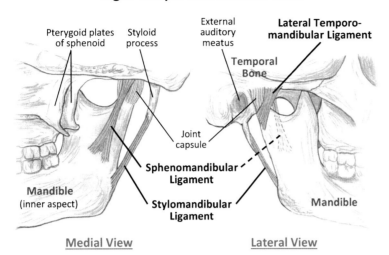

Pterygoid plates of sphenoid · Styloid process · External auditory meatus · **Lateral Temporomandibular Ligament** · **Temporal Bone** · Mandible (inner aspect) · Joint capsule · **Sphenomandibular Ligament** · **Stylomandibular Ligament** · Mandible

<u>Medial View</u>   <u>Lateral View</u>

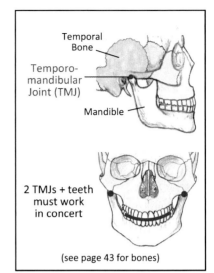

Temporal Bone · Temporomandibular Joint (TMJ) · Mandible

2 TMJs + teeth must work in concert

(see page 43 for bones)

Superior joint cavity · Articular disc (thinner in the middle) · Mandibular Fossa · Articular eminence · Temporal Bone · Retrodiscal Lamina · Superior · Inferior · Condyle · Joint capsule · Neck · Inferior joint cavity · Superior head · Lateral pterygoid muscle · Inferior head · Mandible

⬭ = articular fibrocartilage

<u>Lateral View</u>   (Sagittal section)

Superior joint cavity · Inferior joint cavity · Temporal bone · Articular disc · Condyle of mandible · Medial discal ligament · Lateral discal ligament · Capsular ligament · Capsular ligament

<u>Posterior View</u>   (Coronal section)

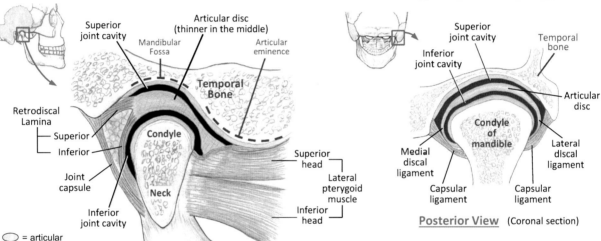

Opening and closing the mouth involves two mechanisms:
1. Rotation of condyle on inferior aspect of disc
2. Translation of superior aspect of disc on temporal bone

Mandibular Fossa · Articular eminence · Superior Retrodiscal Lamina (stretched) · Hinge action predominates · Glides under articular eminence (+ some hinge action)

Early phase of opening:
Primarily rotation of condyle on disc; lateral TM ligament goes taut.

Later phase of opening:
Primarily translation of disc + condyle on articular eminence.

Temporomandibular Joint	
Ligament	**Function**
Temporomandibular Lig. (lateral)	The main TMJ stabilizer. Limits downward, lateral, and posterior motion of the condyle.
Sphenomandibular Lig.	Limits anterior and downward motion, stabilizing during opening.
Stylomandibular Lig.	Assists in limiting anterior motion and lateral deviation.
Articular Disc	Cushions contact between mandibular condyle and temporal bone, and facilitates hinging and gliding movements.
Superior Retrodiscal Lamina	Tethers the disc from behind to resist pulling it too far anterior during opening. During closing, recoil helps pull disc backward.
Discal Ligs. (medial, lateral)	Stabilize the disc position on the condyle.

Upper Cervical Complex – Joints and Ligaments

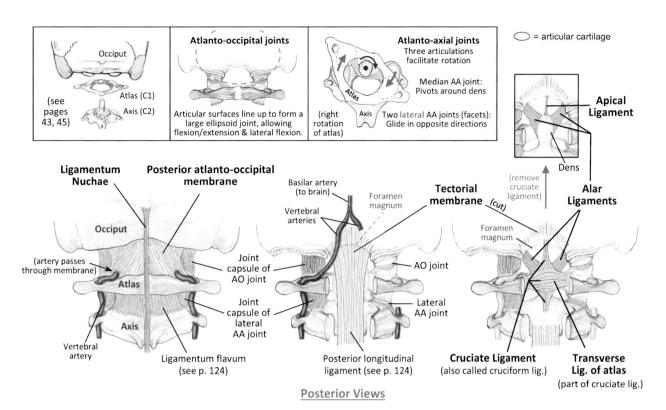

Atlanto-occipital joints
Articular surfaces line up to form a large ellipsoid joint, allowing flexion/extension & lateral flexion.

Atlanto-axial joints
Three articulations facilitate rotation

Median AA joint: Pivots around dens

(right rotation of atlas)

Two *lateral* AA joints (facets): Glide in opposite directions

⬭ = articular cartilage

Occiput
Atlas (C1)
Axis (C2)
(see pages 43, 45)

Apical Ligament

Dens

(remove cruciate ligament)

Alar Ligaments

Ligamentum Nuchae   **Posterior atlanto-occipital membrane**

Occiput

(artery passes through membrane)

Atlas

Axis

Vertebral artery

Ligamentum flavum (see p. 124)

Basilar artery (to brain)

Vertebral arteries

Foramen magnum

Joint capsule of AO joint

Joint capsule of lateral AA joint

Posterior longitudinal ligament (see p. 124)

Tectorial membrane *(cut)*

AO joint

Lateral AA joint

Foramen magnum

Cruciate Ligament
(also called cruciform lig.)

Transverse Lig. of atlas
(part of cruciate lig.)

Posterior Views

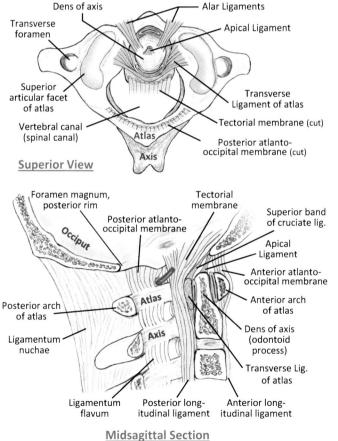

Dens of axis
Transverse foramen
Alar Ligaments
Apical Ligament
Superior articular facet of atlas
Transverse Ligament of atlas
Vertebral canal (spinal canal)
Tectorial membrane (cut)
Atlas
Posterior atlanto-occipital membrane (cut)
Axis

Superior View

Foramen magnum, posterior rim
Tectorial membrane
Posterior atlanto-occipital membrane
Superior band of cruciate lig.
Apical Ligament
Anterior atlanto-occipital membrane
Anterior arch of atlas
Dens of axis (odontoid process)
Transverse Lig. of atlas
Occiput
Atlas
Axis
Posterior arch of atlas
Ligamentum nuchae
Ligamentum flavum
Posterior longitudinal ligament
Anterior longitudinal ligament

Midsagittal Section
(Left side of skull and neck, viewed from the inside)

Atlanto-occipital (AO) & Atlanto-axial (AA) Joints	
Ligament	**Function**
Ligamentum Nuchae (Nuchal Lig.)	Limits excessive flexion of the neck & head (occiput to C7). Attachment site for superficial neck muscles.
Posterior atlanto-occipital membrane	Limits AO joint flexion. Posterior boundary of spinal canal (continuation of the ligamentum flavum).
Tectorial membrane	Adds to stability of AO & AA joints. Anterior boundary of spinal canal (continuation of the posterior longitudinal ligament).
Transverse Lig. of the atlas (horizontal part of cruciate)	Strongly holds dens against atlas, completing the AO pivot joint. Prevents posterior displacement of dens (protecting spinal cord).
Cruciate Lig. (vertical parts)	Superior longitudinal: Stabilizes dens to basilar part of occiput. Inferior longitudinal: Vertical strap down to the body of the axis (C2).
Alar Ligs.	Taut in AO joint flexion. Limit excessive rotation of head-and-atlas relative to dens of the axis.
Apical Lig.	Connects dens to rim of foramen magnum. Limits vertical movement between the occiput, atlas & axis.
Anterior atlanto-occipital membrane	Stabilizes during extension at the AO joint (continuation of the anterior longitudinal ligament).

Vertebral Column – Joints and Ligaments

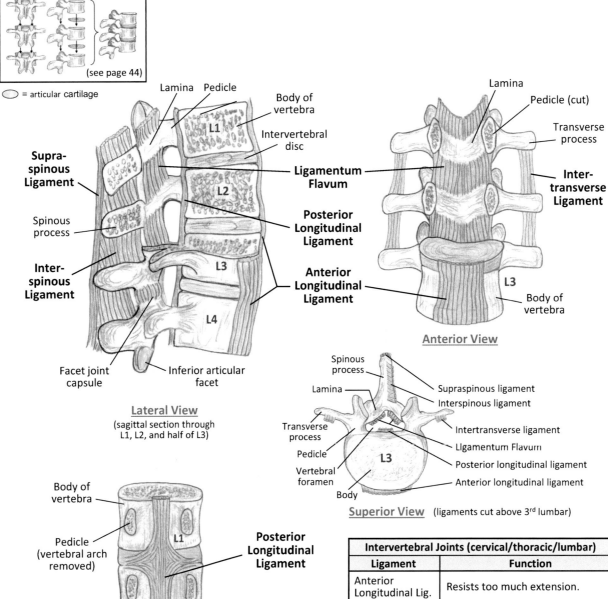

(see page 44)

◯ = articular cartilage

Lateral View
(sagittal section through
L1, L2, and half of L3)

Lamina · Pedicle · Body of vertebra · Intervertebral disc

Supra-spinous Ligament

Ligamentum Flavum

Spinous process

Posterior Longitudinal Ligament

Inter-spinous Ligament

Anterior Longitudinal Ligament

Facet joint capsule · Inferior articular facet

Anterior View

Lamina · Pedicle (cut) · Transverse process · **Inter-transverse Ligament** · Body of vertebra

Superior View (ligaments cut above 3rd lumbar)

Spinous process · Lamina · Transverse process · Pedicle · Vertebral foramen · Body

Supraspinous ligament · Interspinous ligament · Intertransverse ligament · Ligamentum Flavum · Posterior longitudinal ligament · Anterior longitudinal ligament

Posterior View

Body of vertebra · Pedicle (vertebral arch removed) · Transverse process · **Inter-transverse Ligament**

Posterior Longitudinal Ligament · **Ligamentum Flavum** · **Iliolumbar Ligament**

Iliac crest · Sacrum

Intervertebral Joints (cervical/thoracic/lumbar)	
Ligament	**Function**
Anterior Longitudinal Lig.	Resists too much extension.
Posterior Longitudinal Lig.	Resists too much flexion. Protects anterior border of the spinal canal.
Ligamentum Flavum	Connects adjacent lamina, stabilizing during flexion. Protects posterior border of the spinal canal.
Interspinous Lig.	Resists too much flexion.
Supraspinous Lig.	Resists too much flexion.
Intertransverse Lig.	Limits lateral flexion to the opposite side.
Note: The above ligaments run the entire length of the spine.	
Iliolumbar Lig.	Restrains movement at the lumbosacral junction (L5/S1). Helps stabilize SI joints.

Thorax – Joints and Ligaments

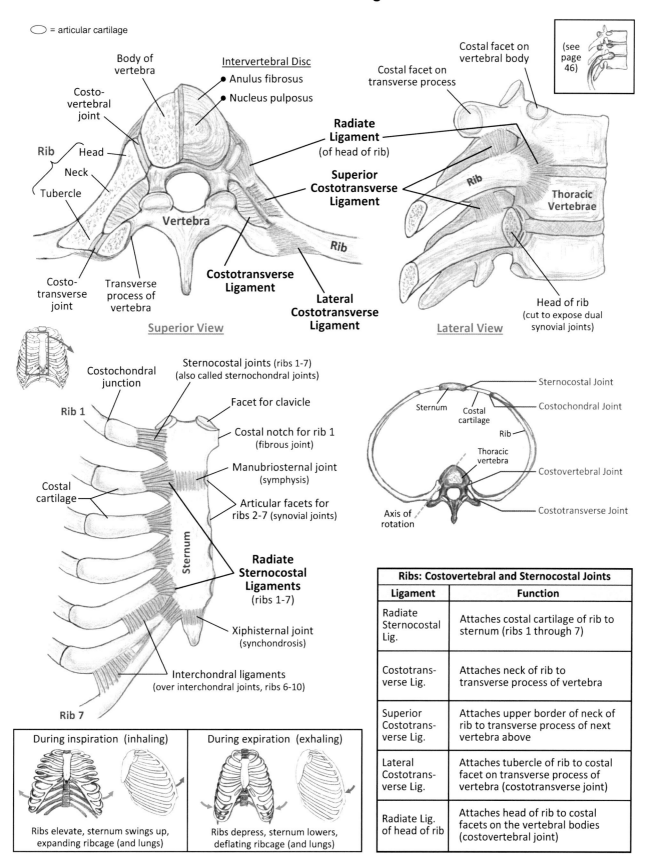

◯ = articular cartilage

Superior View

Body of vertebra

Costo-vertebral joint

Rib { Head, Neck, Tubercle

Costo-transverse joint

Transverse process of vertebra

Vertebra

Intervertebral Disc
- Anulus fibrosus
- Nucleus pulposus

Radiate Ligament
(of head of rib)

Superior Costotransverse Ligament

Costotransverse Ligament

Rib

Lateral Costotransverse Ligament

Lateral View

(see page 46)

Costal facet on vertebral body

Costal facet on transverse process

Rib

Thoracic Vertebrae

Head of rib
(cut to expose dual synovial joints)

Costochondral junction

Sternocostal joints (ribs 1-7)
(also called sternochondral joints)

Rib 1

Facet for clavicle

Costal notch for rib 1
(fibrous joint)

Manubriosternal joint
(symphysis)

Costal cartilage

Articular facets for ribs 2-7 (synovial joints)

Sternum

Radiate Sternocostal Ligaments
(ribs 1-7)

Xiphisternal joint
(synchondrosis)

Interchondral ligaments
(over interchondral joints, ribs 6-10)

Rib 7

Sternocostal Joint

Sternum

Costal cartilage

Rib

Costochondral Joint

Thoracic vertebra

Costovertebral Joint

Axis of rotation

Costotransverse Joint

Ribs: Costovertebral and Sternocostal Joints	
Ligament	**Function**
Radiate Sternocostal Lig.	Attaches costal cartilage of rib to sternum (ribs 1 through 7)
Costotrans-verse Lig.	Attaches neck of rib to transverse process of vertebra
Superior Costotrans-verse Lig.	Attaches upper border of neck of rib to transverse process of next vertebra above
Lateral Costotrans-verse Lig.	Attaches tubercle of rib to costal facet on transverse process of vertebra (costotransverse joint)
Radiate Lig. of head of rib	Attaches head of rib to costal facets on the vertebral bodies (costovertebral joint)

During inspiration (inhaling)

Ribs elevate, sternum swings up, expanding ribcage (and lungs)

During expiration (exhaling)

Ribs depress, sternum lowers, deflating ribcage (and lungs)

Pelvis – Joints and Ligaments

⬭ = articular cartilage

(see page 47)

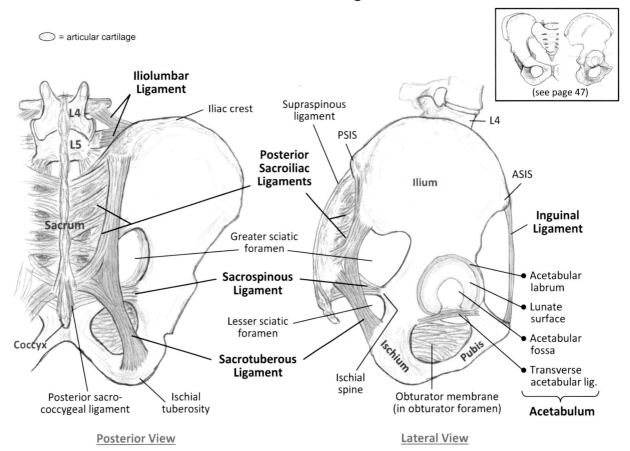

Iliolumbar Ligament

L4

L5

Iliac crest

Sacrum

Coccyx

Posterior sacro-coccygeal ligament

Ischial tuberosity

Supraspinous ligament

PSIS

Posterior Sacroiliac Ligaments

Greater sciatic foramen

Sacrospinous Ligament

Lesser sciatic foramen

Sacrotuberous Ligament

Posterior View

L4

Ilium

ASIS

Inguinal Ligament

Acetabular labrum

Lunate surface

Acetabular fossa

Transverse acetabular lig.

Ischium

Pubis

Ischial spine

Obturator membrane (in obturator foramen)

Acetabulum

Lateral View

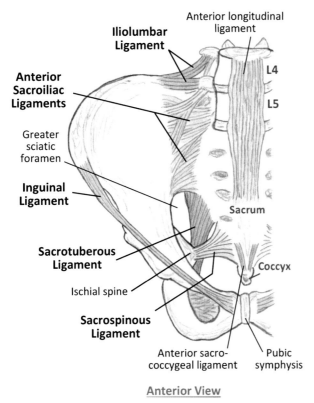

Iliolumbar Ligament

Anterior longitudinal ligament

Anterior Sacroiliac Ligaments

L4

L5

Greater sciatic foramen

Inguinal Ligament

Sacrum

Sacrotuberous Ligament

Coccyx

Ischial spine

Sacrospinous Ligament

Anterior sacro-coccygeal ligament

Pubic symphysis

Anterior View

Pelvis:	Lumbosacral Junction, Sacroiliac (SI) Joints, Sacrococcygeal Joint	
Ligament	**Function**
Iliolumbar Lig.	Restrains movement at the lumbosacral junction (L5/S1). Helps stabilize SI joints.
Sacroiliac Ligs. (anterior & posterior)	Main stabilizers of sacroiliac (SI) joints. Limit rotation/gliding in SI joints.
Sacro-tuberous Lig.	Limits anterior rotation of sacrum at SI joints (nutation), stabilizing when SI joints are bearing weight of the body.
Sacro-spinous Lig.	Stabilizes sacrum vs. hip bone. Defines boundary between greater and lesser sciatic foramen.
Sacro-coccygeal Ligs. (ant., post., lat.)	Stabilize joint between sacrum and coccyx.
Inguinal Lig.	Superior anchor for the fascia latae, inferior anchor for abdominal muscles, "roof" for passage of nerves, vessels, and muscles between abdomen and thigh.

35164

Movement of the Face and Jaw

Muscle Group 6

Masseter	Occipitofrontalis
Temporalis	Platysma
Lateral pterygoid	Suprahyoids group
Medial pterygoid	Infrahyoids group

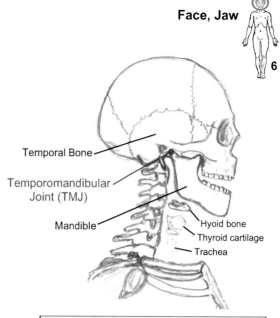

Joint

(Joint details: p. 122)

The first four of the muscles in this group move the mandible at the temporomandibular joint. The remaining muscles are involved with moving the face, jaw, and anterior neck/throat.

Temporomandibular Joint (TMJ)

Condyle of **mandible** ◄► mandibular fossa of **temporal** bone

Complex Type: Condyloid/gliding/hinge
Movements of the jaw available at the TMJ:
    Elevation, Depression
    Protraction, Retraction (Protrusion, Retrusion)
    Lateral Deviation

Note: There is a moveable articular disc (cartilage) between the bones at the TMJ.

Other Structures and Movements

The following are not individual actions of bones at joints, but are body functions that involve coordinated contractions of the muscles of the face, jaw, and anterior neck.

Mastication (chewing)
    Involves movement of TMJ (see above) along with movement of the tongue, cheeks, and lips.

Facial Expression
    Many muscles move the tissue of the face.

Deglutition (swallowing)
    Swallowing involves a complex series of movements of the tongue, throat, and anterior neck muscles.

Speech
    Muscles of the jaw, mouth, tongue, face, and soft palate are used when forming spoken words.

Sight
    Muscles close and open the eyelids, and small muscles move the eyeballs in their sockets.

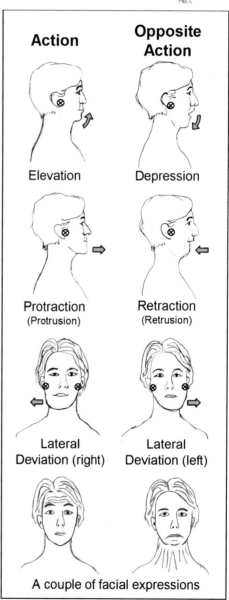

Action	Opposite Action
Elevation	Depression
Protraction (Protrusion)	Retraction (Retrusion)
Lateral Deviation (right)	Lateral Deviation (left)

A couple of facial expressions

Face, Jaw

6 Bones, Bony Landmarks, Other Structures

Muscles that move the face and jaw have attachments on the skull, mandible, hyoid bone, fascia, sternum, and others. Review the bony landmarks and other structures listed below, referring to the drawings in Chapter 2, page 43-46.

Cranial Bones: (p. 43)

Occiput
     External occipital protuberance
     Superior nuchal line

Temporal (2)
     Styloid process
     Mastoid process
     Zygomatic arch
     Mandibular fossa

Parietal (2)
Frontal

Sphenoid
     Pterygoid plates, lateral and medial (p. 122)

Temporal Fossa:
     Flat area on side of skull covering
     portions of the temporal, parietal,
     frontal, and sphenoid bones

Facial Bones: (p. 43)

Maxilla (2)
Zygomatic (2)
Nasal (2)

Mandible
     Condyle of the mandible
     Coronoid process
     Ramus
     Angle
     Body

Hyoid Bone (p. 43)

Sternum (p. 46)
     Manubrium

Other Structures
     Galea aponeurotica   (p. 129)
     Thyroid cartilage   (p. 127)

Muscles of Facial Expression

Humans have a multitude of muscles that move the tissue of the face. Most of these muscles of **facial expression** are shown in this illustration. Note that two of these muscles, occipitofrontalis and platysma, are also included in the Group 6 tables.

In addition to expressing emotions, these muscles provide important functions such as closing the eyes and mouth, holding in the cheeks while chewing food, and shaping sounds while speaking.

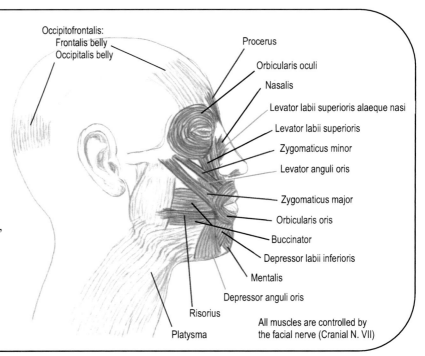

All muscles are controlled by the facial nerve (Cranial N. VII)

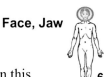

Muscle Group 6 - Muscles that move the face and jaw are illustrated as a group on this page. The four pages that follow have tables and figures that describe each muscle individually, and provide many ways of comparing and contrasting the muscles to each other.

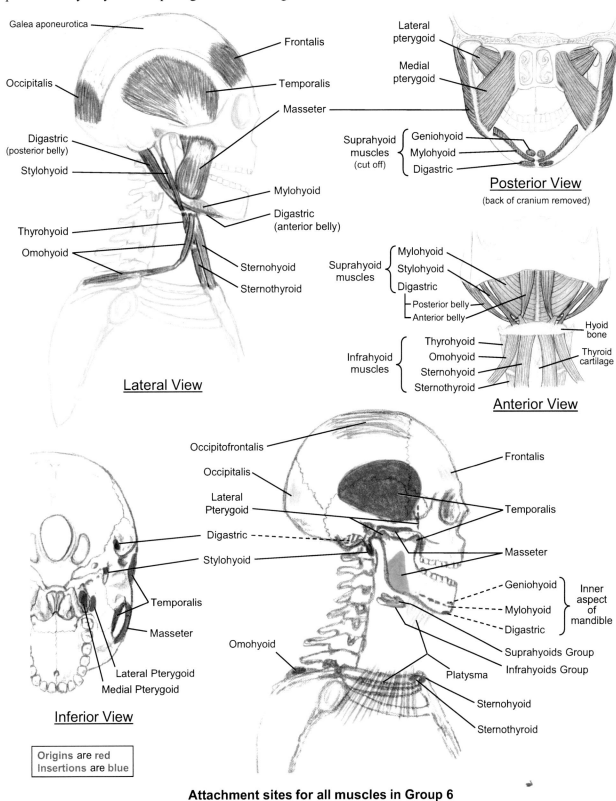

Attachment sites for all muscles in Group 6

Mandible moves at the TMJ=Temporomandibular joint, UL=Unilateral action, BL=Bilateral action

Group 6: Muscles Acting On

Face, Jaw	Origin	Insertion	Action
Masseter moves the mandible	Zygomatic arch	Angle and ramus of the mandible (Has 2 bellies: superficial & deep)	<u>BL</u>: Elevation of the mandible
Temporalis moves the mandible	Temporal fossa and fascia	Coronoid process of the mandible	<u>BL</u>: Elevation and retraction of mandible.
Lateral Pterygoid moves the mandible	<u>Lower head</u>: *Lateral* surface of lateral pterygoid plate of sphenoid bone <u>Upper Head</u>: Greater wing of sphenoid	Neck of mandible and articular disc of TMJ	<u>BL</u>: Protrusion of mandible, assists depression of mandible. <u>UL</u>: Lateral deviation of mandible to the opposite side.
Medial Pterygoid moves the mandible	<u>Deep head</u>: Fossa between lateral and medial pterygoid plates <u>Superficial head</u>: Tuberosity of maxilla	Medial (inner) surface of angle of mandible (forms a "sling" with the masseter muscle on the outside)	<u>BL</u>: Assists elevation of mandible. <u>UL</u>: Lateral deviation of mandible to the opposite side.
Occipitofrontalis moves the brows	Galea aponeurotica	<u>Frontalis belly</u>: Skin and fascia above the eyebrows. <u>Occipitalis belly</u>: Superior nuchal line of occiput	Raises the eyebrows, wrinkles the forehead
Platysma moves the mandible and skin	Fascia over the pectoralis major	Lower mandible, subcutaneous tissue of lower face & angle of mouth	Pulls angle of mouth downward and thoracic skin upward. Assists depression of the mandible
Suprahyoids group *Geniohyoid, Mylohyoid, Stylohyoid, Digastric*	Underside of mandible, styloid process, mastoid process (Digastric has 2-bellies, origins at mastoid process and mandible)	Hyoid bone	*When the mandible is stable*: Elevation of the hyoid when swallowing. *When the hyoid is stable*: Depression of the mandible.
Infrahyoids group *Sternohyoid, Sternothyroid, Omohyoid, Thyrohyoid*	Manubrium of sternum, medial clavicle, superior border of scapula (omohyoid)	Hyoid bone and thyroid cartilage	Depression and stabilization of the hyoid bone and thyroid cartilage.

(larger illustrations on page 133)

Table 6 (A) - Face, Jaw - Origin, Insertion, Action

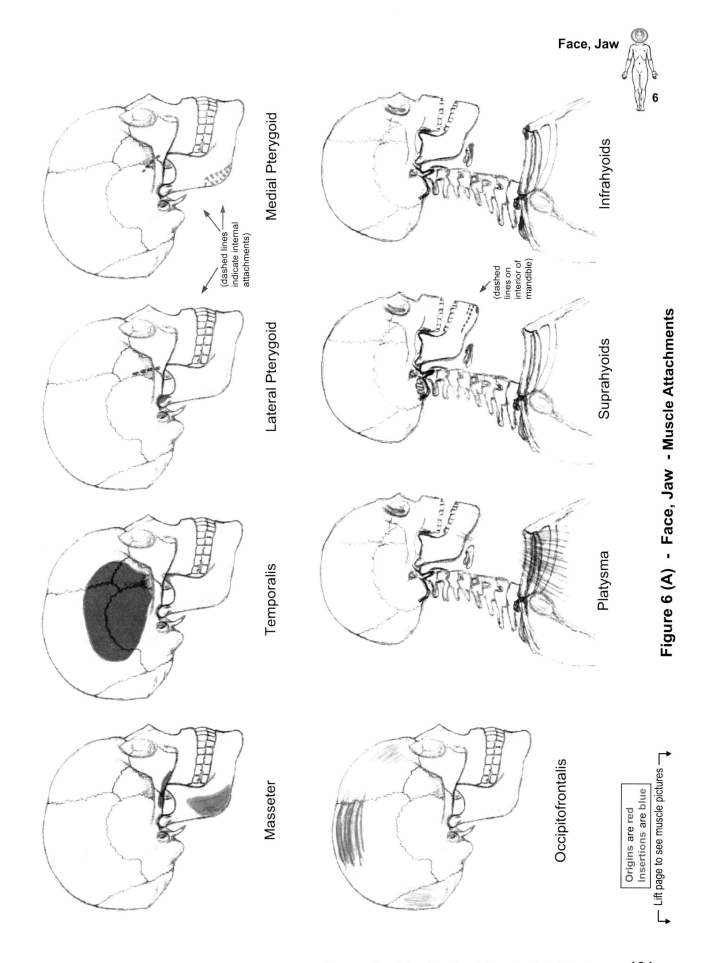

Medial Pterygoid

(dashed lines indicate internal attachments)

Lateral Pterygoid

Temporalis

Masseter

Infrahyoids

(dashed lines on interior of mandible)

Suprahyoids

Platysma

Occipitofrontalis

Origins are red
Insertions are blue

Lift page to see muscle pictures

Figure 6 (A) - Face, Jaw - Muscle Attachments

Group 6:

Mandible moves at the two TMJs (Temporomandibular Joints), UL=Unilateral action, BL=Bilateral action, ✓=Both UL & BL action, N=Nerve

Muscles Acting On Face, Jaw	Elevation of mandible	Depression of mandible	Protrusion/ Protraction of mandible	Retrusion/ Retraction of mandible	Lateral Deviation of mandible	Other	Innervation	Cr. V	Cr. VII	Cr. XII	C1	C2	C3
1. Masseter	✓			✓ assist (deep belly)			Trigeminal N. (Cranial N. V)	N					
2. Temporalis	✓			✓ (posterior fibers)		Many movements due to multiple fiber directions: Anterior = vertical, Middle = diagonal, Posterior = horizontal	Trigeminal N. (Cranial N. V)	N					
3. Lateral Pterygoid		✓ assist	✓		UL to opposite side	Pulls artcular disc forward when opening mouth	Trigeminal N. (Cranial N. V)	N					
4. Medial Pterygoid	✓ assist		✓ may assist		UL to opposite side	This and masseter create a "sling" around angle of the mandible	Trigeminal N. (Cranial N. V)	N					
5. Occipitofrontalis: Frontalis belly, Occipitalis belly						Raises eyebrows, wrinkles forehead	Frontalis: Temporal branch Facial N. (Cr.VII) Occip: Posterior auricular br. Facial N. (Cr.VII)		N				
6. Platysma		✓ assist				Pulls angle of mouth downward and thoracic skin upward	Facial N. (Cr. VII)		N				
7. Suprahyoids group Geniohyoid, Mylohyoid, Stylohyoid, Digastric				✓ assist		Elevates hyoid (when mandible is stable), or depresses mandible (when hyoid is stable)	G: Hypoglossal XII,C1 M: Trigeminal N. (V) S: Facial N. (VII) D: Trgiem.V,Facial	N	N	N	N		
8. Infrahyoids group Sternohyoid, Sternothyroid, Omohyoid, Thyrohyoid		✓ assist				Depresses and stabilizes the hyoid bone	Ansa cervicalis C1,C2,C3				N	N	N

(More muscles for the action) —→

Innervation

B3

Table 6 (B) - Face, Jaw - Synergists & Antagonists

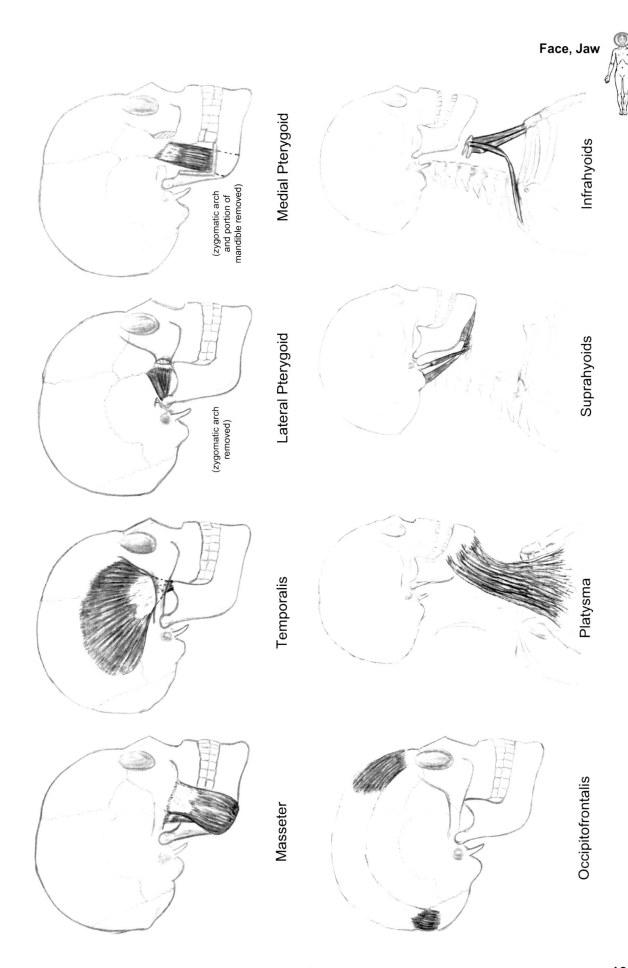

Medial Pterygoid

(zygomatic arch and portion of mandible removed)

Lateral Pterygoid

(zygomatic arch removed)

Temporalis

Masseter

Infrahyoids

Suprahyoids

Platysma

Occipitofrontalis

Figure 6 (B) - Face, Jaw - Muscle Pictures

Note-taking page ~ (palpation, how to lengthen/shorten, cautions, common uses, etc.)

Muscle Group 6 - Muscles Acting on the Face, Jaw

1. Masseter

2. Temporalis

3. Lateral Pterygoid

4. Medial Pterygoid

5. Occipitofrontalis   *(Occipitalis & Frontalis)*

6. Platysma

7. Suprahyoids Group   *(Geniohyoid, Mylohyoid, Stylohyoid, Digastric)*

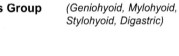

8. Infrahyoids Group   *(Sternohyoid, Sternothyroid, Omohyoid, Thyrohyoid)*

Movement of the Neck and Head

Muscle Group 7

Sternocleidomastoid (SCM)	Splenius capitis
Scalenes group ⤵ (anterior, middle, posterior)	Splenius cervicis
	Semispinalis capitis
Longus capitis & longus colli	Levator scapula (reversed O/I)
Suboccipital group	Trapezius, upper fibers (reversed O/I)

Joints

(Joint details: p. 123)

The muscles in this group primarily move the neck and head. Some are also used in the inhalation phase of breathing (reversed O/I actions). Two of the muscles also move the scapula, as described previously in Chapter 4, Muscle Group 1.

Atlanto-occipital Joint (AO)
　　Occipital condyles ◄► Superior facets of C1 (atlas)
　　Ellipsoid joint
　　　　Flexion & Extension　(head rocks forward and back-
　　　　　　　　　　　　　　　　ward on C1: "stiff necked yes")
　　　　Lateral flexion　　　(tilt side to side: "duh")

　　(the AO joint is also called the **Occipito-atlantal (OA)** joint)

Atlantoaxial Joint (AA) Atlas/Axis = C1/C2, has 2 parts:

　• **Atlanto-odontoid Joint**　　(also called median AA joint)
　　　Inner anterior arch of **C1** ◄► Odontoid process of **C2**
　　　Pivot joint (allows rotation)

　• **Atlantoaxial Facet Joints (2)**　(also called lateral AA joints)
　　　Pairs:　**C1** inferior facets ◄► **C2** superior facets
　　　Gliding joints (Rotation as they glide in opposite directions)

　　　C1/C2 has more rotation than any other spinal segment, and the axis of rotation is at the median AA joint (p. 123).

Intervertebral Joints (C2–T1, have 2 parts):
(please review page 119)

　• **Intervertebral Discs**
　　　Between vertebral bodies
　　　Amphiarthrotic/Cartilaginous joint

　• **Intervertebral Facet Joints (paired)**　(zygapophyseal joints)
　　　Pairs:　Inferior facets of vertebra above ◄► Superior
　　　　　　　facets of vertebra below
　　　Gliding joints

(C2-T1 intervertebral joints allow all six actions shown in box)

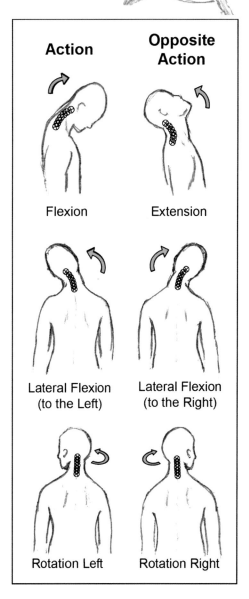

Action / **Opposite Action**

Flexion　　Extension

Lateral Flexion (to the Left)　　Lateral Flexion (to the Right)

Rotation Left　　Rotation Right

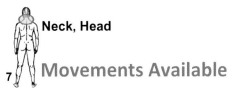

Neck, Head

Movements Available

To move the head and neck, muscles anchor below and pull on structures above. Movement dynamics can be divided into three categories:

Head Movement: Head sitting on Atlas (C1) moves without the neck moving.
- Muscles have a short span – from C1 and C2 to the occiput.

Neck-Initiated Movement: Neck is pulled by a muscle, and the head goes along with it.
- Muscles insert on the cervical spine, and do not cross over to the skull.

Head-Initiated Movement: Skull is pulled by a muscle, and the neck "usually" goes along with it.
- Muscles span several vertebrae and insert on the occiput, creating a complex dynamic between head and neck.
- The head may tilt or rotate along with moving the neck.

Deep Anterior Neck Muscles

(Prevertebral Muscles)

There are four muscles that lie deep in the anterior neck. Some of these **prevertebral muscles** are not included in the Group 7 tables, so they are summarized here for completeness. Three of the muscles insert on the base of the occiput, just anterior or lateral to the foramen magnum, and the fourth spans all cervical and the upper 3 thoracic vertebrae. They assist flexion of the neck/head, and the RCL assists lateral tilting of the head on C1.

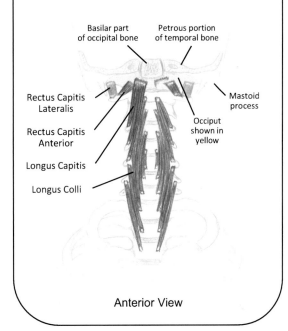

Anterior View

Bones, Bony Landmarks, Other

Muscles that move the neck and head have attachments on the skull, vertebrae, upper thorax, and shoulder girdle. Review the bony landmarks and other structures listed below, referring to the drawings in Chapter 2, pages 40-46.

Skull (p. 43)
    Occiput
        External occipital protuberance
        Superior nuchal line, Inferior nuchal line
        Occipital condyles
        Foramen magnum
    Temporal bone (mastoid process)

Sternum, upper 2 ribs, scapula, and clavicle (p. 40, 46)

Focus: Cervical spine (p. 45, 123)

Cervical vertebrae have:
    Transverse foramen in TVPs (for blood vessels)
    Bifid spinous processes (except C1 & C7)
    Nearly horizontal facets

Atlas (C1)
    No SP, broader TVPs
    No Body (anterior arch instead)
    Superior facets are where the occiput sits

Axis (C2)
    Odontoid process (dens) above,
        Dens fits into anterior arch of C1
    "Body" articulates to C3 below

Middle and lower cervicals (C3 – C7)
    "Normal" cervical vertebrae

Nuchal Ligament (p. 123)
    Also called Ligamentum Nuchae
    Attachment site for the more superficial muscles

Muscle Group 7 - **Muscles that move the neck and head** are illustrated as a group on this page. The following four pages have tables and figures that describe each muscle individually, and provide many ways of comparing and contrasting the muscles to each other.

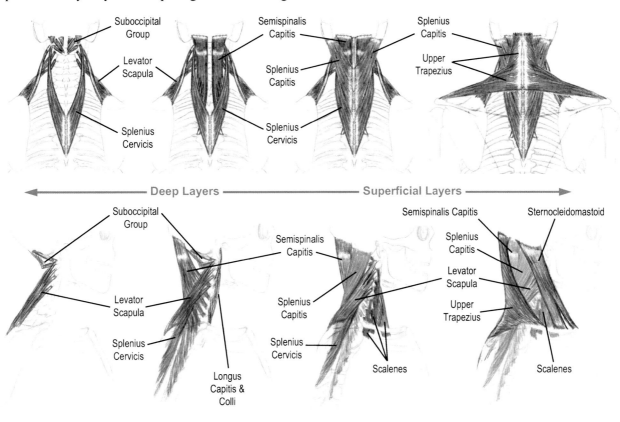

Note: Some of the muscles in this group use reversed O/I actions.

Base of Skull – Inferior View

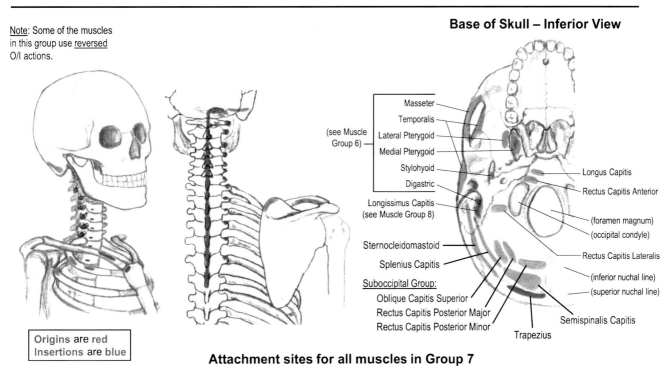

Origins are red
Insertions are blue

Attachment sites for all muscles in Group 7

Group 7: Muscles Acting On

TVP=Transverse process of vertebra, SP=Spinous process of vertebra, UL=Unilateral action, BL=Bilateral action

Neck, Head	Origin	Insertion	Action
Sternocleidomastoid (SCM) moves the head and neck	Sternal head: Manubrium of the sternum Clavicular head: Medial third of the clavicle *Overall Description:* Medial clavicle, and manubrium of the sternum	Mastoid process of the temporal bone, (and lateral part of superior nuchal line of occiput)	**BL:** Flexion of the neck. (also extension at atlanto-occipital joint, and assists inhalation by lifting ribcage) **UL:** Lateral flexion of head/neck, rotation of head to opposite side. (rotating also makes face turn upward)
Scalenes: Anterior Scalene Middle Scalene Posterior Scalene move the neck	Anterior: TVP's C3-C6 Middle: TVP's C2-C7 Posterior: TVP's C5-C7 *Overall Description:* TVP's of C2-C7	Anterior: Anterior Rib 1 Middle: Lateral Rib 1 Posterior: Lateral Rib 2 *Overall Description:* Ribs 1 & 2	**BL:** Raise ribs #1 & 2 for inhalation, assist flexion of the neck (ant.&mid.). **UL:** Lateral flexion of neck (ant.&mid.--assist rotation to opp. side)
Longus Capitis, Longus Colli move the head and neck	Capitis: TVP's of C3-C5 Colli: TVP's of C3-C5, and Anterior bodies of C5-T3	Capitis: Inferior surface of occiput (anterior to the foramen magnum) Colli: Anterior arch/bodies C1-C4, & TVP's of C5-C6	**BL:** Flexion of the head/neck. (**UL:** May assist lateral flexion and rotation of the head/neck)
Suboccipitals Group move the head • Rectus Capitis Posterior Major • Rectus Capitis Posterior minor • Oblique Capitis Superior • Oblique Capitis Inferior	RCP Maj: SP of C2 RCP Min: Posterior tubercle of C1 OCS: TVP of C1 OCI: SP of C2 *Overall Description:* SP's & TVP's of C1 and C2 (atlas and axis)	RCP Maj: } RCP Min: } Inferior nuchal line OCS: } of occiput OCI: TVP of C1 *Overall Description:* Lower occipital bone & TVP's of C1	**BL:** Rock the head back into extension (all) **UL:** Lateral flexion of the head (RCPM, RCPm, and OCS) Rotation to the same side (OCI)
Splenius Capitis moves the head and neck	Lower half of nuchal ligament (from C3-C6), and SP's of C7-T3	Mastoid process of the temporal bone, (and lateral part of superior nuchal line of occiput - deep to SCM insertion)	**BL:** Extension of the head/neck. **UL:** Rotation of head/neck to the same side, lateral flexion of the head/neck
Splenius Cervicis moves the neck	SP's of T3-T6	TVP's of C1-C3	**BL:** Extension of the neck. **UL:** Rotation of the neck to the same side, lateral flexion of the neck
Semispinalis Capitis moves the head and neck	TVP's of C4-C7 and T1-T6	Occipital bone (between the superior and inferior nuchal lines)	**BL:** Extension of the head/neck. *(see Muscle Group 8 for description of the complete semispinalis muscle)*
Levator Scapula This is reversed O/I action, i.e., scapula is held fixed, so moves the neck *(See also Muscle Group 1)*	TVP's of C1-C4	Superior angle of scapula	*With scapula held fixed:* **BL:** Extension of neck. **UL:** Lateral flexion of neck, rotation of neck to same side
Trapezius, upper fibers This is reversed O/I action, i.e., scapula is held fixed, so moves the head & neck *(See also Muscle Group 1)*	Upper fibers: Occiput, nuchal ligament, and SP of C7	Upper fibers: Lateral clavicle	*With scapula held fixed:* **BL:** Extension of head/neck. **UL:** Lateral flexion of head/neck, and rotation to opposite side.

Table 7 (A) - Neck, Head - Origin, Insertion, Action

(larger illustrations on page 141)

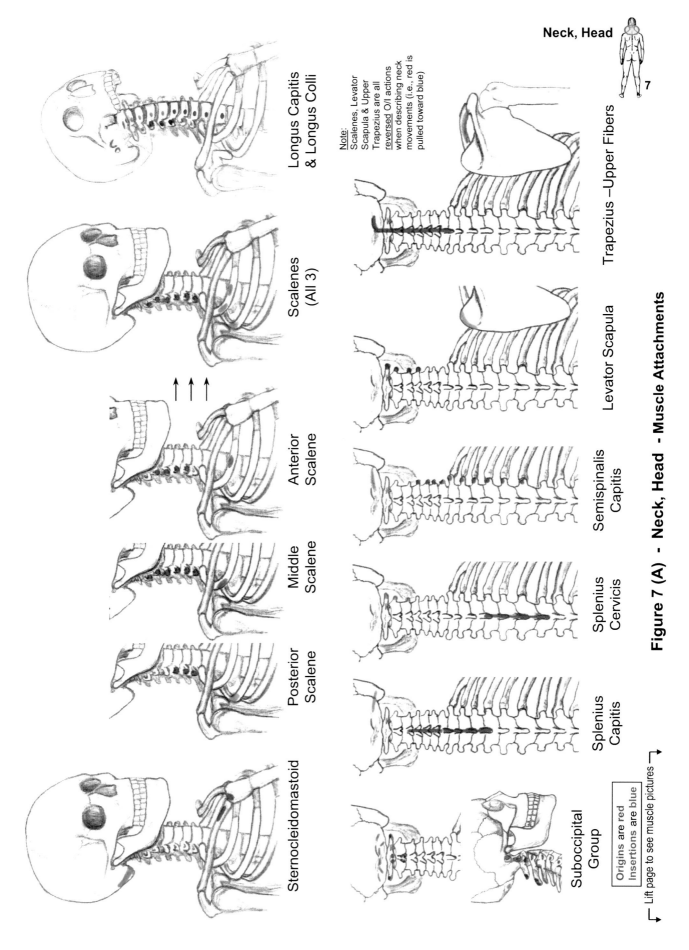

Longus Capitis & Longus Colli

Note:
Scalenes, Levator Scapula & Upper Trapezius are all reversed O/I actions when describing neck movements (i.e., red is pulled toward blue)

Trapezius –Upper Fibers

Scalenes (All 3)

Levator Scapula

Anterior Scalene

Semispinalis Capitis

Middle Scalene

Splenius Cervicis

Posterior Scalene

Splenius Capitis

Sternocleidomastoid

Suboccipital Group

Figure 7 (A) - Neck, Head - Muscle Attachments

Origins are red
Insertions are blue

Lift page to see muscle pictures

Group 7:

UL=Unilateral action, BL=Bilateral action, N=Nerve, AO jt.=Atlanto-occipital joint

Muscles Acting On — Neck, Head

Muscles Acting On: Neck, Head	Flexion	Extension	Lateral Flexion	Rotation to same side	Rotation to opp. side	Inhalation	(other)
1. Sternocleidomastoid	BL neck	BL may assist (AO jt. only)	UL head/neck		UL head/neck	BL assist (lifts upper rib cage)	Helps stabilize head
2. Scalenes: Anterior Scalene, Middle Scalene, Posterior Scalene	BL neck (Ant. & Mid.)		UL neck (all)		UL assist (Ant. & Mid.)	BL (raises ribs 1 & 2)	Helps stabilize neck
3. Longus Capitis / 4. Longus Colli	BL head/neck						
5. Suboccipitals Group — Rectus Capitis Posterior Major, Rectus Capitis Posterior minor, Oblique Capitis Superior, Oblique Capitis Inferior		BL head (all)	UL head (RCPM, RCPm, OCS)	UL head (OCI)			
6. Splenius Capitis		BL head/neck	UL head/neck	UL head/neck			
7. Splenius Cervicis		BL neck	UL neck	UL neck			
8. Semispinalis Capitis		BL or UL head/neck					This is part of a spinal muscle (see Group 8)
9. Levator Scapula (reversed O/I action, i.e., scapula held fixed)		BL neck	UL neck	UL neck			This muscle is also in Group 1 (moves scapula)
10. Trapezius, Upr fibers (reversed O/I action, i.e., scapula held fixed)		BL head/neck	UL head/neck		UL head/neck		This muscle is also in Group 1 (moves scapula)
(More muscles for the action) --->		See also Group 8	See also Group 8	See also Group 8		See also Group 9	

Innervation

Muscles Acting On: Neck, Head	Innervation	Cr. XI	C1	C2	C3	C4	C5	C6	C7	C8
1. Sternocleidomastoid	Spinal Accessory N. (Cranial N. XI), and C2, C3	N		N	N					
2. Scalenes	Anterior rami: Ant. C5, C6; Mid. C3-C8; Post. C6-C8				N	N	N	N	N	N
3. Longus Capitis / 4. Longus Colli	Ventral rami of C1-C6		N	N	N	N	N	N		
5. Suboccipitals Group	Suboccipital N. (C1)		N							
6. Splenius Capitis	Dorsal rami of middle cervicals					N	N	N		
7. Splenius Cervicis	Dorsal rami of lower cervicals								N	
8. Semispinalis Capitis	Dorsal rami of C1-C5		N	N	N	N	N			
9. Levator Scapula	Dorsal scapular N. (C5), and C3, C4				N	N	N			
10. Trapezius, Upr fibers	Spinal Accessory N. (Cranial N. XI), and C3, C4	N			N	N				

B4

Table 7 (B) - Neck, Head - Synergists & Antagonists

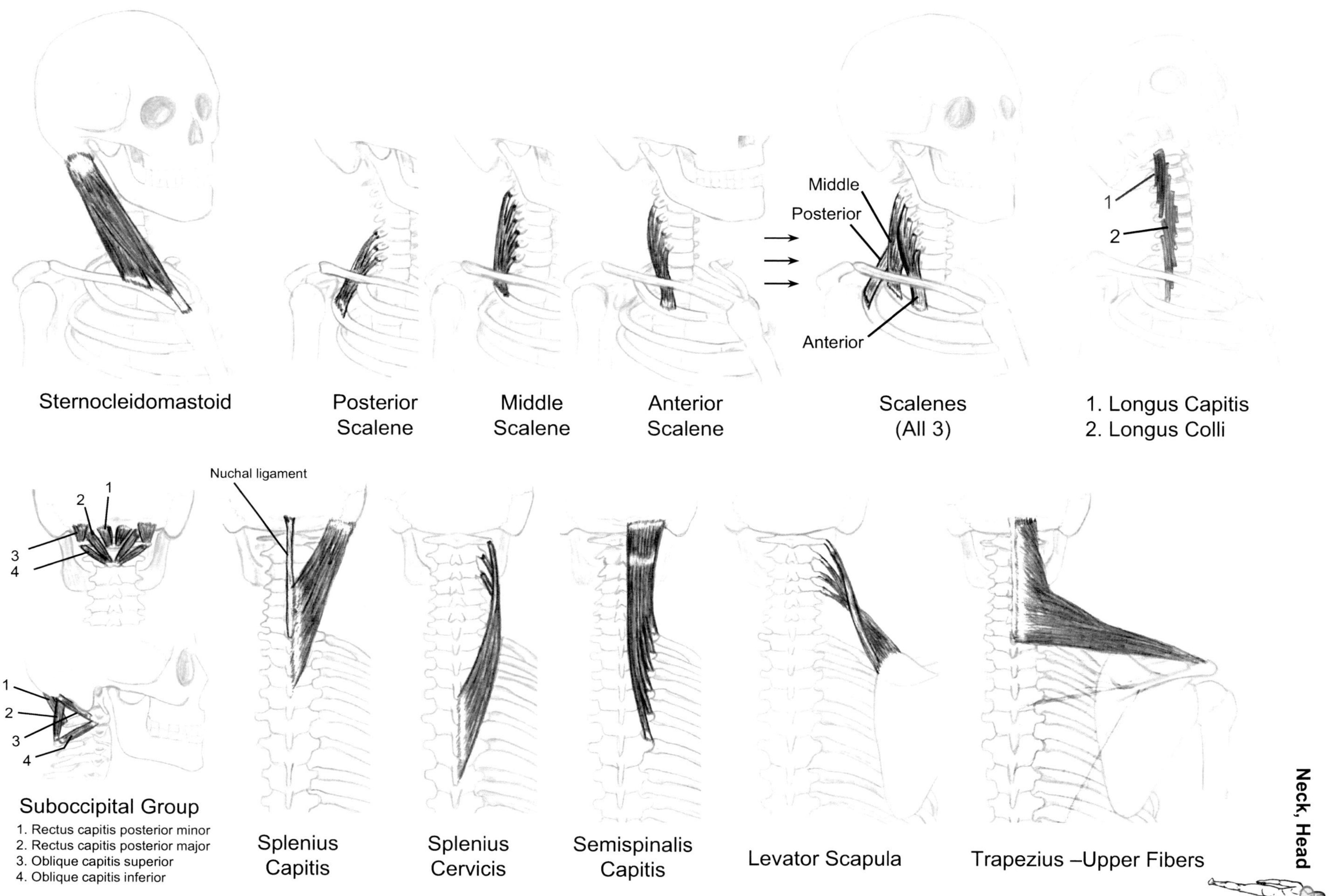

Middle
Posterior
Anterior
1
2
Sternocleidomastoid
Posterior Scalene
Middle Scalene
Anterior Scalene
Scalenes (All 3)
1. Longus Capitis
2. Longus Colli
Nuchal ligament
1
2
3
4
Suboccipital Group
1. Rectus capitis posterior minor
2. Rectus capitis posterior major
3. Oblique capitis superior
4. Oblique capitis inferior
Splenius Capitis
Splenius Cervicis
Semispinalis Capitis
Levator Scapula
Trapezius –Upper Fibers
Neck, Head
7

Figure 7 (B) - Neck, Head - Muscle Pictures

Note-taking page ~ (palpation, how to lengthen/shorten, cautions, common uses, etc.)

Muscle Group 7 - Muscles Acting on the **Neck, Head**

1. Sternocleidomastoid

2. Scalenes

Middle
Posterior

Anterior

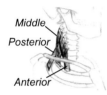

3. Longus Capitis
4. Longus Colli

3
4

5. Suboccipitals Group

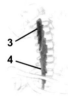

6. Splenius Capitis

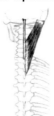

7. Splenius Cervicis

8. Semispinalis Capitis

9. Levator Scapula   *Reversed O/I action (i.e., scapula held fixed)*

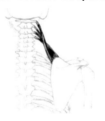

10. Trapezius, Upper fibers   *Reversed O/I action (i.e., scapula held fixed)*

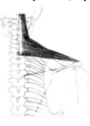

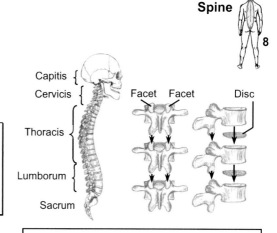
Movement of the Spine

Muscle Group 8

Erector Spinae Group:	Transversospinal Group:
Spinalis	Semispinalis
Longissimus	Multifidis
Iliocostalis	Rotatores
	Other: Quadratus lumborum

Capitis {
Cervicis {
Thoracis {
Lumborum {
Sacrum

Facet   Facet   Disc

Joints

(Joint details: p. 124)

This group is generally called simply "the back muscles" or "the paraspinal muscles". The muscles are all located on the posterior axial skeleton, and move the axial body in extension, rotation, and lateral bending.

Atlanto-occipital Joint (AO)
Atlantoaxial Joint (AA) = C1/C2
> (above 2 joints: see Group 7: Movement of the Neck & Head, page 135)

Intervertebral Joints (have 2 components):
> (please review page 119)

> • **Intervertebral Discs (all vertebrae C2 through S1)**
> Between vertebral bodies
> Amphiarthrotic/Cartilaginous joints
> Movements: Compress, twist, tilt in all directions

> • **Intervertebral Facets (all vertebrae C1 through S1)**
> <u>Pairs:</u> Inferior facets of vertebra above ◄► Superior
> facets of vertebra below
> Gliding joints

(C2-S1 intervertebral joints allow all six actions shown in box)

Sacroiliac Joints
> Lateral **sacrum** ◄► Medial **ilium**
> Part gliding , part fibrous/synarthrotic

Costovertebral & Costotransverse Joints
> Posterior **ribs** ◄► Thoracic **vertebrae**
> (Will be covered in the Thorax/Breathing section, page 151)

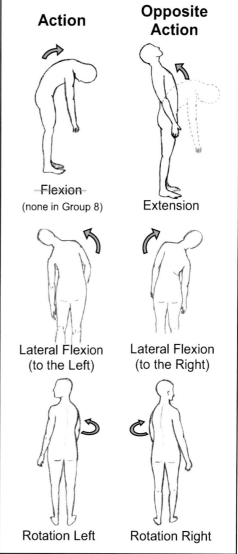

Action — **Opposite Action**

Flexion
(none in Group 8)

Extension

Lateral Flexion (to the Left)

Lateral Flexion (to the Right)

Rotation Left

Rotation Right

Movements

Movements of the spine are: Flexion, extension, right & left lateral flexion, right & left rotation

The cervical, thoracic, and lumbar sections of the spine have different amounts and types of mobility. These differences are due to the facet shapes & slants, lengths/slopes of spinous and transverse processes, disc thicknesses, ribs, ligaments, and other factors. The following table summarizes the structure and mobility of the different sections of the spine.

Summary of Vertebral Column by Section

Type	Vert.	Curvature	Structure of Vertebrae	Movement / Mobility
Cervical	7	Lordotic (secondary)	Small oval body, SPs short & horizontal, SPs bifid at tip, facets nearly horizontal (~30°)	Good mobility in flexion/extension & rotation, sidebending limited somewhat by TVPs and body shape, nuchal ligament resists over-flexion.
Thoracic	12	Kyphotic (primary)	Thin disc, long sloped SPs, facets nearly vertical facing front/back (in coronal plane, on a slight arc), ribs attach	Generally limited, some rotation is allowed, facets and sloped SPs limit extension, ribs and facets restrict sidebending
Lumbar	5	Lordotic (secondary)	Thick disc, short SPs, vertical facets facing side to side (in sagittal plane)	Mobile in flexion/extension and lateral flexion, rotation limited by facets
Sacrum	5 (fused)	Kyphotic (primary)	Fused	No movement within, but some mobility exists at L5/S1 joint and at sacroiliac joints
Coccyx	2-4 (fused)	Kyphotic (primary)	Fused	Joint between coccyx and sacrum allows movement, and can sublux with a fall on it

Comments

- T11/T12 is the first intervertebral joint above the lumbars that allows good rotation, so is stressed a lot.

- L5/S1 joint is curved forward to match into the tilt of the sacrum – so an anterior pelvic tilt is especially stressful on L5/S1 disc, and can cause L5 to slide forward on S1.

- Be careful to not confuse *spine* flexion with flexion at the *hip joint* (e.g., when bending to touch toes).

Interspinales and Intertransversarii

There are two groups of tiny paired muscles that interconnect vertebrae in the cervical and lumbar spine. They are not included in the Group 8 tables, but are illustrated here for completeness.

C2

Cervical Inter-spinales

Cervical Inter-transversarii

T2

T12

Lumbar Inter-spinales

Lumbar Inter-transversarii

L5

Posterior View

Bones, Bony Landmarks, Other

Group 8 muscles move the spine, and have attachments on the posterior axial skeleton and the hip bone. Review the bony landmarks and other structures listed below, referring to Chapter 2, pages 43-47.

Occiput (p. 43)
Temporal Bone (p. 43) – Mastoid process

Spine (p. 44)
- Cervical, thoracic, and lumbar vertebrae
- Sacrum – L5/S1 joint (with disc and facets)
  – Articulation with hip bones (sacroiliac jt)

Ribs (p. 46)
- 12 ribs each side (7 true ribs, 5 false ribs)
- Bottom two false ribs are "floating ribs"
- *Costo* = Rib, *Chondro* = cartilage
- Costal angle (on posterior aspect of ribs)

Pelvis (p. 47)
- Coxal bones (hip bones)
  Made up of 3 fused bones:
  1. Ilium
     – Iliac crest (posterior medial portion)
  2. Ischium
  3. Pubis
Other Structures
- Thoracolumbar Fascia
  Also called Lumbar Fascia
  Also called Thoracolumbar Aponeurosis (TLA)
- Iliolumbar ligament (p. 124, 126)

Muscle Group 8 - **The back muscles that move the spine** are illustrated as a group on
this page. The next four pages have tables and figures that describe each muscle individually, and
provide many ways of comparing and contrasting the muscles to each other.

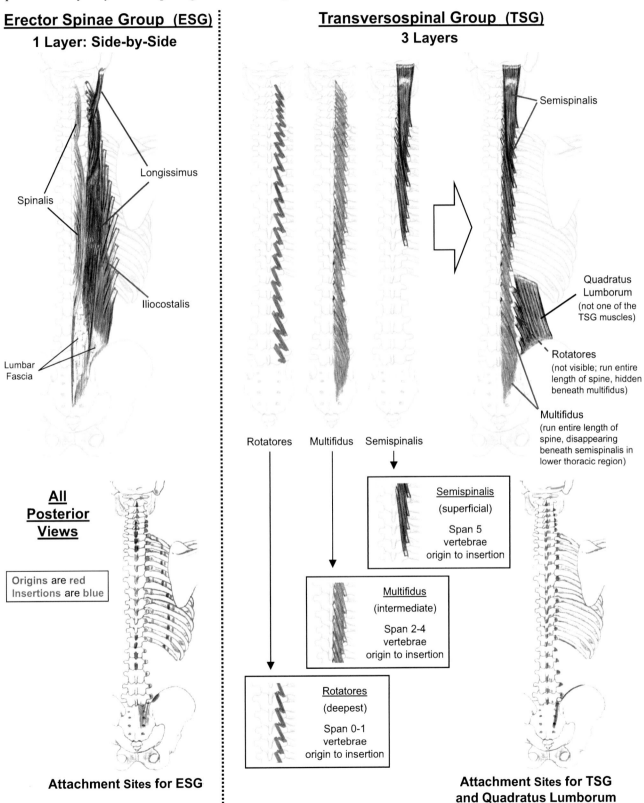

Erector Spinae Group (ESG)
1 Layer: Side-by-Side

Spinalis

Longissimus

Iliocostalis

Lumbar
Fascia

Transversospinal Group (TSG)
3 Layers

Semispinalis

Quadratus
Lumborum
(not one of the
TSG muscles)

Rotatores
(not visible; run entire
length of spine, hidden
beneath multifidus)

Multifidus
(run entire length of
spine, disappearing
beneath semispinalis in
lower thoracic region)

Rotatores   Multifidus   Semispinalis

**All
Posterior
Views**

Origins are red
Insertions are blue

Semispinalis
(superficial)

Span 5
vertebrae
origin to insertion

Multifidus
(intermediate)

Span 2-4
vertebrae
origin to insertion

Rotatores
(deepest)

Span 0-1
vertebrae
origin to insertion

Attachment Sites for ESG

**Attachment Sites for TSG
and Quadratus Lumborum**

Group 8: Muscles Acting On

TVP=Transverse process of vertebra, SP=Spinous process of vertebra, UL=Unilateral action, BL=Bilateral action

Erector Spinae Group – ESG

Spine	Origin	Insertion	Action
Spinalis Cervicis, Thoracis *(most medial of 3 columns of ESG)*	*Overall description:* **SP's** of upper lumbar & lower thoracic vertebrae, and **SP's** of upper thoracic & lower cervical vertebrae	*Overall description:* **SP's** of upper thoracic vertebrae, and **SP's** of upper cervical vertebrae	<u>BL</u> & <u>UL</u>: Extension of the spine
Longissimus Capitis, Cervicis, Thoracis *(intermediate of 3 columns of ESG)*	*Overall description:* **Lumbar fascia,** **TVP's** of all lumbar vertebrae, **TVP's** of upper thoracic & lower cervical vertebrae	*Overall description:* **Ribs** & **TVP's** of the thoracic and cervical vertebrae, and **mastoid process** of temporal bone	<u>BL</u>: Extension of the spine <u>UL</u>: Lateral flexion of the spine (Also, some fibers assist rotation of spine to the same side)
Iliocostalis Cervicis, Thoracis, Lumborum *(most lateral of 3 columns of ESG)*	*Overall description:* **Lumbar fascia,** and the posterior **ribs** #3 – 12 (at the angles of the ribs)	*Overall description:* Posterior aspect of <u>all</u> the **ribs,** and **TVP's** of the lower cervical vertebrae (at the angles of the ribs)	<u>BL</u>: Extension of the spine <u>UL</u>: Lateral flexion of the spine (Also, some fibers assist rotation of spine to the same side)

Transversospinal Group – TSG

Spine	Origin	Insertion	Action
Semispinalis Capitis, Cervicis, Thoracis *(most superficial of 3 layers of TSG)*	**TVP's** of thoracic vertebrae T1-T10 and cervical vertebrae C4-C7	**SP's** of vertebrae above – each spans **5** vertebrae, *and* to the occipital bone (capitis) (occiput attachment Is between superior and inferior nuchal lines)	<u>BL</u>: Extension of the spine (Cervicis,Thor.) Extension of the head (Capitis) <u>UL</u>: Rotation of spine to opposite side (Cervicis and Thoracis)
Multifidus *(intermediate of 3 layers of TSG)*	**Sacrum** and **TVP's** of all vertebrae of the spine (except C1-C3)	**SP's** of vertebrae above – each spans **2 - 4** vertebrae above before inserting	<u>BL</u>: Extension of the spine <u>UL</u>: Rotation of spine to opposite side <u>All</u>: Stabilize vertebrae on each other
Rotatores **(Longus and Brevis)** *(deepest of 3 layers of TSG)*	**Sacrum** and **TVP's** of all vertebrae of the spine (except C1-C2)	**Lamina** of vertebrae above – **Brevis:** Inserts **next** vertebra up **Longus:** Spans **1** vertebra before inserting	<u>BL</u>: Extension of the spine <u>UL</u>: Rotation of spine to opposite side <u>All</u>: Stabilize vertebrae on each other

Other –

Spine	Origin	Insertion	Action
Quadratus Lumborum moves the spine or the hip, or stabilizes rib #12	Iliac crest, iliolumbar ligament	Rib #12, TVP's of L1 - L4	<u>BL</u>: Extension of the lumbar spine <u>UL</u>: Lateral flexion of the lumbar spine *If the spine is held in place:* <u>UL</u>: Raises the ilium (hip hike) <u>BL</u>: Creates anterior pelvic tilt *(Also:* Stabilizes rib #12 during inhalation)

(larger illustrations on page 149)

Table 8 (A) - Spine - Origin, Insertion, Action

Spine

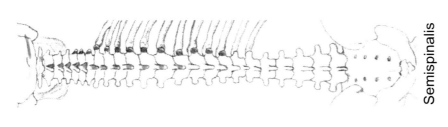

8

Rotatores

Multifidus

Quadratus Lumborum

Semispinalis

Iliocostalis

Figure 8 (A) - Spine - Muscle Attachments

Longissimus

Spinalis

Chapter 5 - Muscles That Move the Axial Skeleton   **147**

Group 8:

UL=Unilateral action, BL=Bilateral action, N=Nerve

Muscles Acting On Spine	Flexion	Extension	Lateral Flexion	Rotation to same side	Rotation to opp. side	Other	(Notes)	Innervation	T12	L1	L2	L3	(all spinal segments)
(1.-3.) --- ERECTOR SPINAE GROUP --- ESG:													
1. Spinalis - cervicis - thoracis		BL or UL					Most <u>medial</u> column of ESG.	Dorsal primary divisions of spinal nerves					N
2. Longissimus - capitis - cervicis - thoracis		BL	UL	UL *(may assist) to same side*		Upper portions of ESG muscles move the head and neck, lower portions of ESG muscles move the spine and trunk.	<u>Intermediate</u> column of ESG.	Dorsal primary divisions of spinal nerves					N
3. Iliocostalis - cervicis - thoracis - lumborum		BL	UL	UL *(may assist) to same side*			Most <u>lateral</u> column of ESG.	Dorsal primary divisions of spinal nerves					N
(4.-6.) --- TRANSVERSOSPINAL GROUP --- TSG: (deep to ESG)													
4. Semispinalis (capitis,cervicis,thoracis)		BL			UL *to opposite side*	A major function of TSG group	Most superficial of TSG group	Dorsal primary divisions of spinal nerves					N
5. Multifidus		BL			UL *to opposite side*	is to <u>stabilize</u> the spine, one vertebra	Next deepest	Dorsal primary divisions of spinal nerves					N
6. Rotatores (longus and brevis)		BL			UL *to opposite side*	on another.	Deepest	Dorsal primary divisions of spinal nerves					N
(7.) --- OTHER:													
7. Quadratus Lumborum		BL (lumbar)	UL (lumbar)			<u>Reverse OI:</u> UL: "hip hike" BL: anter. pelvic tilt	Used in breathing: Stabilizes rib #12 during inhalation	Lumbar plexus (T12, L1-L3)	N	N	N	N	
(More muscles for the action) ---->	See also Group 9				See also Group 9			**Innervation**					

Table 8 (B) - Spine - Synergists & Antagonists

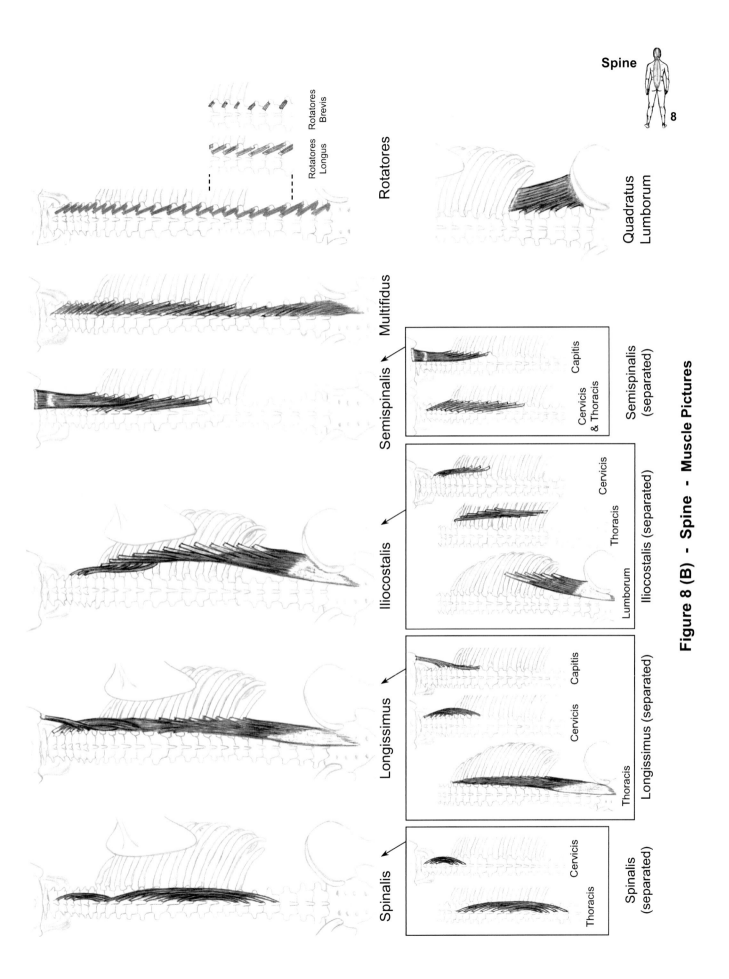

Rotatores Brevis

Rotatores Longus

Rotatores

Quadratus Lumborum

Multifidus

Semispinalis

Capitis

Cervicis & Thoracis

Semispinalis (separated)

Iliocostalis

Cervicis

Thoracis

Lumborum

Iliocostalis (separated)

Longissimus

Capitis

Cervicis

Thoracis

Longissimus (separated)

Spinalis

Cervicis

Thoracis

Spinalis (separated)

Spine

Figure 8 (B) - Spine - Muscle Pictures

Spine

Note-taking page ~ (palpation, how to lengthen/shorten, cautions, common uses, etc.)

8

Muscle Group 8 - Muscles Acting on the **Spine**

1. Spinalis

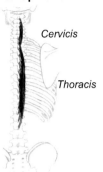

Cervicis

Thoracis

2. Longissimus

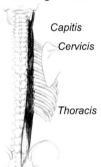

Capitis
Cervicis

Thoracis

3. Iliocostalis

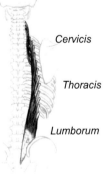

Cervicis

Thoracis

Lumborum

7. Quadratus Lumborum

4. Semispinalis

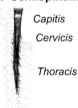

Capitis

Cervicis

Thoracis

5. Multifidus

6. Rotatores

Longus Brevis

Comparison of Transversospinal Muscles

Semispinalis   *Multifidus*   *Rotatores*
                                Longus & Brevis

Movement of the Thorax, Abdomen, Breathing

Muscle Group 9

Abdominal Group:	Other muscles:
Rectus abdominis	External intercostals
External oblique	Internal intercostals
Internal oblique	Serratus posterior superior
Transverse abdominis	Serratus posterior inferior
	Levator costae
Diaphragm	Transversus Thoracis

Joints

(Joint details: p. 125-126)

The muscles in this group move the trunk of the body. This includes flexing and twisting the upper body, compressing the abdomen, and moving the ribs up and down while breathing.

Intervertebral Joints (Discs + Facets)

(see previous section: Group 8 – Movement of the Spine, page 143)

Rib Joints – Anterior: (for rib joints, please review page 46)

- **Sternocostal Joints (J1)**   (also called sterno*chondral* joints)

    Sternum ◄► Costal cartilages of **ribs** (Ribs 1 to 7)
    1: Fibrous Joint
    2-7: Gliding Joints

- **Costochondral Joints (J2)**

    Ribs ◄► Costal cartilages (Ribs 1 to 10: Fibrous junctions of bone to cartilage)

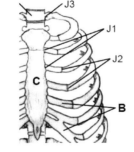

Rib Joints – Posterior:

- **Costovertebral Joints (J3)**
    Head of **rib ◄►** Costal facets on **vertebral bodies**
    Gliding Joints

- **Costotransverse Joints (J4)**
    Tubercle of **rib ◄►** Costal facet on **TVP of vertebra**
    Gliding Joints

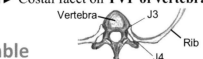

Movements Available

Spine/Trunk:
    Flexion, Extension, R&L Lateral Flexion, R&L Rotation

Ribs – Elevation, Depression

Abdomen – Compression of abdominal contents

Lungs – Breathing (see next page)

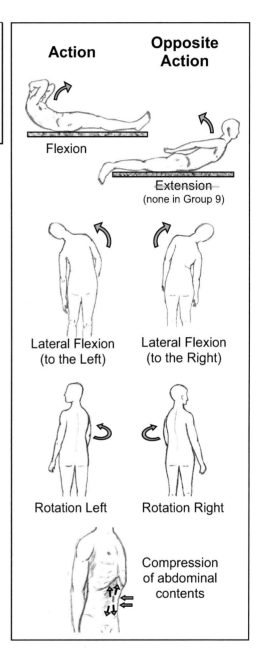

Action	Opposite Action

Flexion

Extension
(none in Group 9)

Lateral Flexion (to the Left) | Lateral Flexion (to the Right)

Rotation Left | Rotation Right

Compression of abdominal contents

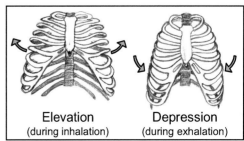

Elevation
(during inhalation)

Depression
(during exhalation)

9 Respiration

Inhalation Phase (also called inspiration)

Quiet Inhalation – The diaphragm muscle contracts, pulling its central tendon downward. This spreads and elevates the lower ribs and pulls the floor of the thoracic cavity downward, causing air to suck into the lungs. The abdominal contents are pushed down, causing the belly to protrude.

Deep and Forced Inhalation – Rib-lifter muscles are recruited as needed to draw more air into the lungs. A common recruitment order is: Scalenes, external intercostals, levator costae, sternocleidomastoid, pectoralis minor, serratus posterior superior, pectoralis major (esp. with arms raised or braced on hips). Actual order of muscle recruitment varies greatly depending on habit, emotion, posture, etc.

Note: The ribcage expands in all directions as the ribs elevate:
Lateral   – Ribs swing out and up (bucket handles)   – The most movement
Anterior – Sternum raises and swings out (pump handle) – Medium movement
Posterior– Back expands as angles of ribs rise   – Slight movement

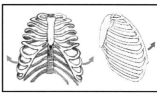

Exhalation Phase (also called expiration)

Quiet Exhalation – A passive process: relaxation of the previously active diaphragm. Air is expelled due to elastic recoil of lungs and ribs being allowed back down and in.

Forced Exhalation – Muscles are recruited to compress the abdomen (abdominal muscles) and pull depression of the ribs (internal intercostals, serratus posterior inferior, transversus thoracis, quadratus lumborum, iliocostalis). Forced exhalation muscles are also used for speech, singing, coughing, sneezing, vomiting, defecation.

Bones, Bony Landmarks, Other Structures

Muscles that move the thorax and abdomen have attachments on the spine, ribs, pelvis, sternum, and fascia. Review the bony landmarks and other structures listed below, referring to Chapter 2, pages 44-47.

Spine (p. 44)
    Thoracic vertebrae
    Lumbar vertebrae

Pelvis (p. 47)

    Landmarks on ilium & pubis:
        Iliac crest
        Anterior Superior Iliac Spine (ASIS)
        Pubic crest
        Pubic symphysis
        Pubic tubercle

Sternum (p. 46)
    Xiphoid process

Ribs (p. 46, 125)
    12 ribs each side (7 true ribs, 5 false ribs)
    Bottom two false ribs are "floating ribs"

    Articulation with sternum in front
    Articulation with thoracic vertebrae in back
    Costal cartilage
    Costal margin / lower thoracic "aperture"
    Costal angle (posterior angle of ribs)

Other Structures (p. 153)
    Lumbar fascia (thoracolumbar fascia)
    Abdominal aponeurosis
    Rectus sheath
    Linea alba
    Inguinal ligament
        - Spans from ASIS to the pubic tubercle
    Thoracic, abdominal and pelvic organs

Muscle Group 9 - **Muscles that move the thorax and abdomen and facilitate breathing**

are illustrated as a group on this page. The next four pages have tables and figures that describe each muscle individually, and provide many ways of comparing and contrasting the muscles to each other.

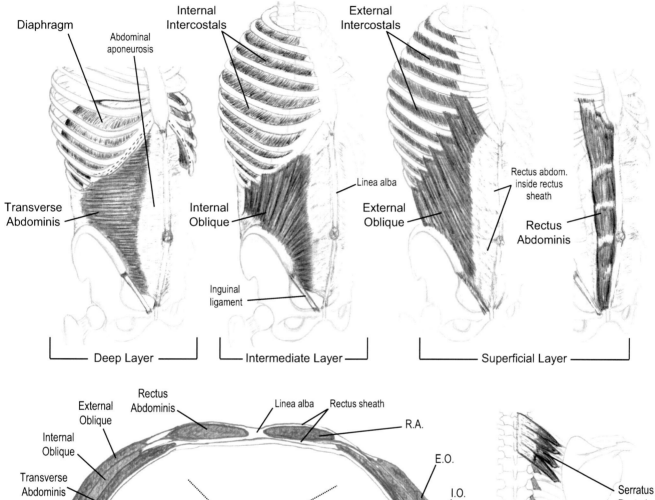

Diaphragm

Abdominal aponeurosis

Internal Intercostals

External Intercostals

Transverse Abdominis

Internal Oblique

External Oblique

Linea alba

Rectus abdom. inside rectus sheath

Rectus Abdominis

Inguinal ligament

— Deep Layer —

— Intermediate Layer —

— Superficial Layer —

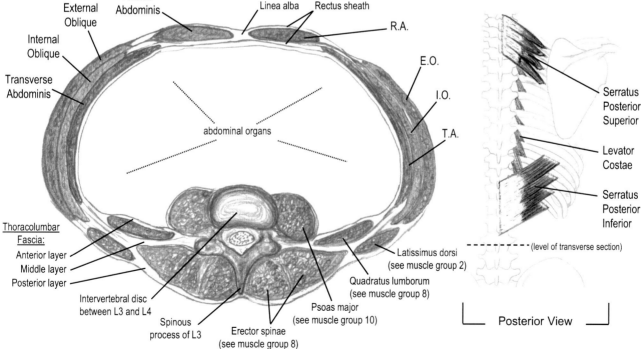

External Oblique

Rectus Abdominis

Linea alba

Rectus sheath

Internal Oblique

Transverse Abdominis

R.A.

E.O.

I.O.

T.A.

abdominal organs

Serratus Posterior Superior

Levator Costae

Serratus Posterior Inferior

Thoracolumbar Fascia:
Anterior layer
Middle layer
Posterior layer

Intervertebral disc between L3 and L4

Spinous process of L3

Erector spinae (see muscle group 8)

Psoas major (see muscle group 10)

Quadratus lumborum (see muscle group 8)

Latissimus dorsi (see muscle group 2)

- - - - (level of transverse section)

— Posterior View —

Transverse Section at the Level of 3rd Lumbar Vertebra (L3)

SP=Spinous process of vertebra, TVP=Transverse process of vertebra, UL=Unilateral action, BL=Bilateral action

Group 9: Muscles Acting On Thorax, Abdomen, Breathing	Origin	Insertion	Action
Rectus Abdominis moves the trunk	Pubic crest and symphysis pubis	Costal cartilages of ribs #5-7, Xiphoid process of sternum	Flexion of the spine, Compress abdom. contents (assist) *When spine is stabilized:* Pulls pubic bone up (posterior pelvic tilt)
External Oblique moves the trunk	Lower 8 ribs, anterior-lateral aspect. (Interdigitates serratus anterior)	Anterior iliac crest, inguinal ligament, abdominal aponeurosis to the linea alba	BL: Flexion of the spine, Compression of abdominal contents UL: Lateral flexion of the spine, Rotation to the *opposite* side
Internal Oblique moves the trunk	Lumbar fascia, iliac crest, lateral inguinal ligament	Last 3 or 4 ribs (lower margins), abdominal aponeurosis to the linea alba	BL: Flexion of the spine, Compression of abdominal contents UL: Lateral flexion of the spine, Rotation to the *same* side.
Transverse Abdominis compresses the abdomen	Lower 6 ribs (inner surface), lumbar fascia, iliac crest, lateral inguinal ligament	Abdominal aponeurosis to the linea alba	Compression of abdominal contents
Diaphragm muscle of respiration	Bodies of upper lumbar vertebrae, interior surface of lower ribs & xiphoid process	Central tendon of the diaphragm (The diaphragm is shaped like a dome or umbrella. The central tendon is a large clover-shaped aponeurosis at the top of the dome that is *not* attached to any bones.)	Draws down the central tendon, creating inhalation. (The movement increases the volume inside the thoracic cavity. It also expands the *lower* ribs in all directions, and compresses down on the abdominal contents.)
External Intercostals move the ribs	Inferior border of rib above *Between all ribs.*	Superior border of rib below (angle of fibers follows the external oblique muscle fibers)	Draw ribs upward during inhalation (Assists rotation of thoracic spine to opposite side)
Internal Intercostals move the ribs	Superior border of rib below *Between all ribs.*	Inferior border of rib above (angle of fibers follows the internal oblique muscle fibers)	Draw ribs downward during exhalation (Assists rotation of thoracic spine to same side)
Serratus Posterior Superior moves the ribs	SPs of vertebrae C6 - T2	Posterior upper ribs (ribs #2 - 5)	Draws ribs upward during inhalation
Serratus Posterior Inferior moves or stabilizes the ribs	SPs of vertebrae T11 - L2	Posterior lower ribs (ribs #9 - 12)	Draws ribs downward and backward. Stabilizes lower ribs against the upward pull of the diaphragm (during inhalation).
Levator Costae move the ribs	TVPs of vertebrae C7 and T1 - T11	Posterior ribs 1 - 12 Brevis: Attach to rib below (ribs 1-12) Longus: Attach 2nd rib below (ribs 10-12)	Draw ribs upward during inhalation
Transversus Thoracis moves the ribs	Inner surface of lower sternum, xiphoid process, and nearby costal cartilages	Fans out to the inner aspect of the costal cartilages of ribs 2 - 6	Draw ribs downward during exhalation

Table 9 (A) - Thorax, Abdomen, Breathing - Origin, Insertion, Action

(larger illustrations on page 157)

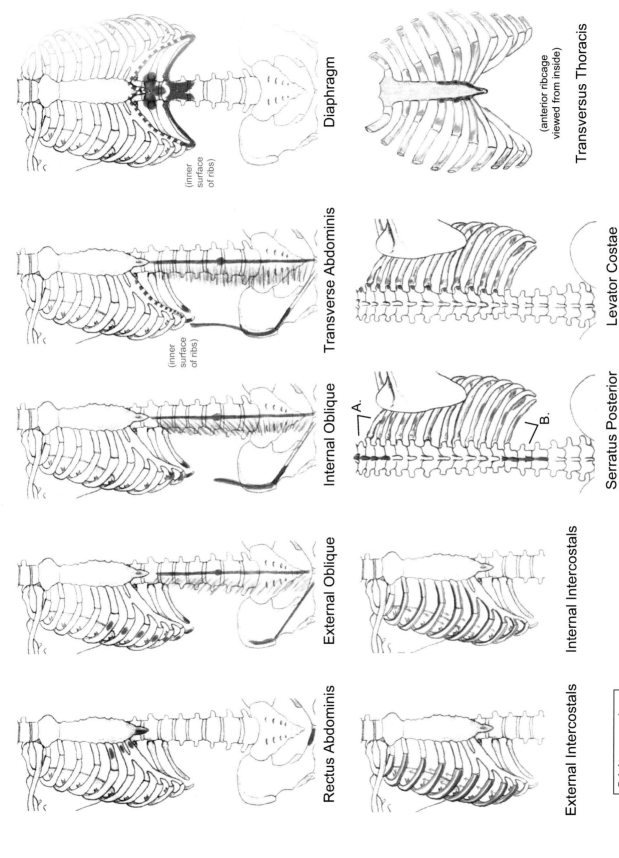

Diaphragm

(inner surface of ribs)

Transversus Thoracis

(anterior ribcage viewed from inside)

Transverse Abdominis

(inner surface of ribs)

Levator Costae

Internal Oblique

Serratus Posterior
A: Superior, B: Inferior

A.

B.

External Oblique

Internal Intercostals

Rectus Abdominis

External Intercostals

Origins are red
Insertions are blue

Lift page to see muscle pictures

Figure 9 (A) - Thorax, Abdomen, Breathing - Muscle Attachments

UL=Unilateral action, BL=Bilateral action, ✓=Both UL & BL action, N=Nerve

Group 9: Thorax, Abdomen, Breathing

Muscles Acting On	Flexion	Extension (none)	Lateral Flexion	Rotation	Compress Abdominal Contents	Inhalation/ Inspiration	Exhalation/ Expiration	Other	Innervation	C3 to C5 / T1 to T4	T5	T6	T7	T8	T9	T10	T11	T12	L1
1. Rectus Abdominis	✓				✓ assist				Intercostal nerves (T6-T12)			N	N	N	N	N	N	N	
2. External Oblique	BL		UL	UL to opposite side	✓		✓	Interdigitates w/ Serratus Anterior & Lat. Dorsi	Intercostal nerves (T8-T12)					N	N	N	N	N	
3. Internal Oblique	BL		UL	UL to same side	✓		✓		Intercostal (T8-12) iliohypogastric N. (T12,L1) & ilioinguinal N. (L1)					N	N	N	N	N	N
4. Transverse Abdominis					✓		✓ forced exhalation, cough, etc.	Interdigitates w/ Diaphragm	Intercostal (T7-12) iliohypogastric N. (T12,L1) & ilioinguinal N. (L1)				N	N	N	N	N	N	N
5. Diaphragm					(✓)→ (downward, pushes out abdominals)	✓		Draws central tendon down, and expands lower ribs	Phrenic nerve (C3, C4, C5)	N									
6. External Intercostals						✓ Draw ribs upward			Intercostal nerves (segmental)	N	N	N	N	N	N	N	N	N	
7. Internal Intercostals							✓ Draw ribs downward		Intercostal nerves (segmental)	N	N	N	N	N	N	N	N	N	
8. Serratus Post. Superior						✓ Raises ribs			Ventral rami of T1-T4	N									
9. Serratus Post. Inferior							✓ Draws ribs down	Counters pull of diaphragm	Ventral rami of T9-T12						N	N	N	N	
10. Levator Costae						✓			Intercostal nerves (segmental)	N	N	N	N	N	N	N	N	N	
11. Transversus Thoracis							✓		Intercostal nerves (T2-T6)	N	N	N							
(More muscles for the action) --->	✓	Group 8	see also Group 8	see also Group 8		✓ see p. 152			**Innervation**										

C1

Table 9 (B) - Thorax, Abdomen, Breathing - Synergists & Antagonists

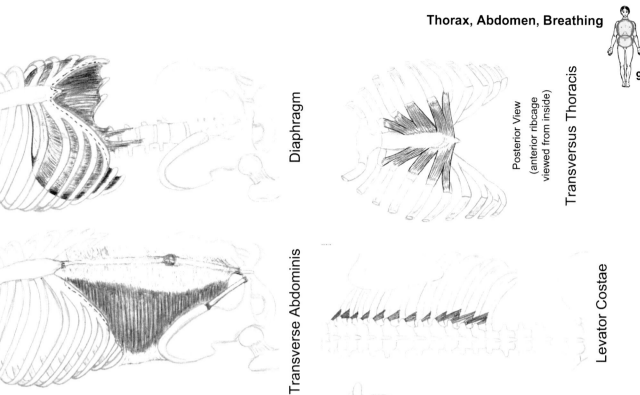

Diaphragm

Transversus Thoracis

Posterior View
(anterior ribcage
viewed from inside)

Transverse Abdominis

Levator Costae

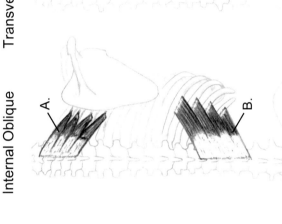

Internal Oblique

Serratus Posterior:
A: Superior, B: Inferior

A.

B.

External Oblique

Internal Intercostals

Rectus Abdominis

External Intercostals

Figure 9 (B) - Thorax, Abdomen, Breathing - Muscle Pictures

Pelvic Floor
(Bonus Group)

9b

Muscles of the Pelvic Floor and Perineum

Muscle	Origin	Insertion	Action	Innervation
Deep Layer: Pelvic Diaphragm				
Levator Ani (part 1): **Puborectalis**	Posterior surface of bodies of pubic bones	None (forms 'puborectal sling' around rectum)	Draws distal rectum forward for fecal continence	Nerve to levator ani (S4)
Levator Ani (part 2): **Pubococcygeus**	Posterior surface of bodies of pubic bones	Anococcygeal ligament, coccyx, perineal body	Supports pelvic organs, helps urinary and fecal continence	Nerve to levator ani (S4), pudendal nerve (S2-S4)
Levator Ani (part 3): **Iliococcygeus**	Tendinous arch of the levator ani, ischial spine	Anococcygeal ligament, coccyx	Supports pelvic organs, helps urinary and fecal continence	Nerve to levator ani (S4)
Coccygeus (ischiococcygeus)	Ischial spine and sacrospinous ligament	Inferior end of sacrum, coccyx	Supports contents of pelvic cavity, pulls coccyx forward	Anterior rami of sacral nerves (S4-S5)
Intermediate Layer: Deep perineal pouch (urogenital diaphragm)				
Deep transverse perineal muscle	Medial aspect of the ischial ramus	Perineal body	Stabilizes the position of the perineal body	Perineal branches of pudendal N. (S2-S4)
Sphincter urethrae (M and F)	Surrounds membranous part of urethra	Surrounds membranous part of urethra	Compresses urethra (male & female)	Perineal branches of pudendal N. (S2-S4)
Compressor urethrae (F only)	Ischiopubic ramus	Wraps around anterior aspect of urethra	Accessory compression of urethra (female)	Perineal branches of pudendal N. (S2-S4)
Sphincter urethrovaginalis (F only)	Perineal body	Wraps around vagina and urethra	Constricts both the vagina and urethra (female)	Perineal branches of pudendal N. (S2-S4)
Superficial Layer: Sphincter, erectile & other				
Superficial transverse perineal muscle	Medial aspect of the ischial tuberosity	Perineal body/central tendon	Stabilizes posterior free edge of the perineal pouch	Pudendal N. (S2-S4)
External anal sphincter	Perineal body and anococcygeal ligament	Surrounds anal canal	Constricts anal canal to maintain fecal continence	Pudendal N. (S2-S3), Anterior rami of S4
Ischiocavernosus	Ischial tuberosity and ischial ramus	Crura of clitoris or penis	Move blood from crura into clitoris or penis	Pudendal N. (S2-S4)
Bulbospongiosis	Perineal body	Corpora cavernosa of clitoris or penis	Removes residual urine after urination, pulses w/ orgasm	Perineal branches of pudendal N. (S2-S4)
Peripheral muscles: Lateral and posterior walls of pelvic bowl				
Obturator Internus	(see muscle group 10, page 170)		Lateral rotation of hip joint	
Piriformis	(see muscle group 10, page 170)		Lateral rotation of hip joint	

A2

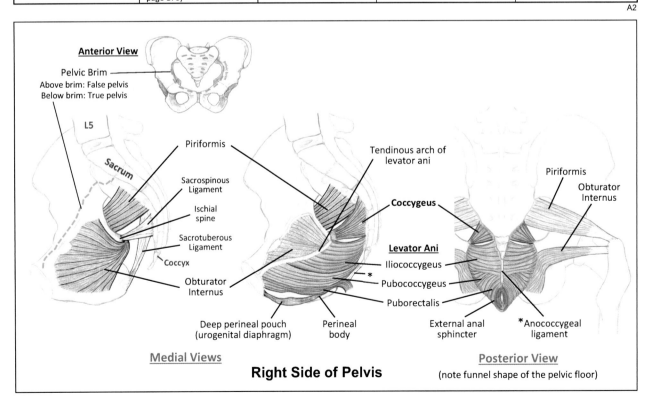

Anterior View

Pelvic Brim
Above brim: False pelvis
Below brim: True pelvis

L5

Sacrum

Piriformis

Sacrospinous Ligament

Ischial spine

Sacrotuberous Ligament

Coccyx

Obturator Internus

Deep perineal pouch (urogenital diaphragm)

Tendinous arch of levator ani

Coccygeus

Levator Ani
Iliococcygeus
*
Pubococcygeus
Puborectalis

Perineal body

Piriformis

Obturator Internus

External anal sphincter

*Anococcygeal ligament

Medial Views

Right Side of Pelvis

Posterior View
(note funnel shape of the pelvic floor)

Muscles of the Pelvic Floor & Perineum
(Female Pelvis)

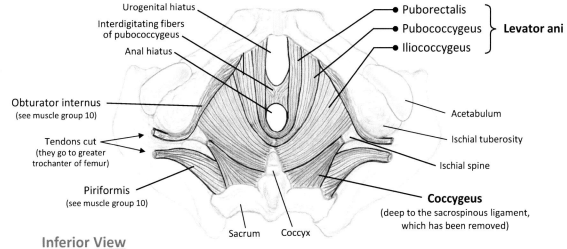

Urogenital hiatus

Interdigitating fibers
of pubococcygeus

Anal hiatus

Puborectalis
Pubococcygeus — **Levator ani**
Iliococcygeus

Obturator internus
(see muscle group 10)

Acetabulum

Ischial tuberosity

Tendons cut
(they go to greater
trochanter of femur)

Ischial spine

Piriformis
(see muscle group 10)

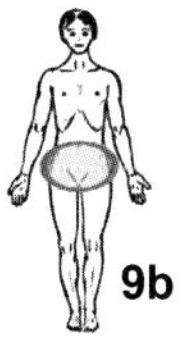

Coccygeus
(deep to the sacrospinous ligament,
which has been removed)

Sacrum   Coccyx

Inferior View

Deep Layer: Pelvic diaphragm

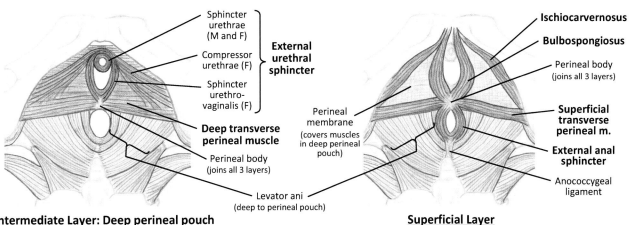

Sphincter
urethrae
(M and F)

**External
urethral
sphincter**

Compressor
urethrae (F)

Sphincter
urethro-
vaginalis (F)

**Deep transverse
perineal muscle**

Perineal body
(joins all 3 layers)

Levator ani
(deep to perineal pouch)

Ischiocarvernosus

Bulbospongiosus

Perineal body
(joins all 3 layers)

**Superficial
transverse
perineal m.**

**External anal
sphincter**

Anococcygeal
ligament

Perineal
membrane
(covers muscles
in deep perineal
pouch)

Intermediate Layer: Deep perineal pouch

(Urogenital diaphragm)

Perineal membrane has been
removed to expose muscles

Superficial Layer

Sphincter, erectile & other muscles

Inferior Views

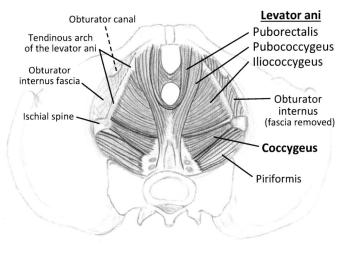

Obturator canal

Tendinous arch
of the levator ani

Obturator
internus fascia

Ischial spine

Levator ani
Puborectalis
Pubococcygeus
Iliococcygeus

Obturator
internus
(fascia removed)

Coccygeus

Piriformis

Superior View

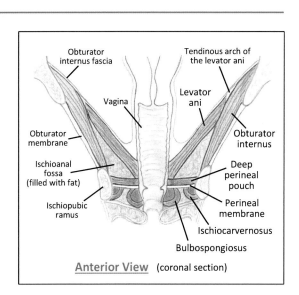

Obturator
internus fascia

Vagina

Obturator
membrane

Ischioanal
fossa
(filled with fat)

Ischiopubic
ramus

Tendinous arch of
the levator ani

Levator
ani

Obturator
internus

Deep
perineal
pouch

Perineal
membrane

Ischiocarvernosus

Bulbospongiosus

Anterior View (coronal section)

Note-taking page ~ (palpation, how to lengthen/shorten, cautions, common uses, etc.)

Muscle Group 9 - Muscles Acting on the **Thorax, Abdomen, Breathing**

1. Rectus Abdominis

6. External Intercostals

2. External Oblique

7. Internal Intercostals

3. Internal Oblique

8. Serratus Posterior Superior

4. Transverse Abdominis

9. Serratus Posterior Inferior

5. Diaphragm

10. Levator Costae

Chapter 6

Muscles That Move the Lower Extremity

Group 10 – Hip Joint (Part 1)

Gluteus maximus
Gluteus medius
Gluteus minimus
Piriformis (1st lateral rotator)
The other 5 lateral rotators
    Gemellus superior
    Obturator internus
    Gemellus inferior
    Obturator externus
    Quadratus femoris
Iliopsoas
    (Iliacus & Psoas major)

p. 167-174

10

Group 11 – Hip Joint (Part 2)

Sartorius
Tensor fascia latae
Pectineus
Adductor brevis
Adductor longus
Adductor magnus
Gracilis

p. 175-182

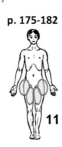

11

Group 12 – Knee (& Hip Joint, Part 3)

Rectus femoris
Vastus lateralis
Vastus intermedius
Vastus medialis
Biceps femoris
Semitendinosus
Semimembranosus
Popliteus

p. 183-190

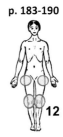

12

Group 13 – Ankle, Foot, Toes

Gastrocnemius
Plantaris
Soleus
Tibialis posterior
Flexor digitorum longus
Flexor hallucis longus
Fibularis longus (peroneus)
Fibularis brevis (peroneus)
Tibialis anterior
Extensor digitorum longus
Extensor hallucis longus

p. 191-197

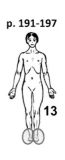

13

Bonus Group

Intrinsic Muscles
of the Foot

p. 198-199

Introduction

The **lower extremity** is the lower-body portion of the appendicular skeleton (see page 37), and includes the hip bone, thigh, leg, and foot. The sacroiliac joints, where the hip bones articulate with the sacrum, are the joints connecting the lower extremities to the trunk.

This chapter describes the muscles that move the various joints within the lower extremity. The muscles are separated into four functional groups, with some overlap of function between groups for muscles that cross multiple joints:

Group 10: Movement of the hip – part 1, which are the "shorter" muscles that move the femur at the hip joint

Group 11: Movement of the hip – part 2, which are the "longer" muscles that move the femur at the hip joint

Group 12: Movement of the knee (which includes multiple-joint muscles that also move the femur at the hip)

Group 13: Movement of the ankle, foot, and toes

At the end of the chapter, a bonus muscle group presents the intrinsic muscles of the foot.

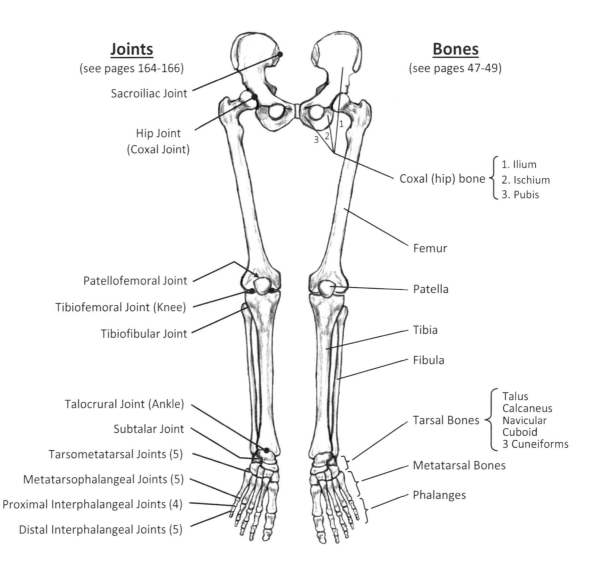

Joints
(see pages 164-166)

Sacroiliac Joint

Hip Joint
(Coxal Joint)

Patellofemoral Joint

Tibiofemoral Joint (Knee)

Tibiofibular Joint

Talocrural Joint (Ankle)

Subtalar Joint

Tarsometatarsal Joints (5)

Metatarsophalangeal Joints (5)

Proximal Interphalangeal Joints (4)

Distal Interphalangeal Joints (5)

Bones
(see pages 47-49)

Coxal (hip) bone {
1. Ilium
2. Ischium
3. Pubis

Femur

Patella

Tibia

Fibula

Tarsal Bones {
Talus
Calcaneus
Navicular
Cuboid
3 Cuneiforms

Metatarsal Bones

Phalanges

Overview of Muscles

The illustration below shows posterior and anterior views of the superficial muscles from groups 10-13. This gives an idea about the overall organization of muscles involved with moving the lower extremity. Note that only muscles that have superficial exposure can be seen. There are also many other muscles at deeper layers that are hidden beneath the superficial muscles.

Joint Details and Ligaments

The joints of the lower extremity begin proximally with the sacroiliac joint, which is the connection of the lower extremity to the sacrum of the axial skeleton. Progressing distally, there are numerous joints at the hip, knee, ankle, and foot. The details and ligaments of these joints are described on the following three pages. Also, see page 126 for ligaments of the pelvis.

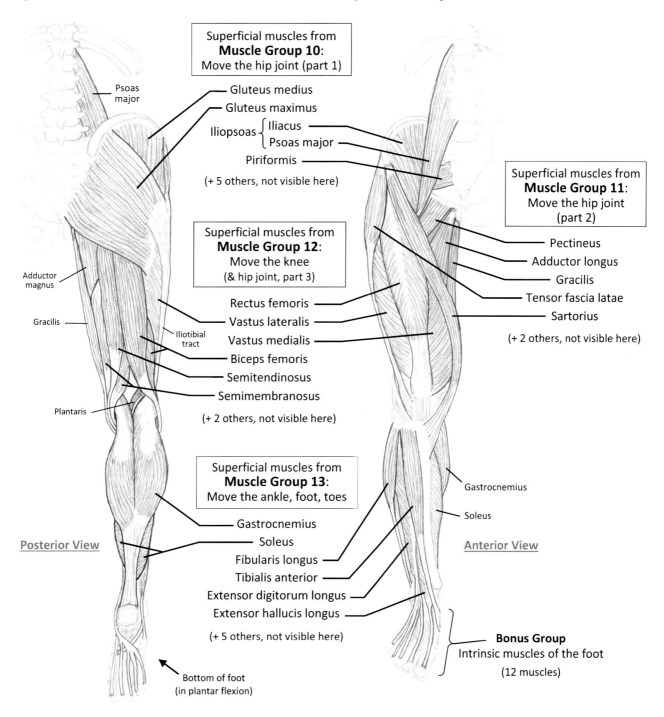

Psoas major

Superficial muscles from
Muscle Group 10:
Move the hip joint (part 1)

Gluteus medius
Gluteus maximus
Iliopsoas { Iliacus
Psoas major
Piriformis
(+ 5 others, not visible here)

Adductor magnus

Gracilis

Iliotibial tract

Superficial muscles from
Muscle Group 12:
Move the knee
(& hip joint, part 3)

Rectus femoris
Vastus lateralis
Vastus medialis
Biceps femoris
Semitendinosus
Semimembranosus
(+ 2 others, not visible here)

Plantaris

Superficial muscles from
Muscle Group 11:
Move the hip joint
(part 2)

Pectineus
Adductor longus
Gracilis
Tensor fascia latae
Sartorius
(+ 2 others, not visible here)

Superficial muscles from
Muscle Group 13:
Move the ankle, foot, toes

Gastrocnemius
Soleus
Fibularis longus
Tibialis anterior
Extensor digitorum longus
Extensor hallucis longus
(+ 5 others, not visible here)

Posterior View

Bottom of foot
(in plantar flexion)

Gastrocnemius

Soleus

Anterior View

Bonus Group
Intrinsic muscles of the foot
(12 muscles)

Hip – Joints and Ligaments

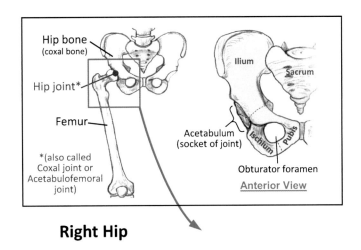

Hip bone (coxal bone)

Hip joint*

Femur

*(also called Coxal joint or Acetabulofemoral joint)

Ilium

Sacrum

Acetabulum (socket of joint)

Ischium

Pubis

Obturator foramen

Anterior View

Right Hip

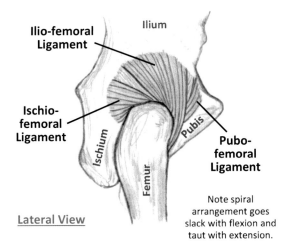

Ilio-femoral Ligament

Ilium

Ischio-femoral Ligament

Ischium

Femur

Pubis

Pubo-femoral Ligament

Lateral View

Note spiral arrangement goes slack with flexion and taut with extension.

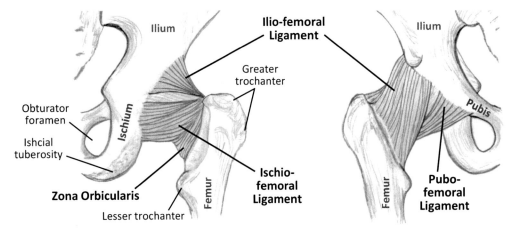

Ilium

Ilio-femoral Ligament

Greater trochanter

Obturator foramen

Ischium

Ishcial tuberosity

Zona Orbicularis

Femur

Lesser trochanter

Ischio-femoral Ligament

Posterior View

Ilium

Pubis

Femur

Pubo-femoral Ligament

Anterior View

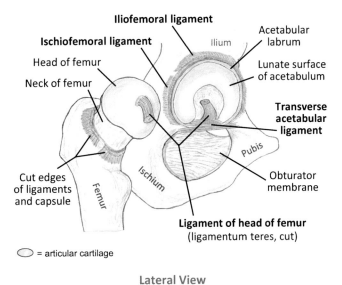

Iliofemoral ligament

Ischiofemoral ligament

Head of femur

Neck of femur

Ilium

Acetabular labrum

Lunate surface of acetabulum

Transverse acetabular ligament

Femur

Ischium

Pubis

Obturator membrane

Cut edges of ligaments and capsule

Ligament of head of femur (ligamentum teres, cut)

◯ = articular cartilage

Lateral View

(Femur removed to expose acetabulum)

Hip Joint	
Ligament	**Function**
Iliofemoral Lig.	Limits extension and lateral rotation.
Ischiofemoral Lig.	Limits extension and medial rotation.
Pubofemoral Lig.	Limits extension and abduction.
Zona Orbicularis	Wraps around neck of femur, resists pulling head of femur away from socket.
Ligament of head of femur	Loosely connects head of femur into the acetabulum, carries blood vessel.
Transverse acetabular Lig.	Completes the acetabular labrum ring, and creates a foramen for vessels to enter the joint.

Knee – Joints and Ligaments

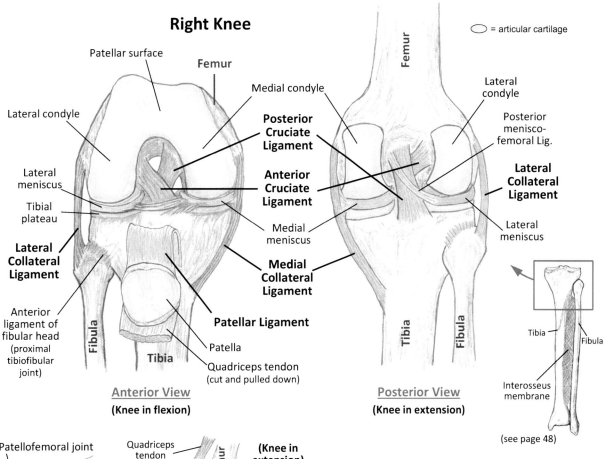

Right Knee

= articular cartilage

Patellar surface

Femur

Medial condyle

Posterior Cruciate Ligament

Anterior Cruciate Ligament

Lateral condyle

Medial meniscus

Lateral meniscus

Tibial plateau

Medial Collateral Ligament

Lateral Collateral Ligament

Anterior ligament of fibular head (proximal tibiofibular joint)

Fibula

Tibia

Patellar Ligament

Patella

Quadriceps tendon (cut and pulled down)

Anterior View
(Knee in flexion)

Femur

Lateral condyle

Posterior menisco-femoral Lig.

Lateral Collateral Ligament

Lateral meniscus

Tibia

Fibula

Posterior View
(Knee in extension)

Tibia — Fibula

Interosseus membrane

(see page 48)

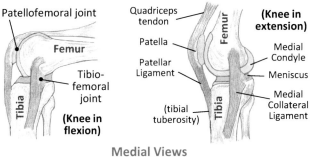

Patellofemoral joint

Femur

Tibia

Tibio-femoral joint

(Knee in flexion)

Quadriceps tendon

Patella

Patellar Ligament

(tibial tuberosity)

Femur

Tibia

(Knee in extension)

Medial Condyle

Meniscus

Medial Collateral Ligament

Medial Views

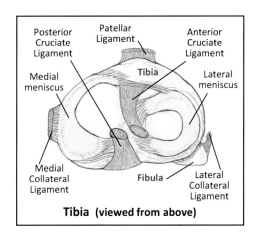

Posterior Cruciate Ligament

Patellar Ligament

Anterior Cruciate Ligament

Medial meniscus

Tibia

Lateral meniscus

Medial Collateral Ligament

Fibula

Lateral Collateral Ligament

Tibia (viewed from above)

Knee: Tibiofemoral Joint & Patellofemoral Joint	
Ligament	**Function**
Medial (Tibial) Collateral Lig. (MCL)	Medial stabilizer, resists valgus forces. Taut when knee is in full extension.
Lateral (Fibular) Collateral Lig. (LCL)	Lateral stabilizer, resists varus forces. Taut when knee is in full extension.
Anterior Cruciate Lig. (ACL)	Prevents anterior displacement of tibia on femur.* Resists hyper-extension and medial rotation. Most frequently injured knee ligament.
Posterior Cruciate Lig. (PCL)	Prevents posterior displacement of tibia on femur.* Resists extreme flexion of knee.
The cruciate ligaments keep the condyles of the femur aligned on the tibial plateau while the knee is flexing and extending. *Note: *Anterior* displacement of the <u>tibia</u> on the femur is equivalent to *posterior* displacement of the <u>femur</u> on the tibia.	
Patellar Lig.	Connects patella to tibia, completing the pulley structure to extend the knee

Ankle and Foot – Joints and Ligaments

Right Foot

◯ = articular cartilage

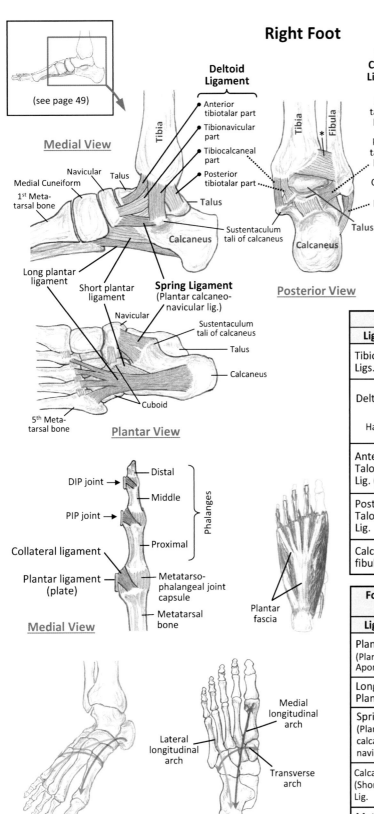

(see page 49)

Deltoid Ligament

Medial View

Anterior tibiotalar part
Tibionavicular part
Tibiocalcaneal part
Posterior tibiotalar part

Tibia
Talus
Talus
Sustentaculum tali of calcaneus
Calcaneus

Navicular
Medial Cuneiform
1st Metatarsal bone

Long plantar ligament
Short plantar ligament
Spring Ligament (Plantar calcaneonavicular lig.)

Navicular
Sustentaculum tali of calcaneus
Talus
Calcaneus
Cuboid
5th Metatarsal bone

Plantar View

Lateral Collateral Ligaments

Anterior talofibular ligament
Posterior talofibular ligament
Calcaneofibular ligament

Tibia
Fibula
*
Talus
Calcaneus

Posterior View

Tibiofibular Ligaments

Posterior TF ligament *
Anterior TF ligament
Intertarsal & metatarsal ligaments

Fibula
Tibia
Talus
Calcaneus
Cuboid
5th Metatarsal
Long plantar ligament

Lateral View

DIP joint → Distal
PIP joint → Middle
Proximal
Phalanges
Collateral ligament
Plantar ligament (plate)
Metatarsophalangeal joint capsule
Metatarsal bone

Medial View

Plantar fascia

Medial longitudinal arch
Lateral longitudinal arch
Transverse arch
(Plantar view)

Arches of the Foot

Ankle: Talocrural Joint & Subtalar Joint	
Ligament	**Function**
Tibiofibular Ligs.	Stabilize the distal tibiofibular joint (a fibrous synarthrotic joint)
Deltoid Lig. — Has 4 parts	Medial stabilizer, limits eversion, resists valgus forces on the ankle — • Anterior tibiotalar • Tibiocalcaneal • Tibionavicular • Posterior tibiotalar
Anterior Talofibular Lig. (ATFL)	Lateral stabilizer, limits inversion and plantarflexion, resists varus forces (most frequently injured ligament)
Posterior Talofibular Lig.	Lateral stabilizer, limits inversion and dorsiflexion, resists varus stress
Calcaneofibular Lig.	Lateral stabilizer, limits inversion and dorsiflexion, resists varus stress

Foot: Tarsal, Metatarsal and Phalangeal Joints (and arches of the foot)	
Ligament	**Function**
Plantar Fascia (Plantar Aponeurosis)	Supports longitudinal arches of foot
Long Plantar Lig.	Supports longitudinal arches of foot
Spring Lig. (Plantar calcaneonavicular Lig.)	Supports medial longitudinal arch of foot. Forms a floor under talonavicular joint, keeping talus from "falling down".
Calcaneocuboid (Short Plantar) Lig.	Supports longitudinal arches deep within the foot, especially the lateral arch
Metatarsophalangeal, PIP, DIP Ligs.	Collateral ligs, Plantar ligs (plates) (Similar to ligaments in the hand – see page 74)

36740

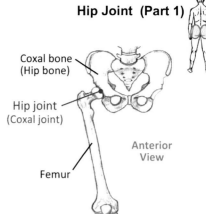

Movement of the Hip Joint (Part 1)

Muscle Group 10

Gluteus maximus	Piriformis (deep lateral rotator #1 of 6)
Gluteus medius	The other 5 lateral rotators:
Gluteus minimus	Gemellus superior, Obturator internus
Iliopsoas { Iliacus &	Gemellus inferior, Obturator externus
Psoas Major	Quadratus femoris

Coxal bone (Hip bone)

Hip joint (Coxal joint)

Anterior View

Femur

Joints

(Joint details: p. 164)

This is the first of three groups of muscles that primarily move the femur at the hip joint (coxal joint). This group contains the "shorter" length muscles that mainly originate on the front or back of the ilium bone of the pelvis, and insert on the greater or lesser trochanter of the femur.

Hip Joint (Coxal Joint)   (also called coxofemoral joint or acetabulofemoral joint)

Head of **Femur** ◄► Acetabulum of the **Hip Bone**

Ball and Socket Joint

Movements Available:

Flexion
Extension
Abduction
Adduction
Lateral Rotation (External Rotation)
Medial Rotation (Internal Rotation)

Other Joints

(Joint details: p. 124, 126)

Postural effects and small movements of the following joints are also created by the muscles in this group:

Sacroiliac Joint
Lateral **Sacrum** ◄► Posterior **Ilium**
Part gliding, part fibrocartilagenous
(affected by piriformis and iliopsoas in this muscle group)

Intervertebral Joints of lumbar vertebrae
Facets and discs
(affected by psoas major in this muscle group)

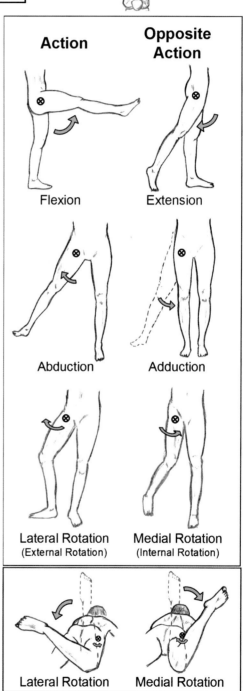

Action   **Opposite Action**

Flexion   Extension

Abduction   Adduction

Lateral Rotation (External Rotation)   Medial Rotation (Internal Rotation)

Lateral Rotation   Medial Rotation

10

Bones, Bony Landmarks, Other Structures

The "short" muscles that move the hip joint mainly have attachments on the pelvis and the femur. Review the bony landmarks and other structures listed below, referring to the diagrams in Chapter 2, pages 47-48.

Hip Bone (Coxal Bone, Os Coxae)   (p. 47)

(Made up of 3 bones fused: Ilium, Ischium, Pubis)

    Landmarks on the Ilium:
        Iliac Fossa
            (anterior-medial surface of wing)
        Iliac Crest
        Posterior Superior Iliac Spine (PSIS)
        Gluteal surface
            (posterior-lateral surface of wing)
        Anterior Gluteal Line
            (a ridge on the gluteal surface,
            between the origins of gluteus
            medius and gluteus minimus)

    Acetabulum)   (p. 164)
        All 3 hip bones (ilium, ischium, pubis)
        intersect in the cavity of this socket

Obturator foramen
        Hole encircled by pubis and ischium

Femur   (p. 48)

    Head
    Neck
    Greater trochanter
    Lesser trochanter
    Gluteal tuberosity

Sacrum   (p. 45)
    Muscles attach on both the posterior and
    anterior surfaces.

Lumbar vertebrae L1-L5, and thoracic T12   (p. 44)
    Anterior bodies and TVP's – (for psoas major)

Other Structures

    Sacrotuberous Ligament   (p. 126)
    Inguinal Ligament   (p. 126)
    Iliotibial Tract / Iliotibial Band (ITB) (p. 177)

Notes

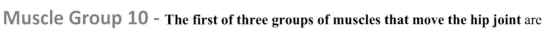

Muscle Group 10 - **The first of three groups of muscles that move the hip joint** are illustrated as a group on this page. The following four pages have tables and figures that describe each muscle individually, and provide many ways of comparing and contrasting the muscles to each other.

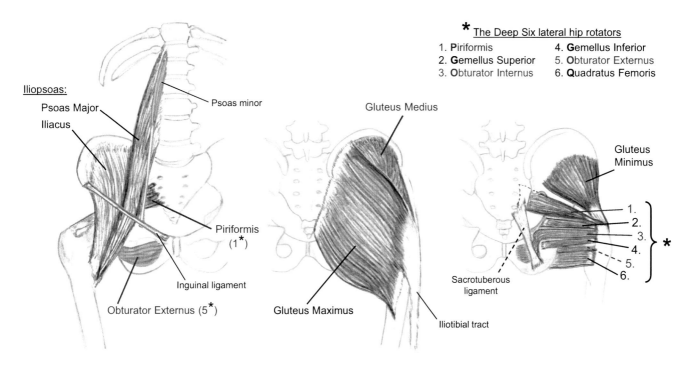

* <u>The Deep Six lateral hip rotators</u>
1. **P**iriformis   4. **G**emellus Inferior
2. **G**emellus Superior   5. **O**bturator Externus
3. **O**bturator Internus   6. **Q**uadratus Femoris

Iliopsoas:
Psoas Major
Iliacus
Psoas minor
Piriformis (1*)
Inguinal ligament
Obturator Externus (5*)

Gluteus Medius
Gluteus Maximus
Iliotibial tract

Gluteus Minimus
1.
2.
3.
4.
5.
6.
*
Sacrotuberous ligament

Anterior View   Posterior Views

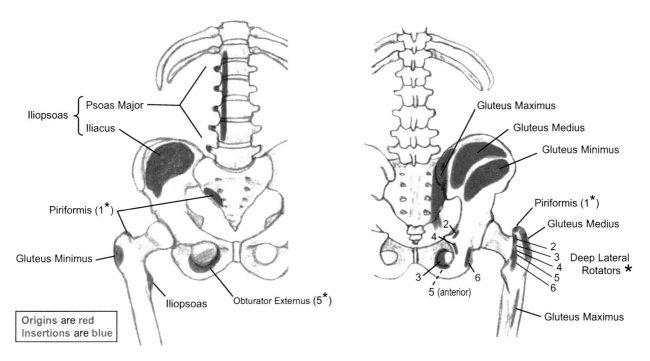

Iliopsoas
Psoas Major
Iliacus
Piriformis (1*)
Gluteus Minimus
Iliopsoas
Obturator Externus (5*)

Origins are red
Insertions are blue

Gluteus Maximus
Gluteus Medius
Gluteus Minimus
Piriformis (1*)
Gluteus Medius
2
3
4
5
6
Deep Lateral Rotators *
2
4
3
5 (anterior)
6
Gluteus Maximus

Attachment sites for all muscles in Group 10

TVP=Transverse process of vertebra, ITB=Iliotibial Band (another name for the iliotibial tract)

Group 10: Muscles Acting On Hip Joint (Part 1)	Origin	Insertion	Action
Gluteus Maximus moves the hip joint	Posterior iliac crest, ilium, and sacrum (also lateral coccyx and sacrotuberous ligament)	Gluteal tuberosity of femur, and the iliotibial tract (ITB)	Extension and lateral rotation at the hip joint (also lower fibers assist adduction, and upper fibers may assist abduction)
Gluteus Medius moves the hip joint	Upper lateral surface of the ilium (upper half of the wing of the ilium, starting just below the iliac crest)	Greater trochanter of femur (lateral aspect)	<u>All fibers:</u> Abduction at the hip joint. <u>Ant. fibers:</u> Assist flexion and medial rotation <u>Post. fibers:</u> Assist extension and lateral rotation
Gluteus Minimus moves the hip joint	Lower lateral surface of the ilium (lower half of the wing of the ilium, inferior to the origin of gluteus medius)	Greater trochanter of femur (anterior aspect)	Abduction and medial rotation at the hip joint. (Also may assist flexion)
Piriformis (Deep Lateral Rotator #1) moves the hip joint	Anterior surface of sacrum	Greater trochanter of femur (superior aspect)	Lateral rotation at the hip joint
The Other 5 Deep Lateral Rotators (#2 - #6) Gemellus superior Obturator internus Gemellus inferior Obturator externus Quadratus femoris	<u>Gemelli & Quad.Fem.:</u> Ischium <u>Obturators:</u> Obturator foramen (ischium & pubis) All Deep 6 Collective: Sacrum, Ischium, and Pubis	Greater trochanter of femur (posterior-medial aspect)	Lateral rotation at the hip joint
Iliopsoas: **Iliacus** and **Psoas Major** Moves the hip joint and the spine	<u>Iliacus:</u> Anterior iliac fossa <u>Psoas Major:</u> Bodies & TVP's of T12 and L1-L5	<u>Both:</u> Lesser trochanter of the femur	Flexion at the hip joint. (May assist lateral rotation at the hip joint) If the femur is fixed (in a standing position): Pulls on lumbar spine, increasing lordosis and anterior pelvic tilt.

(larger illustrations on page 173)

Table 10 (A) - Hip Joint (Part 1) - Origin, Insertion, Action

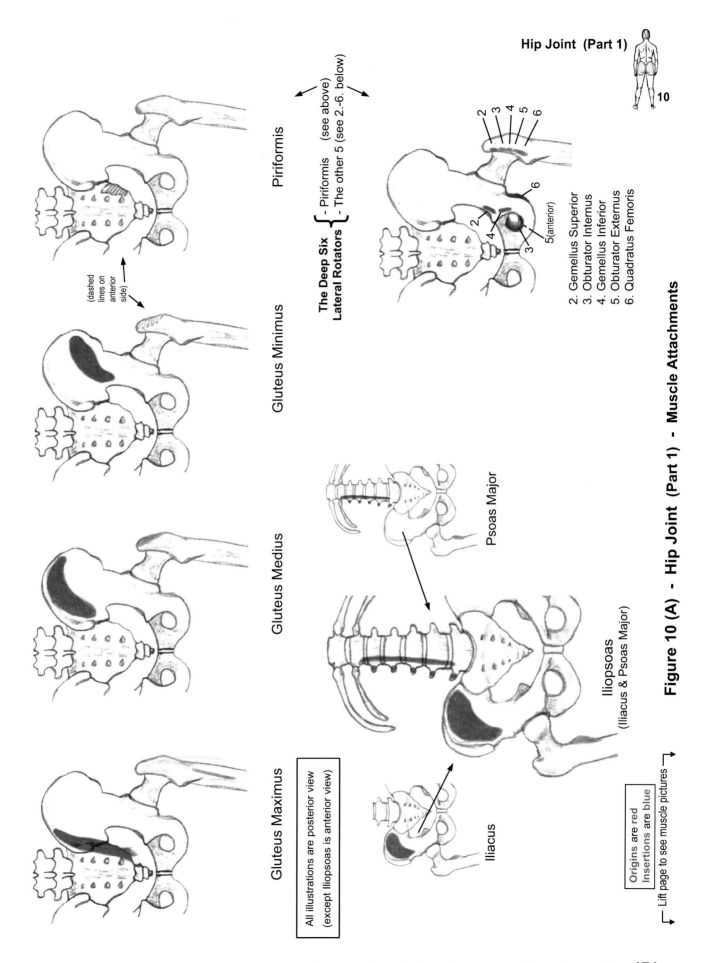

10

Piriformis

(dashed lines on anterior side)

The Deep Six Lateral Rotators { - Piriformis (see above)
- The other 5 (see 2.-6. below)

2. Gemellus Superior
3. Obturator Internus
4. Gemellus Inferior
5. Obturator Externus
6. Quadratus Femoris

Gluteus Minimus

Gluteus Medius

Gluteus Maximus

All illustrations are posterior view (except Iliopsoas is anterior view)

Psoas Major

Iliopsoas (Iliacus & Psoas Major)

Iliacus

Origins are red
Insertions are blue

Lift page to see muscle pictures

Figure 10 (A) - Hip Joint (Part 1) - Muscle Attachments

Group 10:

Muscles Acting On Hip Joint (Part 1)

Hip joint (coxal joint) = Head of femur seated in acetabulum of the hip bone (coxal bone), ➤ =Muscle creates the action, N=Nerve

Muscle	Flexion @ Hip jt.	Extension @ Hip jt.	Abduction @ Hip jt.	Adduction @ Hip jt.	Medial Rotation @ Hip jt.	Lateral Rotation @ Hip jt.	Stabilization of Hip jt.	Other	Innervation	L2	L3	L4	L5	S1	S2
1. Gluteus Maximus		➤	➤ assist (upper fibers)			➤	➤		Inferior gluteal N. (L5, S1, S2)				N	N	N
2. Gluteus Medius	➤ assist (anterior fibers)	➤ assist (posterior fibers)	➤ (all fibers)	➤ assist (lower fibers)	➤ assist (anterior fibers)	➤ assist (post. fibers) when hip is extended	➤ (main hip stabilizer)	This is the primary abductor	Superior gluteal N. (L4, L5, S1)			N	N	N	
3. Gluteus Minimus	➤ may assist		➤		➤		➤		Superior gluteal N. (L4, L5, S1)			N	N	N	
4. Piriformis						➤			Sacral Plexus (S1, S2)					N	N
5. The Other 5 Deep Lateral Rotators Gemellus Superior Obturator Internus Gemellus Inferior Obturator Externus Quadratus Femoris						➤			**GS:** SP- L5, S1, 2 **OI:** SP- L5, S1, 2 **GI:** SP- L4,5, S1 **OE:** Obturator, L3,4 **QF:** SP- L4,5, S1 (SP=Sacral Plexus)		N	N	N	N	N
Iliopsoas: **6. Iliacus**	➤					➤ may assist		Reverse O/I (femur fixed): increases lumbar lordosis, ant. pelvic tilt	**Iliacus:** Femoral N. (L2, L3) **Psoas Major:** Lumbar plexus (L2-L4)	N	N				
7. Psoas Major	➤									N	N	N			
(More muscles for the action) ——>	see also Groups 11, 12	see also Groups 11, 12	see also Group 11	see also Group 11	see also Groups 11, 12	see also Groups 11, 12			**Innervation**						

Table 10 (B) - Hip Joint (Part 1) - Synergists & Antagonists

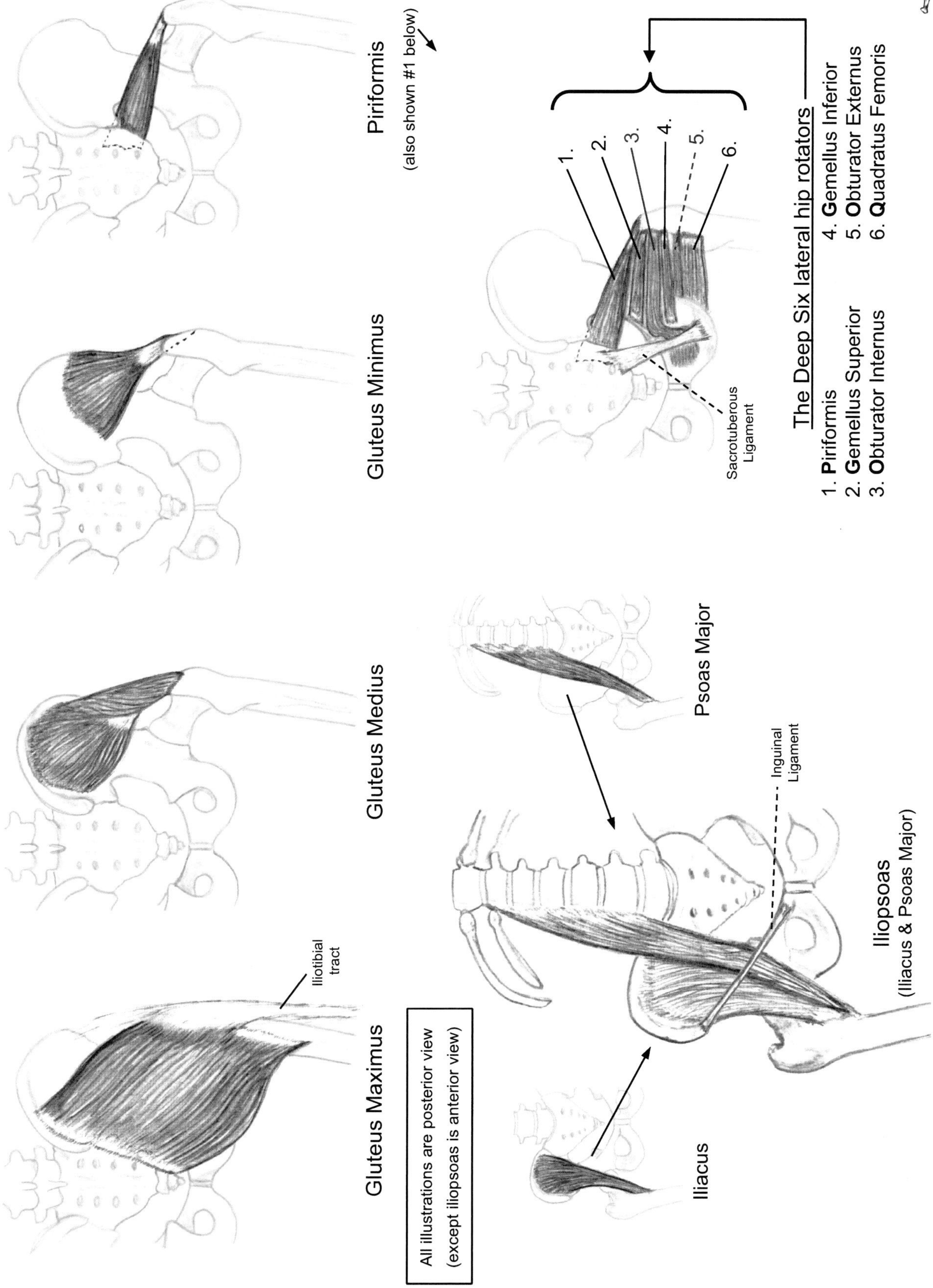

Piriformis
(also shown #1 below)

Gluteus Minimus

Gluteus Medius

Gluteus Maximus

Iliotibial tract

The Deep Six lateral hip rotators

1. Piriformis
2. Gemellus Superior
3. Obturator Internus
4. Gemellus Inferior
5. Obturator Externus
6. Quadratus Femoris

Sacrotuberous Ligament

Psoas Major

Iliopsoas
(Iliacus & Psoas Major)

Inguinal Ligament

Iliacus

All illustrations are posterior view
(except iliopsoas is anterior view)

Figure 10 (B) - Hip Joint (Part 1) - Muscle Pictures

Note-taking page ~ (palpation, how to lengthen/shorten, cautions, common uses, etc.)

10

Muscle Group 10 - Muscles Acting on the Hip Joint (Part 1)

1. Gluteus Maximus

2. Gluteus Medius

3. Gluteus Minimus

4. Piriformis
(Deep Lateral Rotator #1)

5. The Other 5 Deep Lateral Rotators
#2 - #6 *(Piriformis is lateral rotator #1)*

#2. Gemellus superior
#3. Obturator internus
#4. Gemellus inferior
#5. Obturator externus
#6. Quadratus femoris

6. Iliacus

7. Psoas Major

6. + 7. Iliopsoas

Iliacus + Psoas Major
(treated as one muscle)

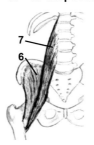

7
6

Movement of the Hip Joint (Part 2)

Muscle Group 11

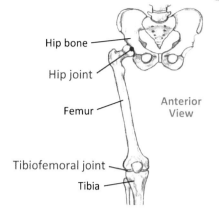

Superficial Long Muscles:	The Adductor Group:
Sartorius	Pectineus
Tensor fascia latae (TFL)	Adductor brevis
	Adductor longus
	Adductor magnus
	Gracilis

Joint

(Joint details: p. 164)

This is the second of three groups of muscles that move the femur at the hip joint (coxal joint). This group contains the "longer" length muscles that mainly originate on the iliac crest and pubic bone, and insert on the posterior shaft of the femur and the proximal end of the tibia.

Hip Joint (Coxal Joint)   (also called acetabulofemoral joint or coxofemoral joint)

Acetabulum of the **Hip Bone** ◄► Head of **Femur**

Ball and Socket Joint

Movements Available:

Flexion
Extension
Abduction
Adduction
Lateral Rotation (External Rotation)
Medial Rotation (Internal Rotation)

Other Joints

(Joint details: p. 165)

Three of the muscles in this group cross both the hip and the knee joints, and therefore also affect the knee (although the *main* knee movers are presented in the next section – Group 12: Movement of the Knee).

Tibiofemoral Joint (TF)

Condyles of **Femur** ◄► Condyles of **Tibia** (tibial plateau)
Modified Hinge Joint
Movements Available:
Flexion, Extension
Medial and Lateral Rotation (when the knee is flexed)

(Note: The TF joint is covered more fully
in the next section – Group 12: Movement of the Knee)

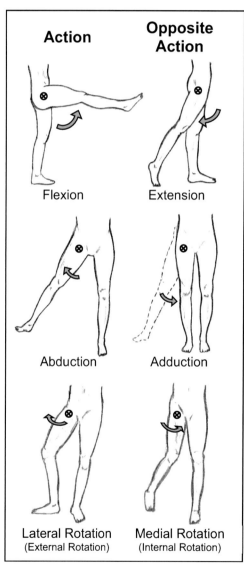

Action	Opposite Action
Flexion	Extension
Abduction	Adduction
Lateral Rotation (External Rotation)	Medial Rotation (Internal Rotation)

Bones, Bony Landmarks, Other Structures

The "long" muscles that move the hip joint have attachments on the hip bone, femur and tibia. Review the bony landmarks and other structures listed below, referring to the drawings in Chapter 2, pages 47-48.

Hip Bone (Coxal Bone, Os Coxae) (p. 47)

(Made up of 3 bones fused: Ilium, Ischium, Pubis)

Landmarks on the Ilium:
Anterior superior iliac spine (ASIS)

Landmarks on the Ischium:
Ischial tuberosity
Ramus of ischium

Landmarks on the Pubis:
Superior ramus of pubis
Pubic crest
Pubic tubercle
Body of pubis
Inferior ramus of pubis
Symphysis pubis

Note: The inferior pubic ramus and the ischial ramus together are called the ischiopubic ramus.

Femur (p. 48)
Condyles
Linea aspera
(medial lip, lateral lip)
Pectineal line
Adductor tubercle

Tibia (p. 48)

Proximal medial shaft (PMS)
Condyles
Lateral tibial tubercle (Gerdy's tubercle)

Other Structures

Fascia Latae	(p. 177)
Iliotibial tract / Iliotibial band (ITB)	"
Pes anserinus	(p. 176)
(on proximal medial shaft (PMS) of tibia)	
Femoral triangle	(p. 176)
Adductor canal	(p. 184)
Adductor hiatus	(p. 177)

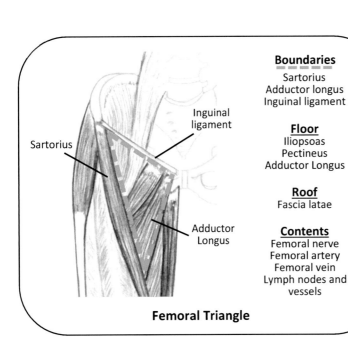

Boundaries
Sartorius
Adductor longus
Inguinal ligament

Floor
Iliopsoas
Pectineus
Adductor Longus

Roof
Fascia latae

Contents
Femoral nerve
Femoral artery
Femoral vein
Lymph nodes and vessels

Inguinal ligament

Sartorius

Adductor Longus

Femoral Triangle

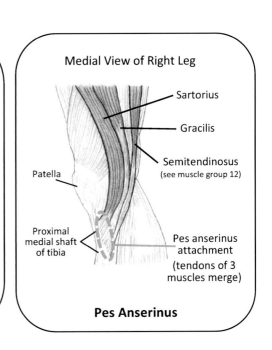

Medial View of Right Leg

Sartorius

Gracilis

Semitendinosus
(see muscle group 12)

Patella

Proximal medial shaft of tibia

Pes anserinus attachment
(tendons of 3 muscles merge)

Pes Anserinus

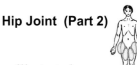

Muscle Group 11 - **The second of three groups that move the hip joint** are illustrated as a group on this page. The following four pages have tables and figures that describe each muscle individually, and provide many ways of comparing and contrasting the muscles to each other.

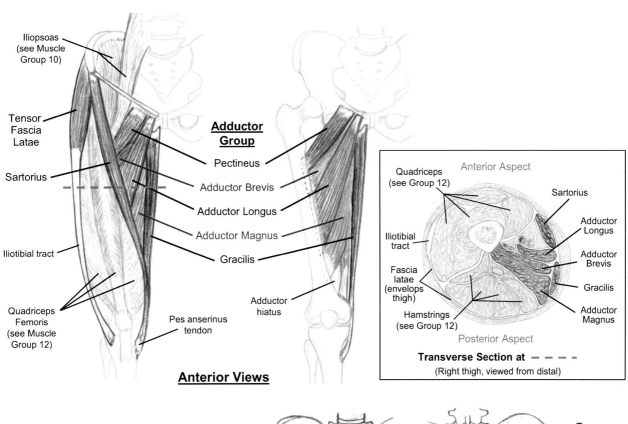

Iliopsoas (see Muscle Group 10)

Tensor Fascia Latae

Sartorius

Iliotibial tract

Quadriceps Femoris (see Muscle Group 12)

Adductor Group

Pectineus

Adductor Brevis

Adductor Longus

Adductor Magnus

Gracilis

Pes anserinus tendon

Adductor hiatus

Anterior Views

Quadriceps (see Group 12)

Iliotibial tract

Fascia latae (envelops thigh)

Hamstrings (see Group 12)

Anterior Aspect

Sartorius

Adductor Longus

Adductor Brevis

Gracilis

Adductor Magnus

Posterior Aspect

Transverse Section at – – – – –
(Right thigh, viewed from distal)

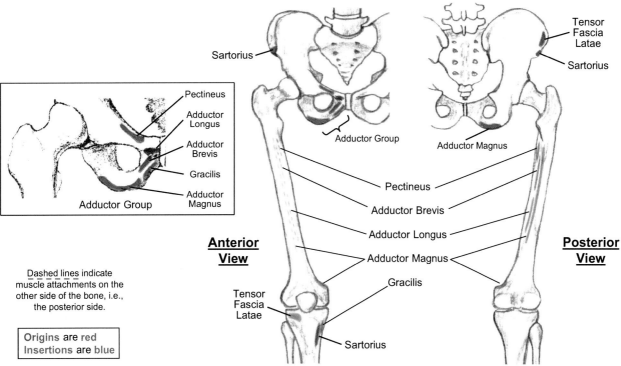

Sartorius

Pectineus

Adductor Longus

Adductor Brevis

Gracilis

Adductor Magnus

Adductor Group

Tensor Fascia Latae

Sartorius

Adductor Group

Adductor Magnus

Pectineus

Adductor Brevis

Adductor Longus

Adductor Magnus

Gracilis

Tensor Fascia Latae

Sartorius

Anterior View

Posterior View

Dashed lines indicate muscle attachments on the other side of the bone, i.e., the posterior side.

Origins are red
Insertions are blue

Attachment sites for all muscles in Group 11

Group 11: Muscles Acting On Hip Joint (Part 2)

	Origin	Insertion	Action
Sartorius moves the hip joint and knee	Anterior Superior Iliac Spine (ASIS) of the hip bone	Proximal medial shaft of tibia (by way of the pes anserinus tendon)	Flexion, abduction, and lateral rotation at the hip joint. Flexion of the knee and medial rotation of the tibia at the flexed knee.
Tensor Fascia Latae moves the hip joint and stabilizes the knee	Iliac crest, just posterior to the ASIS (i.e., next to the sartorius origin)	Iliotibial tract, which continues on to the lateral tubercle of the tibia (Gerdy's tubercle)	Flexion, abduction, and medial rotation at the hip joint Stabilizes the extended knee
Pectineus moves the hip joint	Superior ramus of pubis	Pectineal line of femur (on posterior femur, proximal to linea aspera)	Adduction, flexion, and medial rotation at the hip joint
Adductor Brevis moves the hip joint	Inferior ramus of pubis (near the obturator foramen, lateral to the gracilis attachment)	Proximal linea aspera of femur	Adduction, flexion, and medial rotation at the hip joint
Adductor Longus moves the hip joint	Pubic tubercle	Mid linea aspera of femur	Adduction, flexion, and medial rotation at the hip joint
Adductor Magnus moves the hip joint	<u>Anterior</u>: Inferior ramus of pubis, Posterior: Ramus of ischium, Ischiocondylar: Ischial tuberosity <u>Overall Description</u>: Ischiopubic ramus & ischial tuberosity	Entire linea aspera, and adductor tubercle of femur (with hiatus in between for vessels to pass through)	<u>All fibers</u>: Adduction at the hip joint. <u>Anterior fibers</u>: Flexion and medial rotation at the hip joint. <u>Posterior fibers</u>: Extension at the hip joint
Gracilis moves the hip joint and knee	Inferior ramus of pubis (medial edge of ramus, near the symphysis pubis)	Proximal medial shaft of tibia (by way of the pes anserinus tendon)	Adduction at the hip joint. Flexion of the knee and medial rotation of the tibia at the flexed knee (may assist flexion & medial rotation at the hip joint)

The Adductor Group

(larger illustrations on page 181)

Table 11 (A) - **Hip Joint (Part 2)** - **Origin, Insertion, Action**

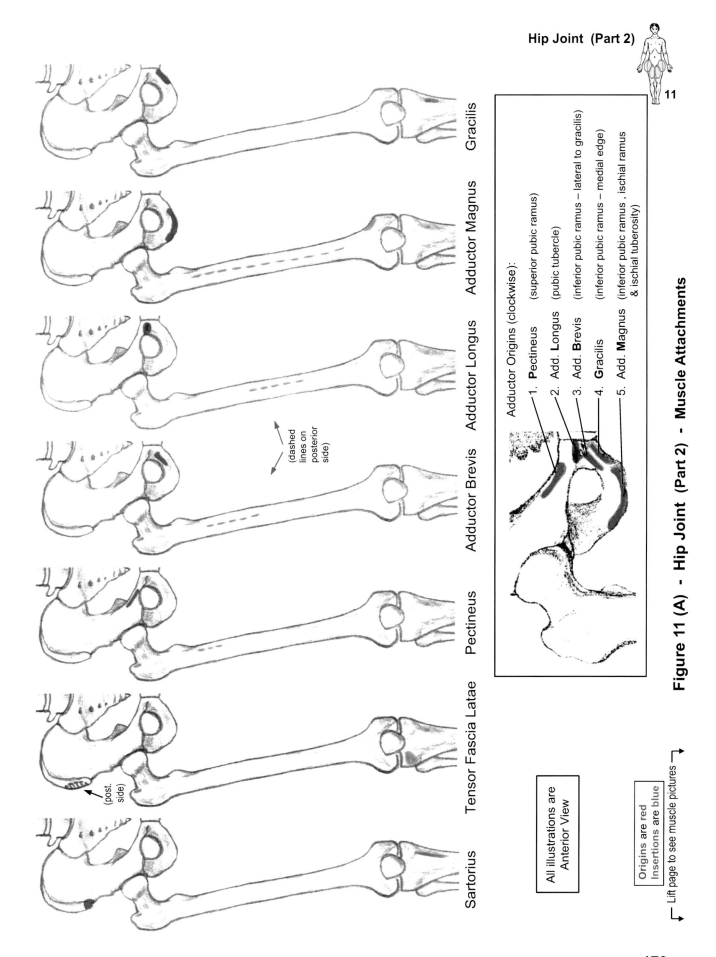

Gracilis

Adductor Magnus

Adductor Longus

(dashed lines on posterior side)

Adductor Brevis

Pectineus

Tensor Fascia Latae

(post. side)

Sartorius

Adductor Origins (clockwise):

1. **Pectineus**   (superior pubic ramus)
2. Add. **Longus**   (pubic tubercle)
3. Add. **Brevis**   (inferior pubic ramus – lateral to gracilis)
4. **Gracilis**   (inferior pubic ramus – medial edge)
5. Add. **Magnus**   (inferior pubic ramus , ischial ramus & ischial tuberosity)

Figure 11 (A) - Hip Joint (Part 2) - Muscle Attachments

All illustrations are Anterior View

Origins are red
Insertions are blue

└ Lift page to see muscle pictures ┘

Hip Joint (Part 2)

Group 11: Muscles Acting On Hip Joint (Part 2)

Knee=Tibiofemoral joint (TF jt.), ✓ =Muscle creates the action, N=Nerve

Muscle	Flexion @ Hip jt.	Extension @ Hip jt.	Abduction @ Hip jt.	Adduction @ Hip jt.	Medial Rotation @ Hip jt.	Lateral Rotation @ Hip jt.	Flexion @ Knee	Other	Innervation	L2	L3	L4	L5	S1	S2	S3
1. Sartorius	✓		✓			✓	✓	Medial rotation of tibia at flexed knee	Femoral N. (L2, L3)	N	N					
2. Tensor Fascia Latae	✓		✓		✓			Stabilizes the extended knee	Superior Gluteal N. (L4, L5, S1)			N	N	N		
3. Pectineus	✓			✓	✓				Femoral N. (L2, L3) (& sometimes Obturator N.)	N	N					
4. Adductor Brevis	✓			✓	✓			(deep to adductor longus)	Obturator N. (L2, L3, L4)	N	N	N				
5. Adductor Longus	✓			✓	✓				Obturator N. (L2, L3, L4)	N	N	N				
6. Adductor Magnus	✓ Anterior fibers (which insert proximally)	✓ Posterior fibers (which insert distally)		✓ All fibers	✓ Anterior fibers			Can be an antagonist to itself (posterior vs. anterior fibers)	Anterior part: Obturator N. (L2,L3,L4) Posterior part: Sciatic N. (L4,L5, S1)	N	N	N	N	N		
7. Gracilis	may assist			✓	may assist		✓	Medial rotation of tibia at flexed knee	Obturator N. (L2, L3)	N	N					
(More muscles for the action) —>	see also Groups 10,12	see also Groups 10,12	see also Group 10	see also Group 10	see also Groups 10,12	see also Groups 10,12	see also Groups 12,13		Innervation							

Table 11 (B) - Hip Joint (Part 2) - Synergists & Antagonists

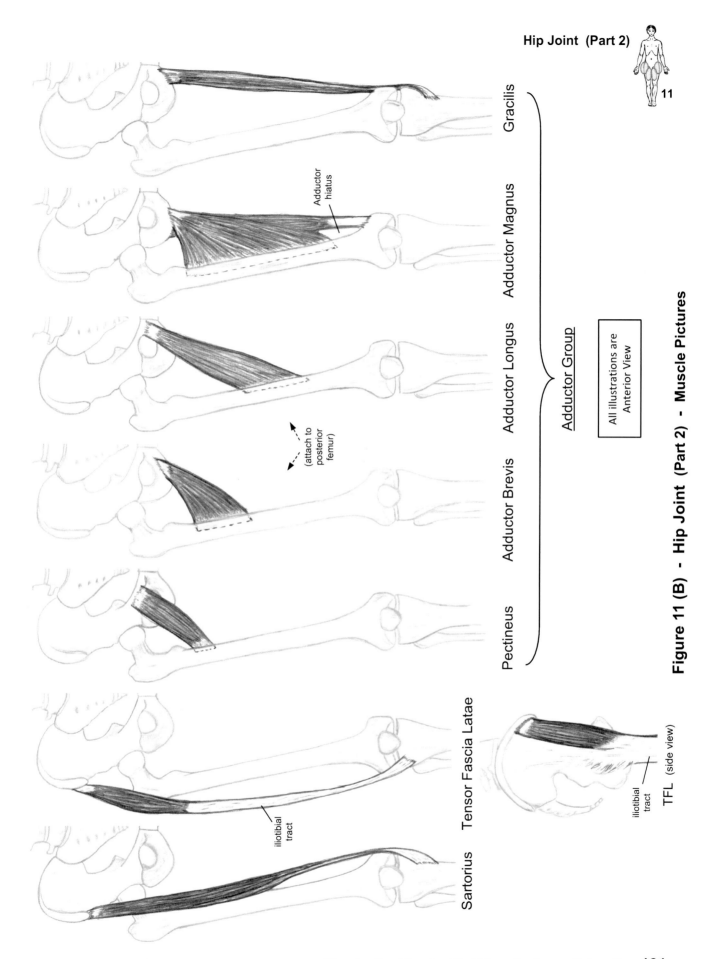

Gracilis

Adductor Magnus

Adductor hiatus

Adductor Longus

(attach to posterior femur)

Adductor Brevis

Pectineus

Adductor Group

All illustrations are Anterior View

Tensor Fascia Latae

iliotibial tract

TFL (side view)

iliotibial tract

Sartorius

Figure 11 (B) - Hip Joint (Part 2) - Muscle Pictures

Note-taking page ~ (palpation, how to lengthen/shorten, cautions, common uses, etc.)

11

Muscle Group 11 - Muscles Acting on the **Hip Joint (Part 2)**

1. Sartorius

5. Adductor Longus

2. Tensor Fascia Latae

6. Adductor Magnus

3. Pectineus

7. Gracilis

4. Adductor Brevis

Movement of the Knee (& Hip Joint, Part 3)

Muscle Group 12

Quadriceps Group:	Hamstrings Group:
Rectus femoris	Biceps femoris
Vastus lateralis	Semimembranosus
Vastus intermedius	Semitendinosus
Vastus medialis	
	Other:
	Popliteus

Joints

(Joint details: p. 164-165)

This group primarily moves the tibia/fibula at the knee. Many of the muscles are also strong movers of the femur at the hip joint, so this is *also* the third of the three groups of hip movers (along with Groups 10 and 11).

Tibiofemoral Joint (TF) – The Knee

Condyles of **Femur** ◄► Condyles of **Tibia** (tibial plateau)

Modified Hinge joint
Movements Available:
    Flexion, Extension
    Medial and Lateral Rotation
      (when the knee is flexed)

Hip Joint
    (See previous section:
    Group 11: Hip Joint, Part 2)

Other Joints

These joints are also involved with movements of the knee:

Patellofemoral
    Posterior **Patella** ◄► Patellar surface of **Femur**
    Gliding joint
    Moves all directions, but primarily up & down

Proximal Tibiofibular
    Proximal lateral **Tibia** ◄► Head of **Fibula**
    Gliding joint
    Very slight movement (subluxation is possible)

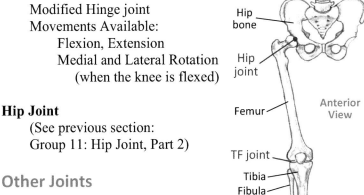

Hip bone
Hip joint
Femur
Anterior View
TF joint
Tibia
Fibula

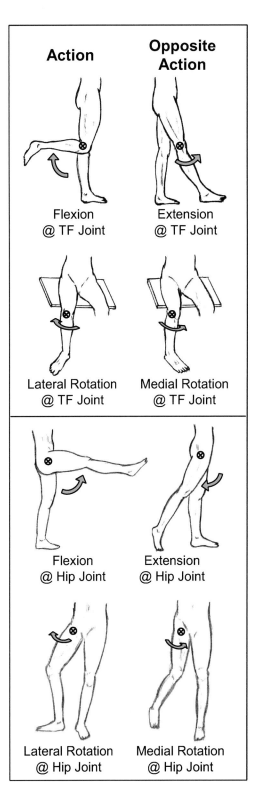

Action	**Opposite Action**
Flexion @ TF Joint	Extension @ TF Joint
Lateral Rotation @ TF Joint	Medial Rotation @ TF Joint
Flexion @ Hip Joint	Extension @ Hip Joint
Lateral Rotation @ Hip Joint	Medial Rotation @ Hip Joint

Bones, Bony Landmarks, Other Structures

Muscles that move knee (and hip) have attachments on the hip bone, femur, patella, tibia and fibula. Review the bony landmarks and other structures listed below, referring to the illustrations in Chapter 2, pages 47-48.

Hip Bone (Coxal Bone, Os Coxae) (p. 47)

> Anterior Inferior Iliac Spine (AIIS)
> Ischial tuberosity

Femur (p. 48)

> Linea aspera
> Greater trochanter
> Lesser trochanter
> Lateral condyle
> Shaft
>> Anterior, Posterior, Lateral, Medial
>> Surfaces
> Patellar Surface

Patella

Fibula (p. 48)

> Head

Tibia (p. 48)

> Tibial tuberosity
> Lateral & Medial Condyles (tibial plateau)
> PMS – Proximal Medial Shaft
> Pes Anserinus attachment

Other Structures:

> Patellar ligament (patellar tendon)   (p. 165)
> Knee ligaments & menisci   (p. 165)
> Pes anserinus tendon   (p. 176)
> Vastus medialis obliquus (VMO)   (p. 184)
> Popliteal Fossa

Notes:

Note that the rectus femoris and all the hamstring muscles are multi-joint muscles, and they are excellent examples for exploring the concepts of active and passive insufficiency and the force-length relationship (see page 33).

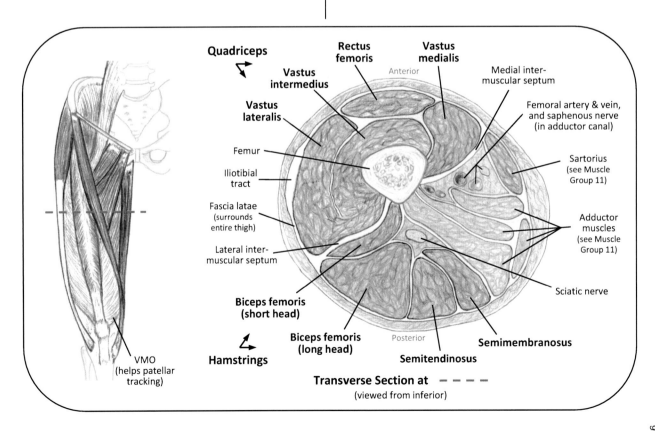

Transverse Section at – – – – –
(viewed from inferior)

Muscle Group 12 - **Muscles that move the knee** (and in many cases the hip) are illustrated
as a group on this page. The next four pages have tables and figures that describe each muscle
individually, and provide many ways of comparing and contrasting the muscles to each other.

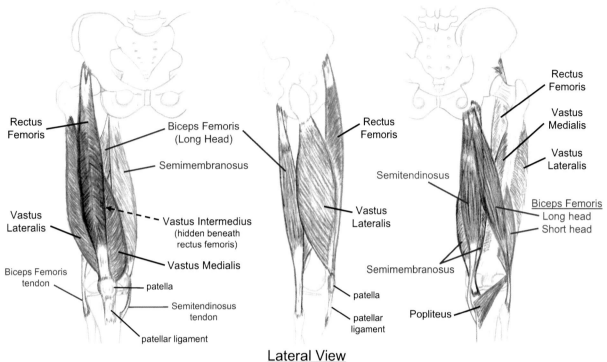

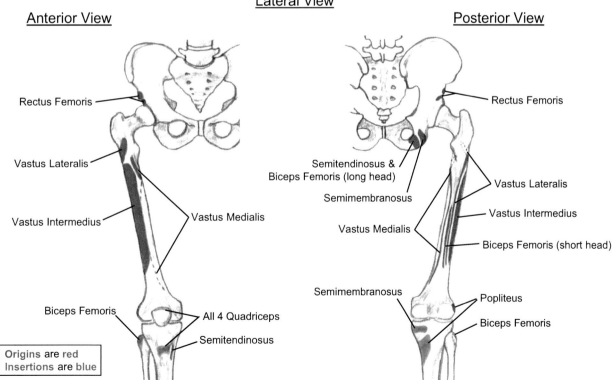

Attachment sites for all muscles in Group 12

Group 12: Muscles Acting On
Knee (& Hip Joint, Part 3)

* The tibia is only capable of rotation (at the tibiofemoral joint) when the knee is in a flexed position.

Knee (& Hip Joint, Part 3)	Origin	Insertion	Action
Rectus Femoris (Quadricep) moves the knee and the hip joint	Anterior Inferior Iliac Spine (AIIS) of the hip bone (and superior margin of the acetabulum just below the AIIS)	Tibial tuberosity via the patellar ligament	Extension at the knee, Flexion at the hip joint
Vastus Lateralis (Quadricep) moves the knee	Posterior *lateral* femur, lateral lip of linea aspera (and wraps to anterior at the base of the greater trochanter)	Tibial tuberosity via the patellar ligament	Extension at the knee
Vastus Intermedius (Quadricep) moves the knee	Anterior and lateral shaft of femur (upper 2/3 of the shaft)	Tibial tuberosity via the patellar ligament	Extension at the knee
Vastus Medialis (Quadricep) moves the knee	Posterior *medial* femur, medial lip of linea aspera (and wraps to anterior at the base of the lesser trochanter)	Tibial tuberosity via the patellar ligament	Extension at the knee (distal portion, the VMO, pulls patella medially so it tracks properly)
Biceps Femoris (Hamstring) moves the knee and the hip joint	<u>Long head:</u> Ischial tuberosity <u>Short head:</u> Lateral lip of linea aspera (distal half)	Head of fibula	*Both* heads: Flexion and lateral rotation* at the knee <u>Long head:</u> Extension and lateral rotation at the hip joint.
Semitendinosus (Hamstring) moves the knee and the hip joint	Ischial tuberosity	Proximal medial shaft of tibia (by way of the pes anserinus tendon)	Flexion and medial rotation* at the knee, Extension and medial rotation at the hip joint
Semimembranosus (Hamstring) moves the knee and the hip joint	Ischial tuberosity	Posterior medial condyle of tibia	Flexion and medial rotation* at the knee, Extension and medial rotation at the hip joint
Popliteus moves the knee	Lateral condyle of the femur	Proximal posterio-medial tibia	Medial rotation* at the knee, May assist flexion at the knee When weight bearing: Lateral rotation of femur, to unlock straightened knee

Anterior Views

Posterior Views

(larger illustrations on page 189)

Table 12 (A) - Knee (& Hip Joint, Part 3) **- Origin, Insertion, Action**

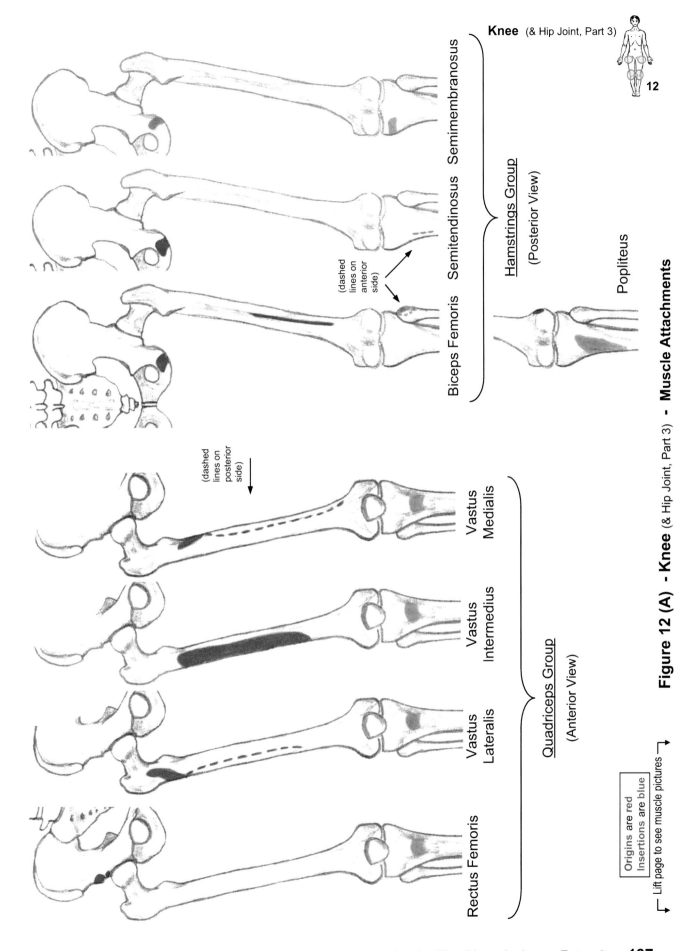

12

Semimembranosus

Semitendinosus

Biceps Femoris

Hamstrings Group
(Posterior View)

(dashed lines on anterior side)

Popliteus

Figure 12 (A) - Knee (& Hip Joint, Part 3) **- Muscle Attachments**

(dashed lines on posterior side)

Vastus Medialis

Vastus Intermedius

Vastus Lateralis

Rectus Femoris

Quadriceps Group
(Anterior View)

Origins are red
Insertions are blue

Lift page to see muscle pictures

Group 12:

Knee=Tibiofemoral joint (TF jt.), ⟍ =Muscle creates the action, N=Nerve

Muscles Acting On **Knee** (& Hip Joint, Part 3)	Flexion @ Knee	Extension @ Knee	Rotation @ Knee	Flexion @ Hip jt.	Extension @ Hip jt.	Medial Rotation @ Hip jt.	Lateral Rotation @ Hip jt.	Other	Innervation	L2	L3	L4	L5	S1	S2	S3
1. Rectus Femoris (Quadricep)		⟍		⟍				Tight Rectus Femoris can cause anterior pelvic tilt.	Femoral N. (L2, L3, L4)	N	N	N				
2. Vastus Lateralis (Quadricep)		⟍						Makes up all of the lateral thigh. It is deep to the iliotibial tract.	Femoral N. (L2, L3, L4)	N	N	N				
3. Vastus Intermedius (Quadricep)		⟍						It is deep to the other 3 quads.	Femoral N. (L2, L3, L4)	N	N	N				
4. Vastus Medialis (Quadricep)		⟍						Distal part (VMO) pulls patella medially so it tracks properly.	Femoral N. (L2, L3, L4)	N	N	N				
5. Biceps Femoris (Hamstring)	⟍		(lateral rotation)		⟍ (long head)		⟍ (long head)	This is the lateral hamstring. It has two heads (long & short).	Long head: Tibial part of sciatic N. (S1, S2, S3) Short hd: Peroneal part of sciatic N. (L5, S1, S2)				N	N	N	N
6. Semitendinosus (Hamstring)	⟍		(medial rotation)		⟍	⟍		Tight hamstrings can cause posterior pelvic tilt.	Tibial part of the sciatic nerve (L5, S1, S2)				N	N	N	
7. Semimembranosus (Hamstring)	⟍		(medial rotation)		⟍	⟍		Semimemb. is broad, flat, bipennate, deep to Semitend.	Tibial part of the sciatic nerve (L5, S1, S2)				N	N	N	
8. Popliteus	⟍ may assist		(medial rotation)					When weight bearing: Lateral rotation of femur, to unlock knee.	Tibial N. (L4, L5, S1)			N	N	N		
(More muscles for the action) --->	see also Groups 11,13			see also Groups 10,11	see also Groups 10,11	see also Groups 10,11	see also Groups 10,11		**Innervation**							

Table 12 (B) - Knee (& Hip Joint, Part 3) - Synergists & Antagonists

26958

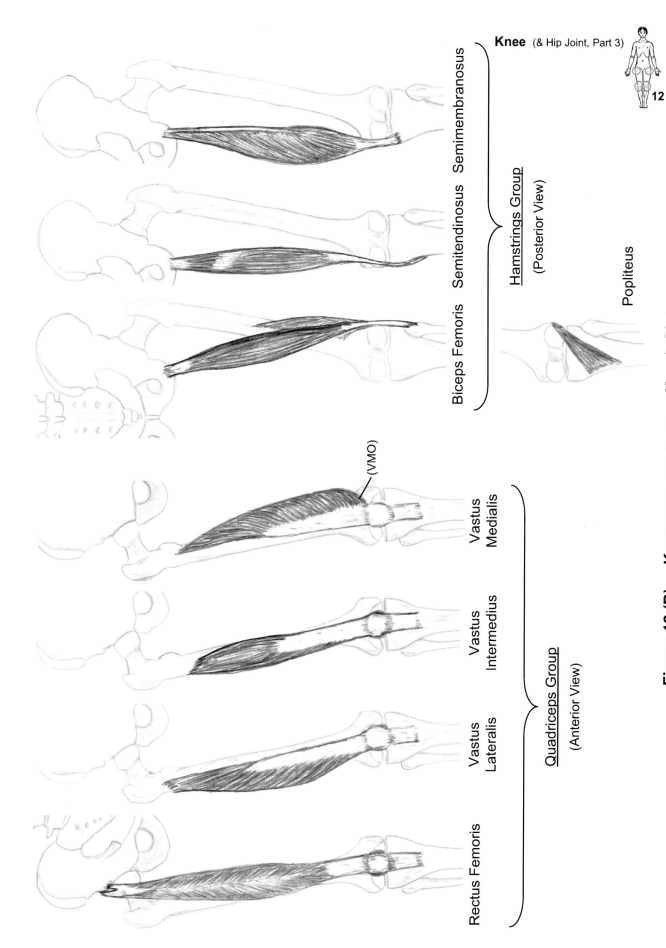

Semimembranosus

Semitendinosus

Hamstrings Group
(Posterior View)

Biceps Femoris

Popliteus

(VMO)

Vastus Medialis

Vastus Intermedius

Quadriceps Group
(Anterior View)

Vastus Lateralis

Rectus Femoris

Figure 12 (B) - Knee (& Hip Joint, Part 3) **- Muscle Pictures**

Muscle Group 12 - Muscles Acting on the **Knee** (& Hip Joint, Part 3)

1. Rectus Femoris

5. Biceps Femoris

2. Vastus Lateralis

6. Semitendinosus

3. Vastus Intermedius

7. Semimembranosus

4. Vastus Medialis

8. Popliteus

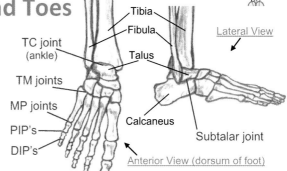

Movement of the Ankle, Foot, and Toes

Muscle Group 13

Gastrocnemius	Fibularis brevis (peroneus b.)
Soleus	Fibularis longus (peroneus l.)
Plantaris	
Tibialis posterior	Tibialis anterior
Flexor digitorum longus	Extensor digitorum longus
Flexor hallucis longus	Extensor hallucis longus

Joints

(Joint details: p. 166)

The muscles in this group move the ankle, foot, and toes. A couple of the muscles also cross the knee joint and therefore affect the knee. There are many joints involved, and it can be challenging to visualize which joints are in play with some of the more complex foot movements.

Talocrural Joint (TC) - Ankle
Distal **tibia** & distal **fibula** ◄► **Talus**
Hinge joint
Movements available: Plantar flexion
Dorsiflexion

Subtalar Joint (Talocalcaneal Joint)
Inferior aspect of **Talus** ◄► Superior aspect of **Calcaneus**
Gliding joint
Movements available: Inversion (Supination)
Eversion (Pronation)

Tarsometatarsal Joints (TM or TMT) (#1-#5)
Distal row of **tarsals** ◄► Bases of **metatarsals**
Gliding joints

Metatarsophalangeal Joints (MP or MTP) (#1-#5)
Heads of **metatarsals** ◄► Bases of proximal **phalanges**
Condyloid joints
Movement of the toes: Flexion, Extension
Abduction, Adduction

(Abduct) (Adduct)

Interphalangeal Joints (PIP and DIP) (#1-#5)
Joints between the **phalanges** of the toes
Hinge joints
Movement of the toes: Flexion, Extension

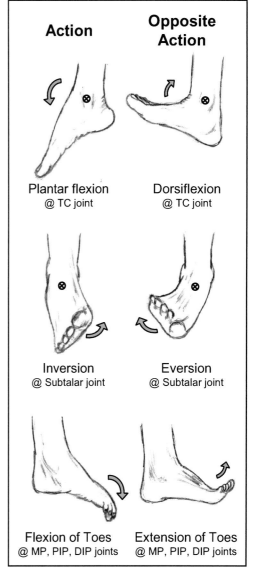

Action	Opposite Action
Plantar flexion @ TC joint	Dorsiflexion @ TC joint
Inversion @ Subtalar joint	Eversion @ Subtalar joint
Flexion of Toes @ MP, PIP, DIP joints	Extension of Toes @ MP, PIP, DIP joints

PIP = Proximal Interphalangeal (between the proximal phalanx and the middle phalanx)
DIP = Distal Interphalangeal (between the middle phalanx and the distal phalanx)
Note: The big toe (hallux) has only 2 phalanges, so has only an IP joint (no PIP or DIP)

Other Joints

The following joints are included here for completeness, but are not considered primary joints involved with ankle/foot/toe movements. They are special combinations of intertarsal joints (interfaces between tarsal bones) that are important when studying the arches and flexibility of the foot.

Transverse Tarsal Joint (also called the midtarsal joint) (p. 49)
Talocalcaneonavicular Joint (TCN)
Longitudinal and transverse <u>arches</u> of the foot (p. 166)

Tripod arches
of the foot

Bones, Bony Landmarks, Other Structures

Muscles that move the ankle, foot and toes have attachments on the bones of the leg, foot, and posterior knee. Review the bony landmarks and other structures listed below, referring to Chapter 2, pages 48-49.

Femur (p. 48)
    Medial and Lateral Condyles
    Medial and Lateral Epicondyles

Tibia (p. 48)
    Medial and Lateral Condyles
    Soleal Line
    Medial malleolus
    Shaft
        Posterior, Anterior, Medial, Lateral
        Combination aspects, e.g., posteriolateral
        Lengthwise positions, e.g.,
        "proximal two-thirds", "middle one-half"

Fibula (p. 48)
    Head
    Lateral malleolus
    Shaft
        Posterior, Anterior, combinations,
        lengthwise positions (as with tibia above)

Ankle & Foot Bones (p. 49)

    Tarsal Bones (7)
        Talus   Calcaneus
        Cuboid   Navicular
        Cuneiforms (3)
            (1st: medial, 2nd: middle, 3rd: lateral)
    Metatarsal Bones (5): 1st=medial to 5th=lateral
        Tuberosity of the 5th metatarsal
        Head, base, and shaft
    Phalanges (14)
        Digit #1 = Hallux (big toe)
            Proximal, Distal phalanges
        Digits #2-#5 = toes medial to lateral
            Proximal, Middle, Distal phalanges
        Head, base, and shaft

Other Structures
Interosseous membrane
Calcaneal tendon (Achilles tendón)
Plantar aponeurosis /plantar fascia
Retinacula: (extensor, flexor, fibular/peroneal)

Tibia
Fibula

Interosseus
membrane

Tendon Arrangements and Compartments of the Leg (see pages 193 and 201)

Medial malleolus tendons: Tibialis Posterior & two Flexor muscles (**TP, FDL, FHL**)
Dorsum of foot tendons: Tibialis Anterior & two Extensor muscles (TA, EHL, EDL)
Lateral malleolus tendons: Fibularis Longus & Fibularis Brevis (FL, FB)
Anatomical Stirrup: Tendons of fibularis longus and tibialis anterior form "stirrup" under foot

Four Leg Compartments: 1. Anterior, 2. Lateral, 3. Deep posterior, 4. Superficial posterior

Intrinsic Muscles of the Foot (see pages 198-199)

There are twelve muscles that reside within the structure of the foot itself. These *intrinsic* muscles of the foot are not included in the Group 13 tables, but a separate table and illustrations are presented as a Bonus Group on pages 198-199.

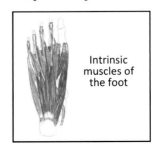

Intrinsic
muscles of
the foot

Muscle Group 13 - Muscles that move the ankle, foot, and toes are illustrated as a group

on this page. The next four pages have tables and figures that describe each muscle individually, and provide many ways of comparing and contrasting the muscles to each other.

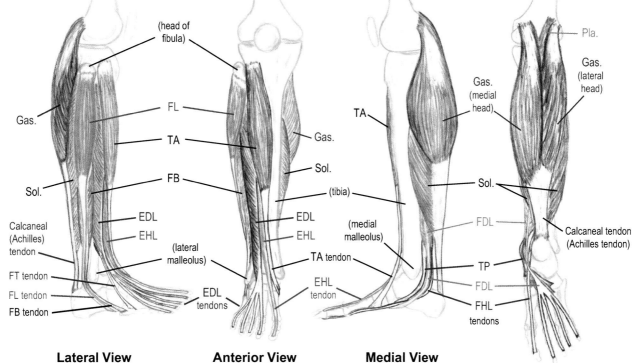

Lateral View   **Anterior View**   **Medial View**

Posterior View

Gas. - Gastrocnemius	FL - Fibularis Longus (Peroneus)	TA - Tibialis Anterior	TP - Tibialis Posterior
Sol. - Soleus	FB - Fibularis Brevis (Peroneus)	EDL - Extensor Digitorum Longus	FDL - Flexor Digitorum Longus
Pla. - Plantaris	FT - Fibularis Tertius (Peroneus)	EHL - Extensor Hallucis Longus	FHL - Flexor Hallucis Longus

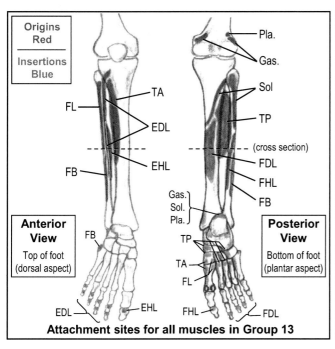

Anterior View
Top of foot
(dorsal aspect)

Posterior View
Bottom of foot
(plantar aspect)

Attachment sites for all muscles in Group 13

Origins Red
Insertions Blue

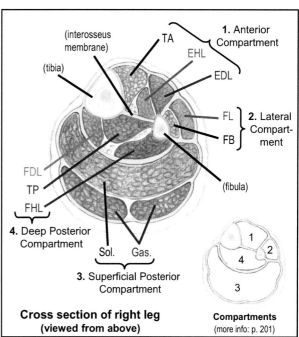

Cross section of right leg
(viewed from above)

Compartments
(more info: p. 201)

Group 13: Muscles Acting On Ankle, Foot, Toes

Joints: DIP & PIP=Distal & Proximal Interphalangeal, MP=Metatarsophalangeal, Toes #1-#5: 1=big toe, 5=little toe

Muscle	Origin	Insertion	Action
Gastrocnemius *moves the ankle and knee*	Posterior condyles of femur (lateral & medial)	Calcaneus via the achilles tendon	Plantar flexion of the ankle, Flexion of the knee (also stabilizes the knee in standing, walking, running)
Plantaris *moves the ankle and knee*	Posterior lateral epicondyle of femur	Calcaneus via the achilles tendon (small spot on the medial side)	Weak plantar flexion of ankle, may assist with inversion of the foot and flexion of the knee
Soleus *moves the ankle*	Proximal posterior shaft and head of fibula, Soleal line & middle medial edge of tibia	Calcaneus via the achilles tendon	Plantar flexion of the ankle
Tibialis Posterior *moves the foot*	Posterior lateral tibia, Posterior medial fibula, and interosseus membrane.	Plantar aspect of all tarsals except talus, and bases of metatarsals #2-4 (Tarsal attachments: calcaneus, navicular, cuboid, 3 cuneiforms)	Inversion of the foot, Plantar flexion of the ankle
Flexor Digitorum Longus *moves toes #2-5 and the foot*	Posterior tibia (starts 1/3 of the way down)	Base of distal phalanges #2-5 (plantar aspect)	Flexion of toes #2-5, Inversion of foot, Plantar flexion of ankle
Flexor Hallucis Longus *moves toe #1 and the foot*	Posterior fibula (starts 1/3 of the way down)	Base of distal phalanx of hallux – big toe (plantar aspect)	Flexion of toe #1 (hallux), Inversion of foot, Plantar flexion of ankle
Fibularis Brevis *(also called Peroneus Brevis)* *moves the foot*	Distal half of fibula (lateral aspect)	Tuberosity of the 5th metatarsal	Eversion of the foot, Assists plantar flexion of ankle
Fibularis Longus *(also called Peroneus Longus)* *moves the foot*	Head and proximal two-thirds of fibula (lateral aspect)	Medial (1st) cuneiform and base of 1st metatarsal (plantar aspect)	Eversion of the foot, Assists plantar flexion of ankle
Tibialis Anterior *moves the foot*	Lateral condyle and proximal half of tibia (lateral aspect) (and interosseus membrane)	Medial (1st) cuneiform and base of 1st metatarsal (medial edge of plantar aspect)	Dorsiflexion of the ankle, Inversion of the foot
Extensor Digitorum Longus *moves toes #2-5 and the foot*	Lateral condyle of tibia, and proximal 2/3 of fibula (anterior aspect)	Middle & distal phalanges #2-5 (dorsal aspect)	Extension of toes #2-5, Dorsiflexion of the ankle, Eversion of the foot
Extensor Hallucis Longus *moves toe #1 and the foot*	Middle portion of fibula (anterior medial aspect) (and interosseus membrane)	Base of distal phalanx of hallux –big toe (dorsal aspect)	Extension of toe #1 (hallux), Dorsiflexion of the ankle (May assist inversion of foot)

Gas. Pla. Sol.

TP FDL FHL

FB FL

TA EDL EHL

(larger illustrations on page 197)

Table 13 (A) - Ankle, Foot, Toes - Origin, Insertion, Action

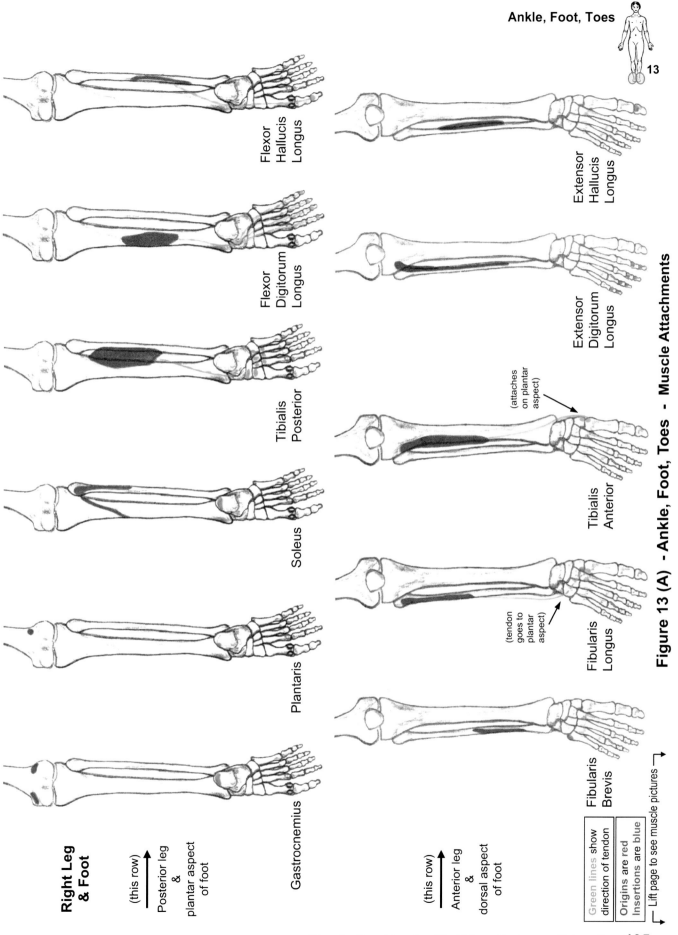

Right Leg & Foot

(this row)
Posterior leg & plantar aspect of foot

Gastrocnemius

Plantaris

Soleus

Tibialis Posterior

Flexor Digitorum Longus

Flexor Hallucis Longus

(this row)
Anterior leg & dorsal aspect of foot

Fibularis Brevis

Fibularis Longus
(tendon goes to plantar aspect)

Tibialis Anterior
(attaches on plantar aspect)

Extensor Digitorum Longus

Extensor Hallucis Longus

Green lines show direction of tendon

Origins are red
Insertions are blue

Lift page to see muscle pictures

Figure 13 (A) - Ankle, Foot, Toes - Muscle Attachments

Group 13:

#1-#5 toes (1=big toe, 5=little toe), Ankle=Talocrural joint (TC jt.), Knee=Tibiofemoral joint (TF jt.), ✓=Muscle creates the action, N=Nerve

Muscles Acting On Ankle, Foot, Toes	Plantar flexion (=flexion) @ Ankle	Dorsiflexion (=extension) @ Ankle	Inversion (@ Subtalar joint)	Eversion (@ Subtalar joint)	Flexion of Toes	Extension of Toes	Flexion @ Knee	Stabilization	Innervation	L4	L5	S1	S2
1. Gastrocnemius	✓						✓	Stabilizes knee	Tibial N. (S1, S2)			N	N
2. Plantaris	may assist		may assist				may assist		Tibial N. (L4, L5, S1)	N	N	N	
3. Soleus	✓								Tibial N. (S1, S2)			N	N
4. Tibialis Posterior	✓		✓					Stabilizer of ankle/foot	Tibial N. (L5, S1)		N	N	
5. Flexor Digitorum Longus	✓		✓		✓ #2-5				Tibial N. (L5, S1)		N	N	
6. Flexor Hallucis Longus	✓		✓		✓ #1 (hallux)				Tibial N. (L5, S1, S2)		N	N	N
7. Fibularis Brevis (Peroneus Brevis)	✓ assist			✓				Helps stabilize foot	Superficial fibular N. *	N	N	N	
8. Fibularis Longus (Peroneus Longus)	✓ assist			✓				PL and TA form "Anatomical stirrup"...	Superficial fibular N. (L4, L5, S1)	N	N	N	
9. Tibialis Anterior		✓	✓					...helping to maintain balance & stabilize foot	Deep fibular N. (L4, L5, S1)	N	N	N	
10. Extensor Digitorum Longus		✓		✓		✓ #2-5			Deep fibular N. (L4, L5, S1)	N	N	N	
11. Extensor Hallucis Longus		✓	may assist			✓ #1 (hallux)			Deep fibular N. (L4, L5, S1)	N	N	N	
(More muscles for the action) ---->								see also Groups 11,12	**Innervation**				

* fibular N. = peroneal N.

B4

Table 13 (B) - Ankle, Foot, Toes - Synergists & Antagonists

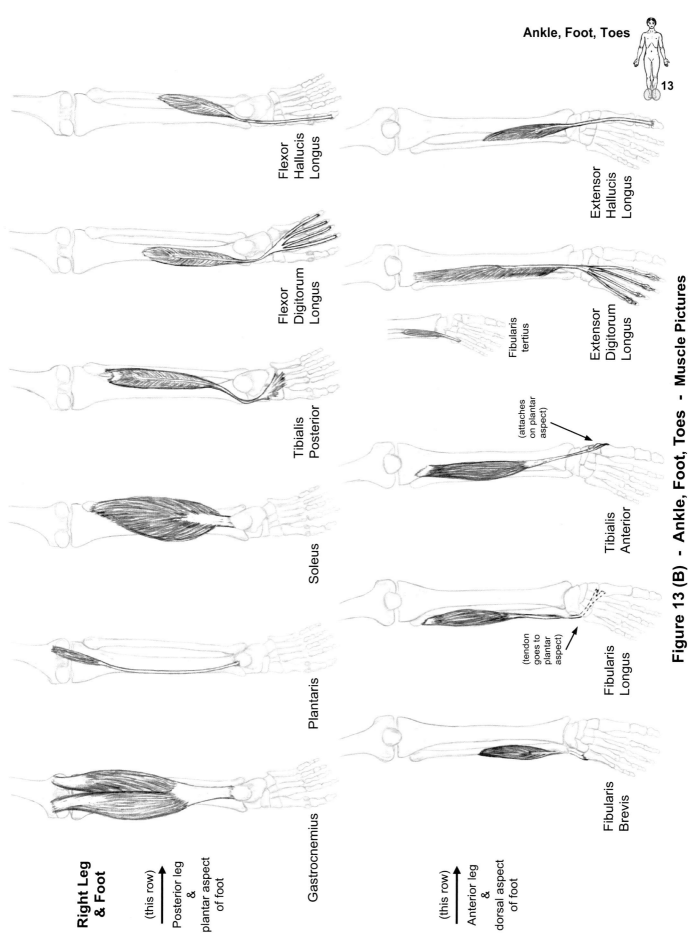

**Right Leg
& Foot**

(this row)

Posterior leg
&
plantar aspect
of foot

Flexor
Hallucis
Longus

Flexor
Digitorum
Longus

Tibialis
Posterior

Soleus

Plantaris

Gastrocnemius

Extensor
Hallucis
Longus

Fibularis
tertius

Extensor
Digitorum
Longus

(attaches
on plantar
aspect)

Tibialis
Anterior

(tendon
goes to
plantar
aspect)

Fibularis
Longus

Fibularis
Brevis

(this row)

Anterior leg
&
dorsal aspect
of foot

Figure 13 (B) - Ankle, Foot, Toes - Muscle Pictures

Intrinsic Muscles of the Foot – Plantar Aspect

Muscle	Origin	Insertion	Action	Innervation
Plantar Layer #1 (superficial)				
Abductor Digiti Minimi	Tuberosity of the calcaneus	Proximal phalanx of the little toe (lateral base)	Abduction and flexion of the little toe	Lateral plantar N. (S2, S3)
Flexor Digitorum Brevis	Tuberosity of the calcaneus	Middle phalanges of toes #2-5 (sides)	Flexion of toes #2-5	Medial plantar N. (L5, S1)
Abductor Hallucis	Tuberosity of the calcaneus	Proximal phalanx of the big toe (medial base)	Abduction and flexion of the big toe	Medial plantar N. (L5, S1)
Plantar Layer #2 (intermediate)				
Lumbrical Muscles (4)	The four tendons of the flexor digitorum longus	The four tendons of the extensor digitorum longus (attach via the medial side of the dorsal digital expansions)	Flexion of toes #2-5 at the metatarsophalangeal joints, Extension of toes #2-5 at the interphalangeal joints	<u>Lumbrical 1:</u> Medial plantar N. (L5, S1) <u>Lumbricals 2-4:</u> Lateral plantar N. (S2, S3)
Quadratus Plantae	Plantar surface of the calcaneus	Tendon of the flexor digitorum longus (lateral margin, before it goes to the 4 toes)	Flexion of toes #2-5 (assists the FDL)	Lateral plantar N. (S2, S3)
Plantar Layer #3 (almost deepest)				
Flexor Digiti Minimi	Base of 5th metatarsal (& peroneus longus tendon)	Proximal phalanx of the little toe (plantar base)	Flexion of the little toe (at the MP joint)	Lateral plantar N. (S2, S3)
Adductor Hallucis	<u>Oblique head:</u> Bases of metatarsals #2-4, <u>Transverse head:</u> Metatarsophalangeal ligaments #3-5	Proximal phalanx of the big toe (lateral base)	Adduction of the big toe	Lateral plantar N. (S2, S3)
Flexor Hallucis Brevis	Cuboid and lateral cuneiform (plantar surfaces)	Proximal phalanx of the big toe (sides of base)	Flexion of the big toe (at the MP joint)	Medial plantar N. (L5, S1)
Plantar Layer #4 (deepest)				
Plantar Interossei (3)	3rd, 4th and 5th metatarsal bones (bases and medial side of shafts)	Bases of the proximal phalanges of toes #3-5 (and the dorsal digital expansions of toes #3-5)	Adduction of toes #3-5, Assist flexion of toes #3-5 at the metatarsophalangeal joints, Assist extension of toes #3-5 at the interphalangeal joints	Lateral plantar N. (S2, S3)

Intrinsic Muscles of the Foot – Dorsal Aspect

Muscle	Origin	Insertion	Action	Innervation
Dorsal Layer #1 (superficial)				
Extensor Digitorum Brevis	Dorsal surface of the calcaneus	Toes #2-4, via the tendons of the extensor digitorum longus (attach to the lateral side of the EDL tendons)	Extension of toes #2-4	Deep fibular N. * (L5, S1)
Extensor Hallucis Brevis	Dorsal surface of the calcaneus	Proximal phalanx of the big toe (dorsal surface of the base of the phalanx)	Extension of the big toe	Deep fibular N. * (L5, S1)
Dorsal Layer #2 (deep) Note: This layer is sometimes considered to be part of plantar layer #4				
Dorsal Interossei (4)	Shafts of metatarsal bones #1-5 (each muscle arises from the sides of two adjacent metatarsal bones)	Bases of the proximal phalanges of toes #2-4 (and the dorsal digital expansions of toes #2-4)	Abduction of toes #2-4, Assist flexion of toes #2-4 at the metatarsophalangeal joints, Assist extension of toes #2-4 at the interphalangeal joints	Lateral plantar N. (S2, S3)

* (formerly called peroneal N.)

Intrinsic Muscles of the Foot

Right Foot – Layers of the Plantar Aspect

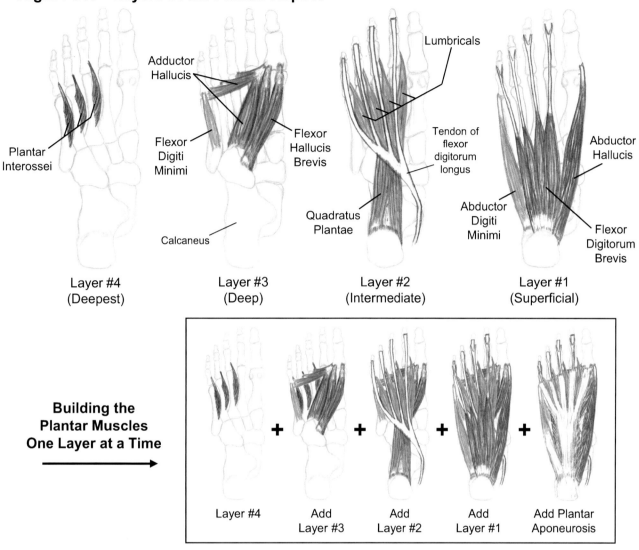

Adductor Hallucis

Lumbricals

Plantar Interossei

Flexor Digiti Minimi

Flexor Hallucis Brevis

Tendon of flexor digitorum longus

Abductor Hallucis

Calcaneus

Quadratus Plantae

Abductor Digiti Minimi

Flexor Digitorum Brevis

Layer #4 (Deepest)

Layer #3 (Deep)

Layer #2 (Intermediate)

Layer #1 (Superficial)

Building the Plantar Muscles One Layer at a Time →

Layer #4 + Add Layer #3 + Add Layer #2 + Add Layer #1 + Add Plantar Aponeurosis

Right Foot – Dorsal Aspect

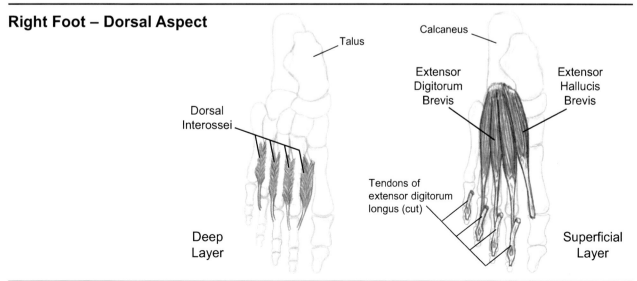

Talus

Calcaneus

Dorsal Interossei

Extensor Digitorum Brevis

Extensor Hallucis Brevis

Tendons of extensor digitorum longus (cut)

Deep Layer

Superficial Layer

Note-taking page ~ (palpation, how to lengthen/shorten, cautions, common uses, etc.)

Muscle Group 13 - Muscles Acting on the **Ankle, Foot and Toes**

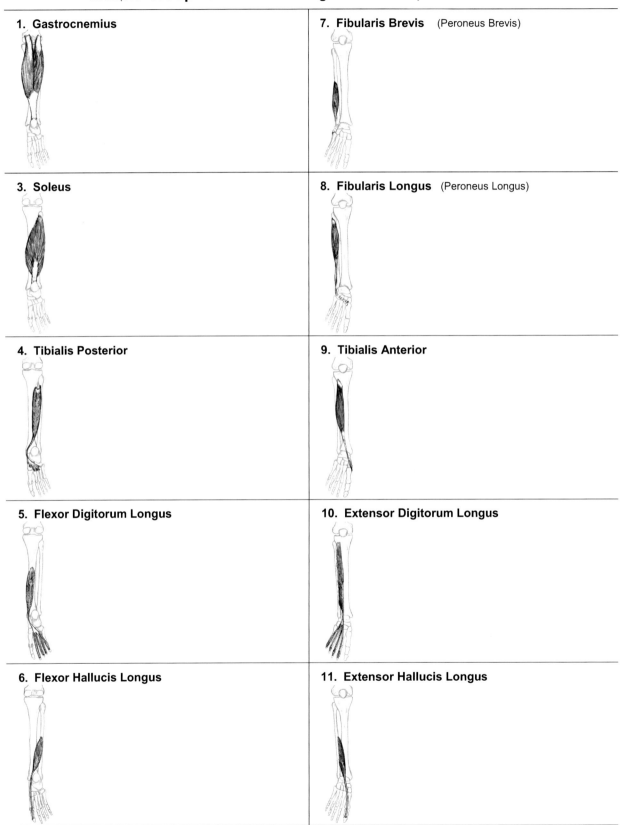

1. Gastrocnemius

3. Soleus

4. Tibialis Posterior

5. Flexor Digitorum Longus

6. Flexor Hallucis Longus

7. Fibularis Brevis (Peroneus Brevis)

8. Fibularis Longus (Peroneus Longus)

9. Tibialis Anterior

10. Extensor Digitorum Longus

11. Extensor Hallucis Longus

Muscles of the Leg - by Compartment

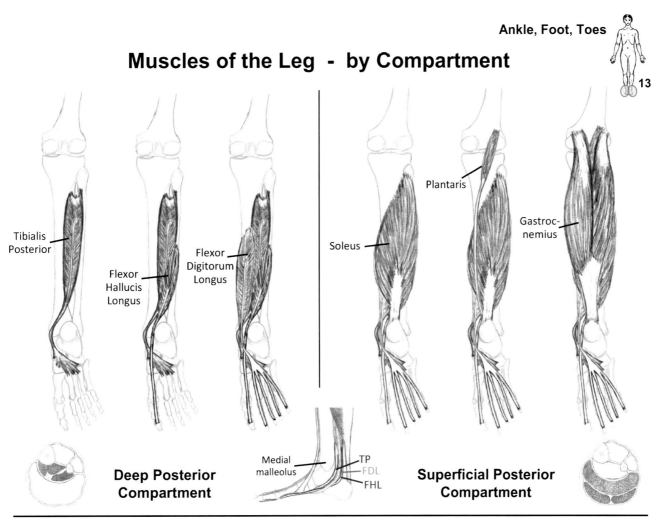

Tibialis Posterior

Flexor Hallucis Longus

Flexor Digitorum Longus

Soleus

Plantaris

Gastroc-nemius

Medial malleolus

TP
FDL
FHL

Deep Posterior Compartment

Superficial Posterior Compartment

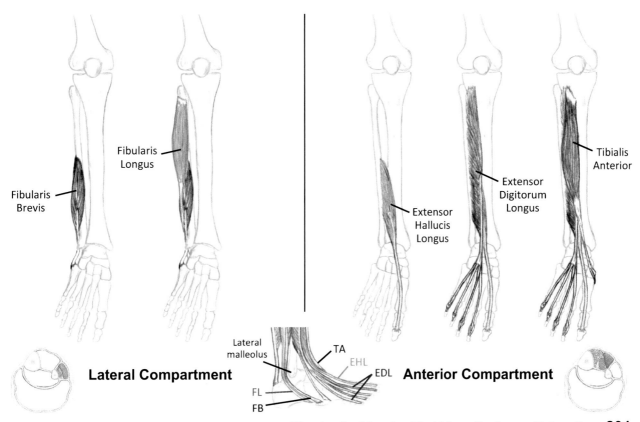

Fibularis Longus

Fibularis Brevis

Extensor Hallucis Longus

Extensor Digitorum Longus

Tibialis Anterior

Lateral malleolus

TA
EHL
EDL

FL
FB

Lateral Compartment

Anterior Compartment

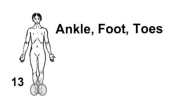 Ankle, Foot, Toes

13

(this page intentionally blank)

Chapter 7

Summary Tables and Illustrations

Introduction

Chapter 7 – Summary Tables provides a handy reference that can be quickly reviewed once you have learned all the muscles in Chapters 4, 5, and 6. It can be used when assessing/analyzing a client's movement patterns or posture, or when performing or teaching stretching and strengthening exercises.

Summary of Muscle Actions – Tables S-1, S-2, and S-3

These tables provide a comprehensive and compact format for analyzing any movement at any joint. Rows and columns can be studied to determine which muscles are acting as synergists, antagonists and stabilizers. Tables S-1, S-2 and S-3 use a format similar to the "B" Tables in Chapters 4-6. For a complete description of how to use "B" Tables, please refer to p. 62 in Chapter 3.

While these tables use a format similar to the "B" Tables in Chapters 4-6, they are different in one important way. For these summary tables, muscles are gathered from *multiple* muscle groups in cases where muscles from different groups move the same structures or joints.

Chapters 4-6 divide the muscles of the body into 13 groups to create a brain-friendly organization. However, the 13 individual B Tables do not always allow analyzing *all* muscles that may move a specific joint or structure. This can happen in Muscle Groups 1-13 because:

- Some muscles move multiple joints. For example, biceps brachii moves both the elbow and the shoulder joints.

- Sometimes in Chapters 4-6 a single joint is presented over more than one group. For example, Muscle Groups 10, 11, and 12 all have muscles that move the hip joint.

The composite organization in this summary chapter provides a single unified table for each body structure or joint, to have a complete picture of the muscles affecting its movements.

Innervation Summary – Table S-4

Table S-4 provides a color-coded list of the major nerves of the body and the muscles they supply. There is also a full body color-coded illustration showing the major nerve trunks and plexuses listed in the table.

Table S-1 -- Summary of Muscle Actions – UPPER EXTREMITY

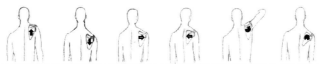

Scapula / Clavicle	Elevation	Depression	Protraction/Abduction	Retraction/Adduction	Lateral / Upward Rotation	Medial / Downward Rotation	Stabilization of Scapula	Muscl Group	Muscle also affects other joints:
Trapezius (upper fibers)	✓				✓		✓	G1	ROI: Head/Neck
Trapezius (middle fibers)				✓			✓	G1	-
Trapezius (lower fibers)		✓			✓		✓	G1	-
Levator Scapula	✓					✓		G1	ROI: Neck
Rhomboid (major & minor)	✓			✓		✓		G1	-
Serratus Anterior			✓		✓		✓	G1	-
Pectoralis Minor		"anterior tilt"						G1	ROI: Breathing
Subclavius		depresses clavicle						G1	ROI: Breathing
Pectoralis Major		✓ (lower/ab fib)						G2	Shoulder Joint
Latissimus Dorsi		✓						G2	Shoulder Joint

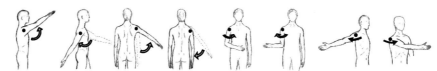

Shoulder Joint	Flexion @ GH jt.	Extension @ GH jt.	Abduction @ GH jt.	Adduction @ GH jt.	Medial Rotation @ GH jt.	Lateral Rotation @ GH jt.	Horizontal Abduction @ GH jt.	Horizontal Adduction @ GH jt.	Muscl Group	Muscle also affects other joints:
Deltoid (anterior fibers)	✓		✓		✓			✓	G2	-
Deltoid (middle fibers)			✓						G2	-
Deltoid (posterior fibers)		✓	✓			✓	✓		G2	-
Supraspinatus			✓						G2	-
Infraspinatus						✓	✓ may assist		G2	-
Teres Minor						✓			G2	-
Subscapularis					✓				G2	-
Pectoralis Major (upper fibers)	✓			✓	✓			✓	G2	-
Pectoralis Major (lower fibers)		✓ (from flexed pos.)		✓	✓				G2	Scapula
Coracobrachialis	✓			✓				✓ assist	G2	-
Latissimus Dorsi		✓		✓	✓				G2	Spine/Trunk. Scapula
Teres Major		✓		✓	✓				G2	-
Biceps Brachii	✓							✓ assist (short head)	G3	Elbow/ Forearm
Triceps Brachii		✓ (long head)		✓ assist (long head)					G3	Elbow

KEY: ✓ = Muscle creates the action, ✓assist = Muscle assists the action, GH = Glenohumeral joint (shoulder joint)
ROI = Reversed Origin/Insertion action (action moves O toward I)

Elbow, Forearm	Flexion @ HU jt.	Extension @ HU jt.	Pronation @ RU jt.	Supination @ RU jt.	Stabilization	Muscl Group	Muscle also affects other joints:
Biceps Brachii	✓			✓		G3	Shoulder Joint
Brachialis	✓					G3	-
Brachioradialis	✓ (handshake)		✓ assist (from sup.)	✓ assist (from pron.)		G3	-
Pronator Teres	✓ assist		✓			G3	-
Pronator Quadratus			✓			G3	-
Supinator				✓		G3	-
Triceps Brachii		✓				G3	Shoulder Joint
Anconeus		✓ assist			✓	G3	-
Extens. carpi radialis long.	✓ assist (handshake)					G4	Wrist
All wrist/digit flexors that attach proximal to elbow	✓ may assist					G4	Wrist

KEY

✓ = Muscle creates the action

✓ assist = Muscle assists the action

HU = Humeroulnar joint (elbow)

RU = Radioulnar joints

RC = Radiocarpal joint (wrist)

Wrist, Hand, Fingers	Flexion @ wrist	Extension @ wrist	Abduction/ Radial Deviation	Adduction/ Ulnar Deviation	Flexion Phalanges	Extension Phalanges	Abduction Phalanges	Adduction Phalanges	Muscl Group	Muscle also affects other joints:
Flexor Carpi Radialis	✓		✓						G4	Elbow
Palmaris Longus	✓				Cups the hand				G4	Elbow
Flexor Carpi Ulnaris	✓			✓					G4	Elbow
Flexor Digitorum Superficialis	✓				✓ fingers				G4	Elbow
Flexor Digitorum Profundus	✓ assist				✓ closed fist				G4	-
Extensor Carpi Radialis Longus		✓	✓						G4	Elbow
Extensor Carpi Radialis Brevis		✓	✓						G4	-
Extensor Carpi Ulnaris		✓		✓					G4	-
Extensor Digitorum		✓				✓ fingers	✓ assist		G4	-
Extensor Indicis		✓ assist				✓ index finger			G4	-
Flexor Pollicis Longus	✓ may assist				✓ thumb				G5	-
Opponens Pollicis					✓ thumb opposition				G5	-
Adductor Pollicis								✓ thumb	G5	-
Abductor Pollicis Longus			✓			✓ thumb	✓ thumb		G5	-
Extensor Pollicis Longus		✓ assist	✓ assist			✓ thumb			G5	-
Extensor Pollicis Brevis			✓ assist			✓ thumb			G5	-

Thumb actions →

Table S-2 -- Summary of Muscle Actions – AXIAL SKELETON

Face, Jaw	Elevation of mandible	Depression of mandible	Protrusion/ Protraction of mandible	Retrusion/ Retraction of mandible	Lateral Deviation of mandible	Other	Muscl Group	Muscle also affects other joints:
Masseter	✓			✓ assist (deep belly)			G6	-
Temporalis	✓			✓ (post. fibers)			G6	-
Lateral Pterygoid		✓ assist	✓		UL to opp. side		G6	-
Medial Pterygoid	✓ assist		✓ may assist		UL to opp. side		G6	-
Occipitofrontalis						raise eyebrows	G6	-
Platysma		✓ assist				tighten skin of neck	G6	-
Suprahyoids Group		✓		✓ assist		elev. hyoid (swallow)	G6	-
Infrahyoids Group		✓ assist				depress hyoid	G6	-

Head, Neck	Flexion	Extension	Lateral Flexion	Rotation *Same* Side	Rotation *Opp.* Side	Comment	Muscl Group	Muscle also affects other joints:
Sternocleidomastoid	BL head/neck	may assist (AO jt. Only)	UL head/neck		UL head/neck		G7	Breathing
Scalene – Anterior	BL neck		UL neck		UL assist	ROI use of muscle	G7	Breathing
Scalene – Middle	BL neck		UL neck			ROI use of muscle	G7	Breathing
Scalene – Posterior			UL neck			ROI use of muscle	G7	Breathing
Longus Capitis	BL head/neck						G7	-
Longus Colli	BL neck		UL may assist				G7	-
Suboccipitals Group		BL head	UL head	UL (OCI only)			G7	-
Splenius Capitis		BL head/neck	UL head/neck	UL head/neck			G7	-
Splenius Cervicis		BL neck	UL neck	UL neck			G7	-
Levator Scapula (scapula held fixed)		BL neck	UL neck	UL neck		ROI use of muscle	G7	Scapula
Trapezius, upper (scapula held fixed)		BL head/neck	UL head/neck		UL head/neck	ROI use of muscle	G7	Scapula
Spinalis (Cervicis)		BL or UL					G8	Spine/Trunk
Longissimus (Capitis)		BL head/neck	UL head/neck	UL head/neck			G8	Spine/Trunk
Longissimus (Cervicis)		BL neck	UL neck	UL neck			G8	Spine/Trunk
Iliocostalis (Cervicis)		BL neck	UL neck	UL neck			G8	Spine/Trunk
Semispinalis (Capitis)		BL or UL head/neck					G8	Spine/Trunk
Semispinalis (Cervicis)		BL neck			UL neck		G8	Spine/Trunk
Multifidus (upper slips)		BL neck			UL neck		G8	Spine/Trunk
Rotatores (upper slips)		BL neck			UL neck		G8	Spine/Trunk

KEY: UL = Unilateral contraction creates the action, BL = Bilateral contraction creates the action, ✓ = Both UL & BL create the action
ROI = Reversed Origin/Insertion (the action moves the origin toward the insertion), AO jt. = Atlantooccipital joint

Head/Neck = Muscle pulls the head, and the head & neck both move with a complex dynamic
Neck = Muscle pulls the neck, and the head goes along for the ride
Head = Muscle pulls the head from C1/C2, so the head moves on top of the spine, *without* the neck being moved

37268

Spine, Trunk, Breathing	Flexion	Extension	Lateral Flexion	Rotation *Same* Side	Rotation *Opp.* Side	Inhalation/ Inspiration	Exhalation/ Expiration	Compress Abdominal Contents	Muscl Group	Muscle also affects other joints:
Spinalis (thoracis)		BL or UL							G8	Head/Neck
Longissimus (thoracis)		BL	UL	UL (assist)					G8	Head/Neck
Iliocostalis (thoracis, lumborum)		BL	UL	UL (assist)			✓ assist		G8	Neck
Semispinalis (thoracis)		BL			UL				G8	Neck
Multifidus		BL			UL				G8	Neck
Rotatores		BL			UL				G8	Neck
Quadratus Lumborum		BL (lumbar)	UL				✓ stabilize rib 12		G8	Hip hike
Psoas Major		BL (↑ lordosis)	UL may assist						G10	Hip Joint
Sternocleidomastoid						assist (ROI)			G7	Head/Neck
Scalenes						✓			G7	Neck
Pectoralis Minor						assist (ROI)			G1	Scapula
Subclavius						assist (ROI)			G1	Clavicle
Diaphragm						✓		✓ (downward)	G9	-
Rectus Abdominis	✓						✓	✓ assist	G9	-
External Oblique	BL		UL		UL		✓	✓	G9	-
Internal Oblique	BL		UL	UL			✓	✓	G9	-
Transverse Abdominis							✓	✓	G9	-
External Intercostals						✓			G9	-
Internal Intercostals							✓		G9	-
Serratus Post. Superior						✓			G9	-
Serratus Post. Inferior							✓		G9	-
Levator Costae						✓			G9	-
Latissimus Dorsi		BL	UL						G2	-

KEY: UL = Unilateral contraction creates the action, BL = Bilateral contraction creates the action, ✓ = Both UL & BL create the action
ROI = Reversed Origin/Insertion (the action moves the origin toward the insertion)

Rotation *Same side* = Front of body moves to same side as the muscle contracting
Rotation *Opp. side* = Front of body moves to opposite side from the muscle contracting

Table S-3 -- Summary of Muscle Actions – LOWER EXTREMITY

Hip Joint	Flexion @ Hip jt.	Extension @ Hip jt.	Abduction @ Hip jt.	Adduction @ Hip jt.	Medial Rotation @ Hip jt.	Lateral Rotation @ Hip jt.	Stabilization of Hip jt.	Muscl Group	Muscle also affects other joints:
Gluteus Maximus		✓	✓ m assist (upper fib.)	✓ assist (lower fib.)		✓		G10	-
Gluteus Medius	✓ assist (anter. fib.)	✓ assist (poster. fib.)	✓		✓ assist (anter. fib.)	✓ assist (poster. fib.)	✓	G10	-
Gluteus Minimus	✓ may assist		✓		✓		✓	G10	-
Piriformis (& other 5 lateral rotators)						✓		G10	-
iliopsoas { Iliacus	✓					✓ may assist		G10	-
Psoas Major	✓					✓ may assist		G10	ROI: Trunk / Lumbar Spine
Sartorius	✓		✓			✓		G11	Knee
Tensor Fascia Latae	✓		✓		✓		✓	G11	Knee
Pectineus	✓			✓	✓			G11	-
Adductor Brevis	✓			✓	✓			G11	-
Adductor Longus	✓			✓	✓			G11	-
Adductor Magnus	✓ (anter. fib.)	✓ (poster. fib.)		✓ (all fibers)	✓ (anter. fib.)			G11	-
Gracilis	✓ may assist			✓	✓ may assist			G11	Knee
Rectus Femoris	✓							G12	Knee
Biceps Femoris		✓ (long head)				✓ (long head)		G12	Knee
Semitendinosus		✓			✓			G12	Knee
Semimembranosus		✓			✓			G12	Knee

KEY: ✓ = Muscle creates the action, ✓assist = Muscle assists the action, ✓may assist = May help action under certain circumstances
(anter. fib.) = Anterior fibers of the muscle, (poster. fib.) = Posterior fibers of the muscle

Knee	Flexion @ Knee	Extension @ Knee	Medial Rotation @ Knee (flexed)	Lateral Rotation @ Knee (flexed)	Stabilization of Knee	Muscl Group	Muscle also affects other joints:
Rectus Femoris		✓				G12	Hip Joint
Vastus Medialis		✓				G12	-
Vastus Lateralis		✓				G12	-
Vastus Intermedius		✓				G12	-
Biceps Femoris	✓			✓		G12	Hip Joint
Semitendinosus	✓		✓			G12	Hip Joint
Semimembranosus	✓		✓			G12	Hip Joint
Popliteus	✓ may assist		✓			G12	-
Sartorius	✓		✓			G11	Hip Joint
Tensor Fascia Latae					✓	G11	Hip Joint
Gracilis	✓		✓		✓	G11	Hip Joint
Gastrocnemius	✓				✓	G13	Ankle
Plantaris	✓ may assist					G13	Ankle

KEY

✓ = Muscle creates the action

✓ assist = Muscle assists the action

Knee = Tibiofemoral Joint (TF jt.)

ROI = Reversed O/I action

Ankle, Foot, Toes	Plantarflex @ Ankle	Dorsiflex @ Ankle	Inversion (subtalar joint)	Eversion (subtalar joint).	Flexion of Toes	Extension of Toes	Stabilization of Ankle/Foot	Muscl Group	Muscle also affects other joints:
Gastrocnemius	✓							G13	Knee
Plantaris	✓ may assist		✓ may assist					G13	Knee
Soleus	✓							G13	-
Tibialis Posterior	✓		✓				✓	G13	-
Flexor Digitorum Longus	✓		✓		✓ #2-5			G13	-
Flexor Hallucis Longus	✓		✓		✓ #1 (hallux)			G13	-
Peroneus Brevis	✓ assist			✓				G13	-
Peroneus Longus	✓ assist			✓			P.L. & T.A. create stirrup	G13	-
Tibialis Anterior		✓	✓				to stabilize foot/ankle	G13	-
Extensor Digitorum Longus		✓		✓		✓ #2-5		G13	-
Peroneus Tertius		✓		✓ assist				G13	
Extensor Hallucis Longus		✓	✓ may assist			✓ #1 (hallux)		G13	-

KEY: ✓ = Muscle creates the action, ✓ assist = Muscle assists the action, ✓ may assist = May help action under certain circumstances
Ankle = Talocrural joint (TC jt.), Hallux = Big toe (digit #1)

Table S-4 -- INNERVATION SUMMARY

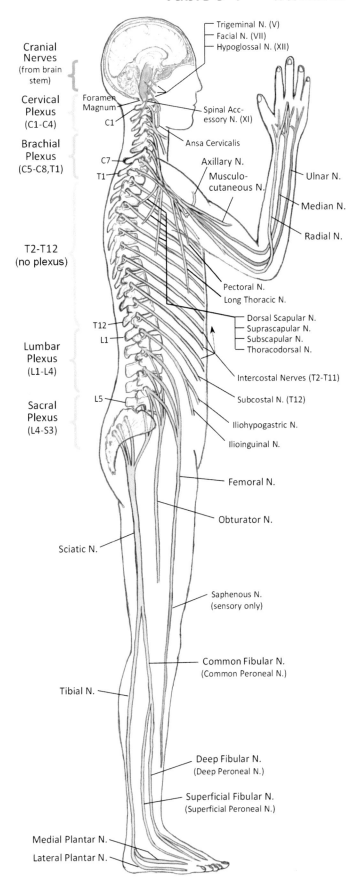

Cranial Nerves (from brain stem)

Cervical Plexus (C1-C4)

Brachial Plexus (C5-C8,T1)

T2-T12 (no plexus)

Lumbar Plexus (L1-L4)

Sacral Plexus (L4-S3)

The set of tables on this and the following page summarize the nerves that supply the muscles of the body. For an overview description of the nervous system, please refer to pages 22-25 in Chapter 1 – Basic Information.

Cranial Nerves		
Nerve Name	**Muscle**	**Segment**
Trigeminal N.	Masseter	Cranial V
Trigeminal N.	Temporalis	Cranial V
Trigeminal N.	Lateral pterygoid	Cranial V
Trigeminal N.	Medial pterygoid	Cranial V
Trigeminal N.	Mylohyoid	Cranial V
Trigeminal N.	Digastric, anterior belly	Cranial V
Facial N.	Digastric, posterior belly	Cranial VII
Facial N.	Stylohyoid	Cranial VII
Facial N.	Occipitofrontalis	Cranial VII
Facial N.	Platysma	Cranial VII
Facial N.	Muscles of facial expression	Cranial VII

Cranial Nerves with	Upper Cervical Nerves	
Hypoglossal N. & C1	Geniohyoid	Cranial XII, and C1
Spinal Accessory N. & ventral rami C2,C3	Sternocleidomastoid	Cranial XI, and C2, C3
Spinal Accessory N. & ventral rami C3,C4	Trapezius	Cranial XI, and C3, C4

Cervical Plexus (Ventral Rami of C1-C4)		
Ansa cervicalis	Sternohyoid	C1,C2,C3
Ansa cervicalis	Sternothyroid	C1,C2,C3
Ansa cervicalis	Omohyoid	C1,C2,C3
Ansa cervicalis	Thyrohyoid	C1,C2,C3
Phrenic N.	Diaphragm	C3,C4,C5
Ventral rami C1-C3	Longus capitis	C1-C3
Ventral rami C2-C6	Longus colli *	C2-C6
Ventral rami C3-C8	Middle scalene *	C3-C8
Ventral rami C3-C5	Levator scapula *	C3-C5
	*muscle has nerve supply from both cervical plexus and brachial plexus	

Dorsal Rami of Cervical Nerves		
Suboccipital N.	Rectus capitis posterior major	C1
Suboccipital N.	Rectus capitis posterior minor	C1
Suboccipital N.	Oblique capitis superior	C1
Suboccipital N.	Oblique capitis inferior	C1
Dorsal rami of upper cervicals	Semispinalis capitis	C1-C5
Dorsal rami of middle cervicals	Splenius capitis	C3-C6
Dorsal rami of lower cervicals	Splenius cervicis	C5-C8

Paraspinal Muscles (Dorsal Rami of Spinal Nerves)		
Dorsal rami (segmental)	Spinalis	C5-T12
Dorsal rami (segmental)	Longissimus	C3-L4
Dorsal rami (segmental)	Iliocostalis	C6-L2
Dorsal rami (segmental)	Semispinalis	C1-T10
Dorsal rami (segmental)	Multifidus	C3-L5
Dorsal rami (segmental)	Rotatores	C2-L5
Dorsal rami (segmental)	Levator costae	C8-T11

17480

Brachial Plexus (Ventral Rami of C5-T1)

Nerve Name	Muscle	Segments
Ventral rami C5,C6	Scalene, anterior	C5,C6
Ventral rami C3-C8	Scalene, middle *	C3-C8
Ventral rami C6-C8	Scalene, posterior	C6-C8
Ventral rami C2-C6	Longus colli *	C2-C6
Dorsal scapular N. (C5) & ventral rami C3, C4	Levator scapula *	C5 & C3,C4
Dorsal scapular N.	Rhomboid major	C5
Dorsal scapular N.	Rhomboid minor	C5
	* muscle has nerve supply from both cervical plexus and brachial plexus	
Subclavian N.	Subclavius	C5,C6
Suprascapular N.	Supraspinatus	C5
Suprascapular N.	Infraspinatus	C5,C6
Upper Subscapular N.	Subscapularis, upper part	C5,C6
Lower Subscapular N.	Subscapularis, lower part	C5,C6
Lower Subscapular N.	Teres major	C5,C6
Long thoracic N.	Serratus anterior	C5,C6,C7
Thoracodorsal N.	Latissimus dorsi	C6,C7,C8
Lateral pectoral N.	Pectoralis major, upper part	C5,C6,C7
Medial pectoral N.	Pectoralis major, lower part	C8,T1
Medial pectoral N.	Pectoralis minor	C8,T1
(Below are the five major "terminal branches" of the brachial plexus)		
Axillary N.	Deltoid	C5, C6
Axillary N.	Teres minor	C5
Musculocutaneous N.	Coracobrachialis	C6,C7
Musculocutaneous N.	Biceps brachii	C5,C6
Musculocutaneous N.	Brachialis	C5,C6
Radial N.	Brachioradialis	C5,C6
Radial N.	Triceps brachii	C7,C8
Radial N.	Anconeus	C7,C8,T1
Radial N.	Supinator	C6
Radial N.	Extensor carpi radialis longus	C6,C7
Radial N.	Extensor carpi radialis brevis	C6,C7
Radial N.	Extensor carpi ulnaris	C6,C7,C8
Radial N.	Extensor digitorum	C6,C7,C8
Radial N.	Extensor indicis	C7,C8
Radial N.	Abductor pollicis longus	C7,C8
Radial N.	Extensor pollicis longus	C6,C7,C8
Radial N.	Extensor pollicis brevis	C7,C8
Median N.	Pronator teres	C6,C7
Median N.	Pronator quadratus	C8,T1
Median N.	Flexor carpi radialis	C6,C7
Median N.	Palmaris longus	C6,C7
Median N.	Flexor digitorum superficialis	C7,C8,T1
Median N.	Flexor pollicis longus	C8,T1
Median N.	Opponens pollicis	C8,T1
Median N.	Abductor pollicis brevis	C8,T1
Median N.	Flexor pollicis brevis, sup. hd	C8,T1
Median N.	Flexor digitorum profundus, to digits 2 & 3	C8,T1
Median N.	Lumbrical muscles, digits 2-3	C8,T1
Ulnar N.	Flexor pollicis brevis, deep hd	C8,T1
Ulnar N.	Flexor digitorum profundus, to digits 4 & 5	C8,T1
Ulnar N.	Lumbrical muscles, digits 4-5	C8,T1
Ulnar N.	Flexor carpi ulnaris	C8,T1
Ulnar N.	Dorsal interossei	C8,T1
Ulnar N.	Palmar interossei	C8,T1
Ulnar N.	Abductor digiti minimi	C8,T1
Ulnar N.	Flexor digiti minimi	C8,T1
Ulnar N.	Opponens digiti minimi	C8,T1
Ulnar N.	Adductor pollicis	C8,T1

Ventral Rami of Thoracic Nerves

Intercostal nerves	External intercostals	T1-T11
Intercostal nerves	Internal intercostals	T1-T11
Intercostal nerves	Serratus posterior superior	T2-T5
Intercostal nerves	Serratus posterior inferior	T9-T12

Abdominal Muscles (Ventral Rami of T6-T12 and L1)

Nerve Name	Muscle	Segments
Intercostal nerves	Rectus abdominis	T6-T12
Intercostal nerves	External oblique	T7-T12
Intercostal N., Iliohypogastric N. & Ilioinguinal N.	Internal oblique	T8-T12, T12-L1, & L1
Intercostal N., Iliohypogastric N. & Ilioinguinal N.	Transverse abdominis	T7-T12, T12-L1, & L1

Lumbar Plexus (Ventral Rami of L1-L4)

Lumbar plexus	Quadratus lumborum	T12,L1-L3
Lumbar plexus	Psoas major	L2,L3,L4
Lumbar plexus	Psoas minor	L1
Femoral N.	Iliacus	L2,L3
Femoral N.	Sartorius	L2,L3
Femoral N.	Rectus femoris	L2,L3,L4
Femoral N.	Vastus lateralis	L2,L3,L4
Femoral N.	Vastus intermedius	L2,L3,L4
Femoral N.	Vastus medialis	L2,L3,L4
Femoral N. (& sometimes Obturator N.)	Pectineus	L2,L3 (L3,L4)
Obturator N.	Adductor brevis	L2,L3,L4
Obturator N.	Adductor longus	L2,L3,L4
Obturator N.	Gracilis	L2,L3
Obturator N.	Adductor magnus, anterior part	L2,L3,L4
Obturator N.	Obturator externus	L3,L4

Sacral Plexus (Ventral Rami of L4-S3)

Inferior gluteal N.	Gluteus maximus	L5,S1,S2
Superior gluteal N.	Gluteus medius	L4,L5,S1
Superior gluteal N.	Gluteus minimus	L4,L5,S1
Superior gluteal N.	Tensor fascia latae	L4,L5,S1
Sacral Plexus	Piriformis	S1,S2
Sacral Plexus	Gemellus superior	L5,S1,S2
Sacral Plexus	Obturator internus	L5,S1,S2
Sacral Plexus	Gemellus inferior	L4,L5,S1
Sacral Plexus	Quadratus femoris	L4,L5,S1
Sciatic N.	Adductor magnus, posterior part	L4,L5,S1
Sciatic N., tibial part	Semitendinosus	L5,S1,S2
Sciatic N., tibial part	Semimembranosus	L5,S1,S2
Sciatic N., tibial part	Biceps femoris, long head	S1,S2,S3
Sciatic N., peroneal part	Biceps femoris, short head	L5,S1,S2
Deep fibular N. *	Extensor digitorum longus	L4,L5,S1
Deep fibular N.	Extensor hallucis longus	L4,L5,S1
Deep fibular N.	Tibialis anterior	L4,L5,S1
Deep fibular N.	Fibularis tertius (peroneus)	L5,S1
Deep fibular N.	Extensor digitorum brevis	L5,S1
Deep fibular N.	Extensor hallucis brevis	L5,S1
Superficial fibular N.	Fibularis brevis (peroneus)	L4,L5,S1
Superficial fibular N.	Fibularis longus (peroneus)	L4,L5,S1
Tibial N.	Popliteus	L4,L5,S1
Tibial N.	Gastrocnemius	S1,S2
Tibial N.	Plantaris	L4,L5,S1
Tibial N.	Soleus	S1,S2
Tibial N.	Tibialis posterior	L5,S1
Tibial N.	Flexor digitorum longus	L5,S1
Tibial N.	Flexor hallucis longus	L5,S1,S2
Medial plantar N.	Flexor digitorum brevis	L5,S1
Medial plantar N.	Abductor hallucis	L5,S1
Medial plantar N.	Flexor hallucis brevis	L5,S1
Medial plantar N.	Lumbrical muscle #1	L5,S1
Lateral plantar N.	Lumbrical muscles #2-4	S2,S3
Lateral plantar N.	Abductor digiti minimi	S2,S3
Lateral plantar N.	Quadratus plantae	S2,S3
Lateral plantar N.	Flexor digiti minimi	S2,S3
Lateral plantar N.	Adductor hallucis	S2,S3
Lateral plantar N.	Plantar interossei	S2,S3
Lateral plantar N.	Dorsal interossei	S2,S3

*(fibular = peroneal)

Dermatomes

A **dermatome** is an area of the skin that is supplied and innervated by a single spinal nerve root. Dermatomes are used in clinical practice to determine if damage has occurred or compression is occurring to spinal nerve roots, or to the region of the spinal cord that leads to those nerve roots. Altered skin sensation may include pain, numbness, itching, tingling, etc.

Note that each area of dermatomes can overlap somewhat into neighboring areas, so that should be considered when assessing clients with potential spinal pathology.

Numbering of Nerve Roots

C1, exits above vertebra C1
C2-C8, exit below vertebrae C1-C7
T1-T12, exit below vertebrae T1-T12
L1-L5, exit below vertebrae L1-L5
S1-S5, exit through foramen in the sacrum

Spine labels
C1, Atlas
C2, Axis
C7
T1
T12
L1
L5
S1
S5
← Coccyx

Anterior body labels
C2,3 — Trigeminal
C2,3
Supraclavicular
C3,4
Superior lateral
T2, T3, T4, T5, T6, T7, T8, T9, T10, T11, T12
Medial brachial
Intercostobrachial
C5,6
T1
Medial antebrachial
Lateral antebrachial
L1
Iliohypogastric
Genitofemoral
S2,3
Ilioinguinal
C5,6
C8, T1
Ulnar
Median
L1,2
C8, T1
C6,7,8
Lateral cutaneous
Posterior cutaneous
Intermediate cutaneous
Medial cutaneous
Obturator
L2,3
Patellar plexus
L3,4
Superficial fibular
L5, S1
Sural
L4,5
L5, S1,2

Posterior body labels
C2,3 — Greater occipital
C3
Lesser occipital
C4
C5
C6
Supraclavicular
T1
C3,4
T2
T3
Superior lateral cutaneous
C5,6
T4
Medial brachial cutaneous
T5
Intercostobrachial
T6
Posterior cutaneous of arm
T1,2
T7
Posterior antebrachial cutaneous
T8
T9
Lateral antebrachial cutaneous
T10
C8
T11
Lateral cutaneous branches
T12
L1, L2
Medial cutaneous of forearm
C5,6
C6,7
L3
Posterior divisions of lumbar nerves
C8, T1
S1
S2
From radial
S3
From ulnar
S4,5 coccygeal
C6,7,8
C8, T1
S1,2,3
Lateral femoral cutaneous
Branches of posterior femoral cutaneous
S1,2,3
L3,4
Anterior femoral
L2,3
Lateral sural cutaneous
Medial crural branches of saphenous
L4,5 S1
Superficial fibular
S1,2
L3,4
Sural nerve
L5,S1
Branch from tibial
S1,2
Lateral plantar
L4,5
Medial plantar

Legend

Colored areas indicate areas of skin sensation supplied by spinal nerve roots.

Uncolored areas illustrate where cutaneous nerves emerge to supply an area of the skin.

(illustrations by Mikael Häggström, used with permission.)

07591

Chapter 8

Study Aids

Many study aids and supporting materials are available to accompany the textbook **Mastering Muscles & Movement: A Brain-Friendly System for Learning Musculoskeletal Anatomy and Basic Kinesiology**. These resources provide a variety of approaches for studying and practicing the information in the book. Study aids are available as downloadable PDF files or as interactive apps on the companion website www.studymuscles.com.

Access to most of the study aids is free to purchasers of the textbook. Educational programs that adopt the textbook also have access to Instructor Resources such as Powerpoint presentations and homework templates.

This chapter describes study aids currently available and provides samples of each. Some resources are in PDF form to be downloaded and printed, while others are interactive apps for online use on computers, tablets or smartphones. In addition, a few of the resources are included in the final pages of this chapter and may be photocopied by the purchaser of this book for their personal use.

Disclaimer: The internet is constantly changing and evolving, and the resources and apps presented in this chapter may or may not be available in the same form as described herein. Some may be removed, some improved or altered, and some new resources may be added.

Downloadable Study Aids

This section lists study aids that can be downloaded as PDF files from the studymuscles.com website by purchasers of the book **Mastering Muscles & Movement**. Only brief descriptions and instructions are offered here. For resources that require a lengthier description, more details and instructions are included on the website.

General-Purpose Skeletons
(Online, or photocopy using pages 221-223)

These are full-page size skeleton drawings - upper body and lower body – to use as practice sheets to draw and write on while you are studying muscles. A good way to use these while saving paper is to insert them into plastic sheet protectors along with a cardboard backing or a manila folder cut to 8½ by 11". They can then be marked and erased many times using fine point dry erase markers (preferably red/blue to match the origin/insertion convention used in this book). In practice we have found that Avery plastic sheet protectors labeled PV-119 work well with dry erase markers.

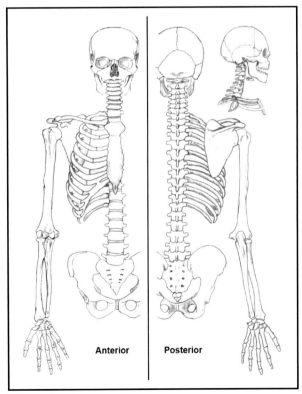

General Purpose Skeleton Pictures

Muscle Tickets
(Online, or photocopy using pages 224-226)

These ticket-sized cards have the muscle names on them. As you study each of the 13 groups of muscles, cut up the muscle tickets and use them to draw out of a hat and randomly test yourself. Each ticket has a small label at the lower right corner, for example "G1-4", that tells which muscle group to go to in the book to read the origin, insertion, etc. The G is for Group, so G1-4 indicates the 4th muscle in Muscle Group 1.

Trapezius	Levator Scapula	Rhomboid Major and Minor	Serratus Anterior
G1-1	G1-2	G1-3	G1-4
Pectoralis Minor	Subclavius		Deltoid
G1-5	G1-6	.	G2-1
Supraspinatus	Infraspinatus	Teres Minor	Subscapularis
G2-2	G2-3	G2-4	G2-5
Pectoralis Major	Coracobrachialis	Latissimus Dorsi	Teres Major
G2-6	G2-7	G2-8	G2-9
Biceps Brachii	Brachialis	Brachioradialis	Pronator Teres

Muscle Tickets

Blank Bone Cards to Draw On
(Online, or photocopy using pages 227-230)

Blank Bone Cards give you a head start for making your own flashcards. Drawing and writing the O/I/A information yourself is like studying the muscle ten times. These flashcard size bone pictures go with each of the 13 muscle groups.

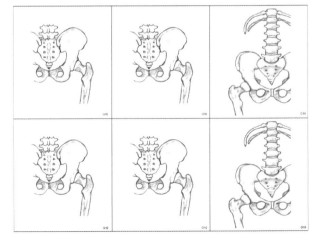

Blank Bone Cards

Bony Landmark Practice Pages
(Online)

These pages provide the bone drawings from Chapter 2 with the labels or words removed to facilitate repetitive practice to memorize bony landmarks.

Chapter 2 of **Mastering Muscles & Movement** contains fully labeled bony landmark drawings. Each page of bone drawings is organized with the bones in one area of the page and a list of bone names, bony landmarks, and joints in a separate area of the page. The arrangement allows you to cover the list of names and use the labels on the drawings to test yourself as you memorize the names. This facilitates learning the landmarks from a *visual* direction, that is, you *see* a place on a bone and you recall its bony landmark name.

To fully learn the bones and bony landmarks, you should be able to recall the information from both visual, as described above, and *verbal* directions. Recalling from the verbal direction means you *read* or *hear* the name of a landmark and you then recall and visualize where it is on the bone.

The bony landmark practice pages include dual versions of the bone drawings from Chapter 2 of the book. One version has the labels removed from the drawings and the list of landmarks is left intact. The other version has the list of landmarks removed and the drawing labels are left intact. With these opposite arrangements, you can memorize the information from both visual and verbal directions. The figure to the right shows an example of these bi-directional practice pages.

A third type of practice page is also included. It gives a larger bone picture with space to simply write the names of the bony landmarks next to the stick pins.

To save paper, the Bony Landmark Practice Sheets can be slipped into a plastic sheet protector as described on page 214, and marked using fine point dry erase markers to allow multiple practice sessions.

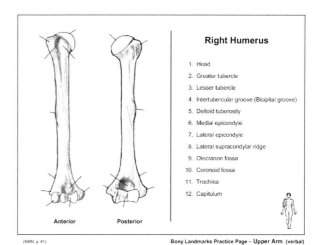

Bony Landmarks – Bi-Directional Practice Pages

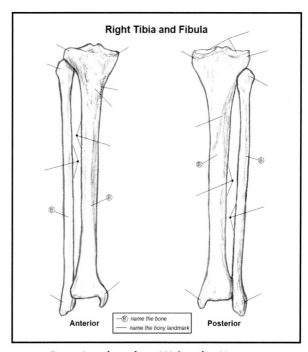

Bony Landmarks – Write the Names

Action Table Practice Pages

These are the Summary Tables from Chapter 7 in a special "practice" format where the ✔ marks have been removed. The learner writes checkmarks in the table cells to test their knowledge of synergists for each action at each joint of the body. They can then check their answers by comparing to the Summary Tables in Chapter 7.

Knee	Flexion @ Knee	Extension @ Knee	Medial Rotation @ Knee (flexed)	Lateral Rotation @ Knee (flexed)	Stabilization of Knee	Muscle Group	Muscle also affects other joints
Rectus Femoris						G12	Hip Joint
Vastus Medialis						G12	-
Vastus Lateralis						G12	-
Vastus Intermedius						G12	-
Biceps Femoris						G12	Hip Joint
Semitendinosus						G12	Hip Joint
Semimembranosus						G12	Hip Joint
Popliteus						G12	-
Sartorius						G11	Hip Joint
Tensor Fascia Latae						G11	Hip Joint
Gracilis						G11	Hip Joint
Gastrocnemius						G13	Ankle
Plantaris						G13	Ankle

Action Table Practice Pages

Study Questions

Study questions are provided to help learners check for comprehension of kinesiology concepts and terminology found in chapter 1, as well as 13 sets of questions to go with the 13 muscle groups in chapters 4, 5, and 6.

Note to instructors: Keys with suggested answers to the study questions are in the Instructor Resources area of the website.

Study Questions – Muscle Group 1   Name:_____

Movement of the Scapula/Clavicle

1. Which of the joints of the shoulder girdle is the only bony attachment of the shoulder girdle to the trunk?

2. Name all the movements that occur at the scapulothoracic joint. Why is this "joint" called a false joint?

3. Name two muscles that pull the scapula toward the spine (retraction).

4. There are several muscles that attach to the scapula. Name two that attach to the medial border.

5. Which muscles are synergists in the concentric action of shrugging the shoulders?

6. What bony landmark of the scapula is the insertion of the pectoralis minor? Describe how a person's upper body would look with a tight/shortened pectoralis minor

Study Questions

Muscle Overview Drawings

These worksheets provide a quick check that the reader can identify the muscles in situ with the other muscles in the group. There are practice sheets for each muscle group presented in chapters 4 through 6 of the book.

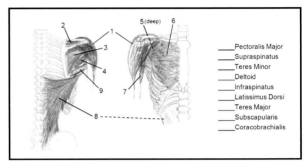

____Pectoralis Major
____Supraspinatus
____Teres Minor
____Deltoid
____Infraspinatus
____Latissimus Dorsi
____Teres Major
____Subscapularis
____Coracobrachialis

Muscle Overview Drawings

Muscle OIA Match-Up Cards

This set of cards provides a way to physically handle and arrange information while you study and memorize muscles. For each muscle, the individual facts (name, pictures, origin, insertion, action) are unpacked onto six separate cards. You can lay out the cards in rows and columns, like playing a game of solitaire, to study and memorize the information (more detailed instructions on website). After laying out the cards per the instructions, you can easily check your work by comparing to the "A" Tables in the book.

NOTE: This is a *lot* of cards (6 cards for every muscle), but some students find that working with their hands, cutting them up and arranging them, really helps them anchor the facts in their brains.

Muscle OIA Match-up Cards

MusclePlus⁺ Flashcards

These full-color flashcards gather the drawings and information for each muscle in the book. They are called **MusclePlus** because the front of each card has a **muscle** illustration **plus** a bone drawing showing muscle attachments in red & blue.

Below are some suggestions on ways to use MusclePlus⁺ cards to build your mastery as outlined on pages 66-68 in Chapter 3. These methods make use of the general-purpose skeleton pictures, inserted in a plastic sheet protector as described on page 214. You could also use red, blue and black colored pencils or fine point markers on any picture of a skeleton on paper. Be sure to apply the generalizations and palpation techniques (page 68).

Practice attachments in a **verbal-to-visual** direction

1. Shuffle cards and stack them so the side with *words* is facing up (you can't see the picture).
2. Select a card, read the muscle name, and try to visualize what the muscle looks like.
3. Read the words for **Origin**, and use a *red* dry erase marker to color the skeleton where the words describe.
4. Read the words for **Insertion** and use a *blue* dry erase marker to color the skeleton.
5. Turn the card over and check if you colored the skeleton accurately.

Practice attachments in a **visual-to-verbal** direction

1. Shuffle the cards and turn them so the side with the *picture* is facing up.
2. Select a card and say the name of the muscle. If you're not sure, briefly check the name at the top back of the card (but don't read anything else yet).
3. Look at the <u>red</u> areas colored on the card and say the names of the bony landmarks indicated. Check if the words you said match the **Origin** on the back of the card.
4. Look at the <u>blue</u> areas colored on the card and name the bony landmarks indicated. Check if the words you said match the **Insertion** on the back of the card.

Study the muscle's shape, fiber directions, and explore the actions the muscle creates.

1. Using a black dry erase marker, draw the muscle onto the bone picture connecting origin to insertion. Show the overall shape and draw lines indicating fiber direction.
2. Visualize the muscle fibers getting shorter (contracting) and pulling the blue insertion toward the red origin, around the joint axis.
3. Recite each action of the muscle while moving your body part in that action. Make sure you demonstrate a clear beginning and ending point to each movement you perform.

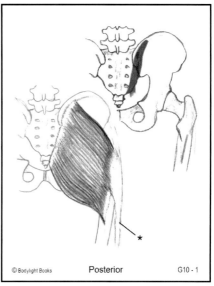

© Bodylight Books   Posterior   G10 - 1

(reduced size, actual size is 3 ¼ " by 4 ¼ ")

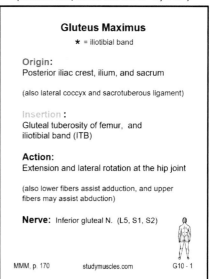

Gluteus Maximus

★ = iliotibial band

Origin:
Posterior iliac crest, ilium, and sacrum

(also lateral coccyx and sacrotuberous ligament)

Insertion :
Gluteal tuberosity of femur, and iliotibial band (ITB)

Action:
Extension and lateral rotation at the hip joint

(also lower fibers assist adduction, and upper fibers may assist abduction)

Nerve: Inferior gluteal N. (L5, S1, S2)

MMM, p. 170   studymuscles.com   G10 - 1

MusclePlus⁺ Flashcards

Apps

Several apps are available on the studymuscles.com website. They are designed to run in a browser as "web apps". Some are fully interactive apps while others are more like enhanced slide presentations that the learner steps through. Currently available apps are:

- Brain-Friendly Muscle Viewer
- MusclePlus⁺ Flashcards
- Atlas of Bones and Bony Landmarks
- Bony Landmark Flashcards
- Muscle Name-and-Click Exercises
- Muscle Layering Demonstrations

Note to instructors: These apps can also be useful for student engagement during class. They can be projected on a screen for students to interact with and even have mini competitions demonstrating their understanding of the material.

Brain-Friendly Muscle Viewer

This app re-creates all the muscle illustrations and information from Chapters 4 through 6 of the textbook, plus adds additional functionality to further study individual muscles. This provides an interactive way to study the muscles using a tablet or laptop computer, while maintaining the brain-friendly approach of the book.

The BFMV app is enhanced beyond what is presented in the book. It allows the learner to "drill down" from the side-by-side muscle screens to view each muscle individually. Clicking on any muscle in a side-by-side screen brings up that individual muscle in its own flashcard-style screen.

While viewing a muscle flashcard-style screen, the user can click/tap to reveal labels that point to the red and blue attachment sites on the illustrations. The labels match the wording used in the Origin and Insertion paragraphs on the right-hand side of the flashcard. This encourages the learner to relate the descriptive words to actual places on the bones.

A few of the screens from the Brain-Friendly Muscle Viewer are presented on the next page.

MusclePlus⁺ Flashcards

This app is the electronic version of the flashcards described on page 217. The app provides on-the-go study and memorization on smartphones, tablets and computers. It's various modes and functions allow studying and self-testing from many different directions. Instructions are provided in the app's help screens and the online user guide.

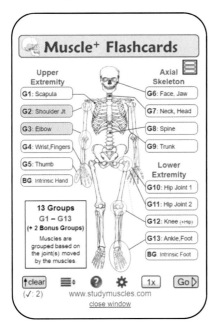
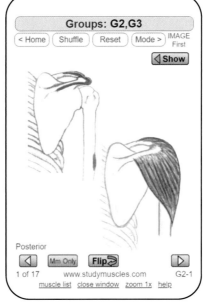
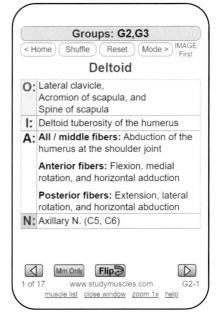

MusclePlus⁺ Flashcard App

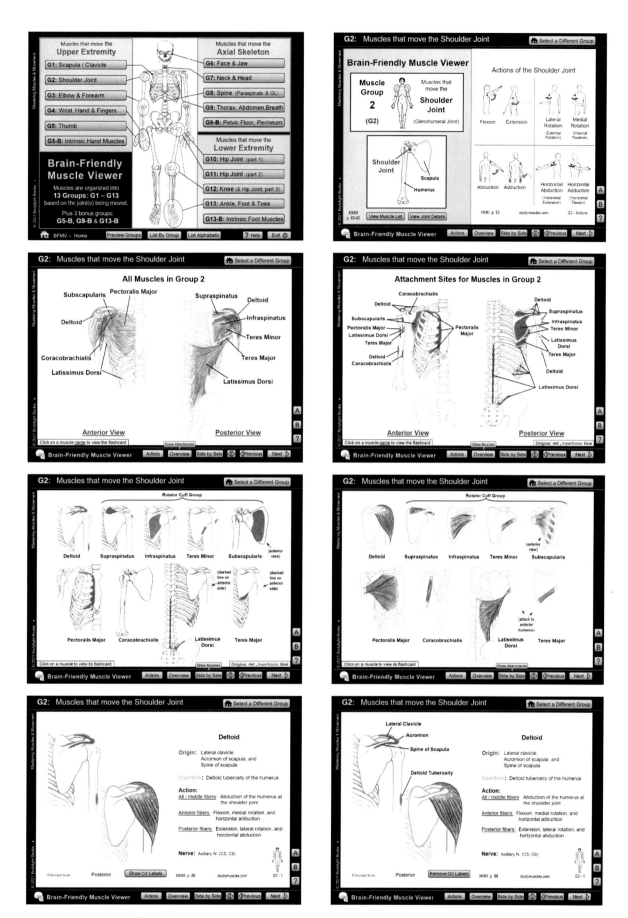

Brain-Friendly Muscle Viewer – Sample Screens

Atlas of Bones & Bony Landmarks

This app is an interactive version of all the bones and bony landmark pages in Chapter 2.

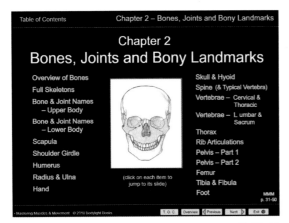

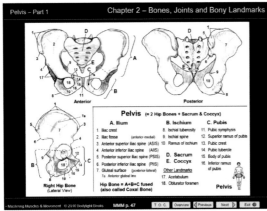

Atlas of Bones & Bony Landmarks App

Bony Landmark Flashcards

This app steps through sets of bones and bony landmarks. It is separated into three sections for Upper Extremity, Axial Skeleton, and Lower Extremity. Within each section you can click/tap on each bone to practice naming its bony landmarks. The app first shows a picture and then the next tap reveals the name of the bone or bony landmark.

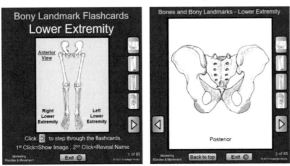

Bony Landmark Flashcards App

Muscle Name-and-Click Exercises

This is a simple full-screen size app that presents the "B" Figures (i.e., the side-by-side muscle illustrations) for the 13 muscle groups in Chapters 4 through 6 of the book. The names of the muscles below each muscle picture are initially hidden. Students point to a muscle, name it, and then click/tap on the muscle picture to reveal the name of the muscle. The app can be used to quickly double-check if the student can identify muscles by how they look and where they are on the body.

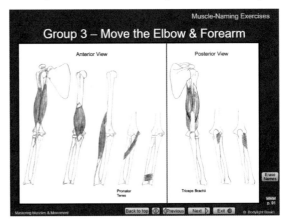

Muscle Name-and-Click App

Muscle Layering Demonstrations

These apps sequentially assemble the layers of muscles for specific muscle groups where layering is difficult to visualize.

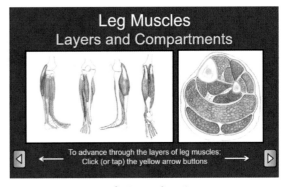

Muscle Layering App

Worksheets to Photocopy

The following pages (221-230) contain worksheets that the purchaser of this book may photocopy for their own personal use.

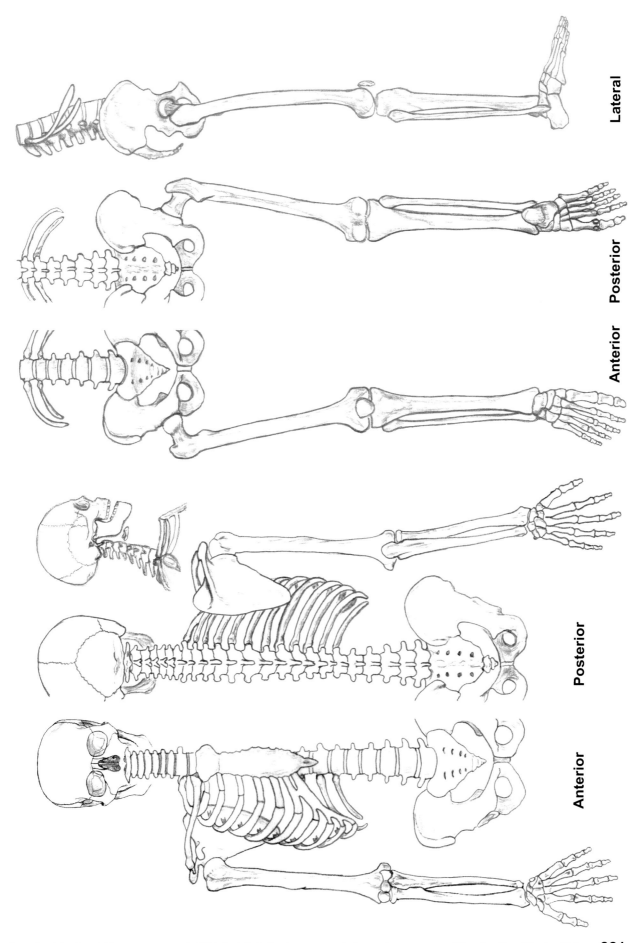

Lateral

Posterior

Anterior

Posterior

Anterior

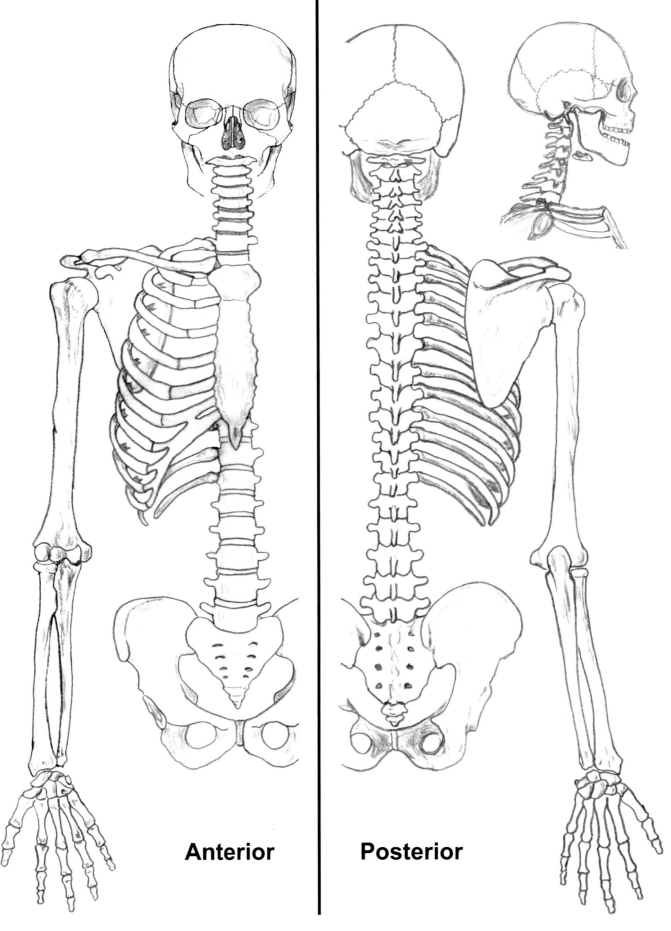

Anterior

Posterior

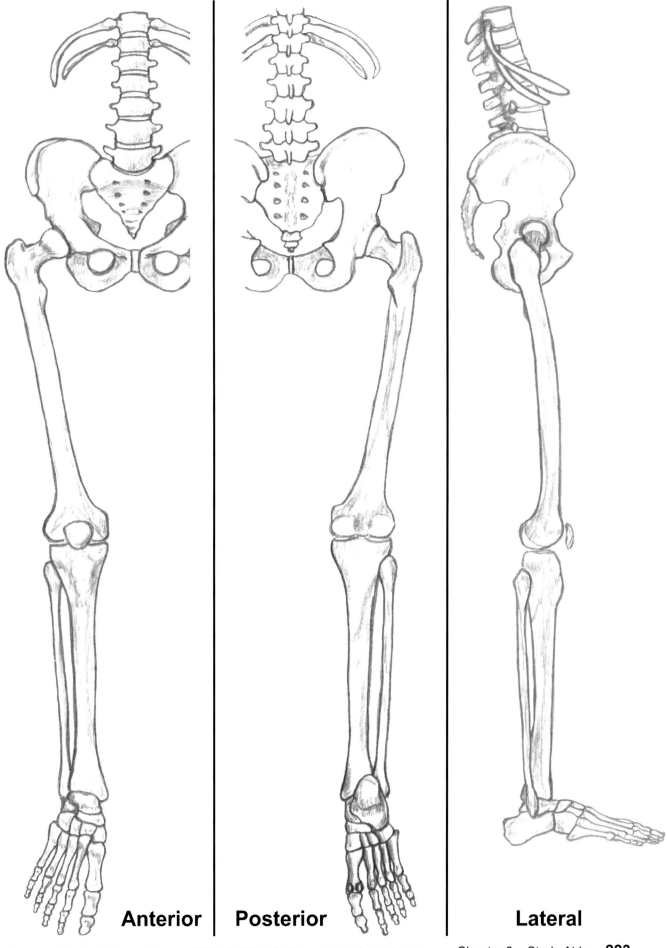

Anterior | **Posterior** | **Lateral**

Trapezius G1 - 1	Levator Scapula G1 - 2	Rhomboid Major and Minor G1 - 3	Serratus Anterior G1 - 4
Pectoralis Minor G1 - 5	Subclavius G1 - 6	 -	Deltoid G2 - 1
Supraspinatus G2 - 2	Infraspinatus G2 - 3	Teres Minor G2 - 4	Subscapularis G2 - 5
Pectoralis Major G2 - 6	Coracobrachialis G2 - 7	Latissimus Dorsi G2 - 8	Teres Major G2 - 9
Biceps Brachii G3 - 1	Brachialis G3 - 2	Brachioradialis G3 - 3	Pronator Teres G3 - 4
Pronator Quadratus G3 - 5	Triceps Brachii G3 - 6	Anconeus G3 - 7	Supinator G3 - 8
Flexor Carpi Radialis G4 - 1	Palmaris Longus G4 - 2	Flexor Carpi Ulnaris G4 - 3	Flexor Digitorum Superficialis G4 - 4
Flexor Digitorum Profundus G4 - 5	Extensor Carpi Radialis Longus G4 - 6	Extensor Carpi Radialis Brevis G4 - 7	Extensor Carpi Ulnaris G4 - 8
Extensor Digitorum G4 - 9	Extensor Indicis G4 - 10	 -	 -
Flexor Pollicis Longus G5 - 1	Flexor Pollicis Brevis G5 - 2	Opponens Pollicis G5 - 3	Adductor Pollicis G5 - 4
Abductor Pollicis Brevis G5 - 5	Abductor Pollicis Longus G5 - 6	Extensor Pollicis Longus G5 - 7	Extensor Pollicis Brevis G5 - 8

Masseter G6 - 1	Temporalis G6 - 2	Lateral Pterygoid G6 - 3	Medial Pterygoid G6 - 4
Occipitofrontalis G6 - 5	Platysma G6 - 6	Suprahyoids Group G6 - 7	Infrahyoids Group G6 - 8
Sternocleidomastoid G7 - 1	Scalene Group (Anterior, Middle, Posterior) G7 - 2	Anterior Scalene G7 – 2 (a)	Middle Scalene G7 – 2 (b)
Posterior Scalene G7 – 2 (c)	Longus Capitis, Longus Colli G7 – 3, 4	Suboccipital Group G7 - 5	Splenius Capitis G7 - 6
Splenius Cervicis G7 - 7	Semispinalis Capitis G7 - 8	Levator Scapula (reversed O/I to move neck) G7 - 9	Trapezius, upper fibers (reversed O/I to move neck) G7 - 10
-	-	-	-
Spinalis G8 - 1	Longissimus G8 - 2	Iliocostalis G8 - 3	Semispinalis G8 - 4
Multifidis G8 - 5	Rotatores G8 - 6	Quadratus Lumborum G8 - 7	-
Rectus Abdominis G9 - 1	External Oblique G9 - 2	Internal Oblique G9 - 3	Transverse Abdominis G9 - 4
Diaphragm G9 - 5	External Intercostals G9 - 6	Internal Intercostals G9 - 7	Serratus Posterior Superior G9 - 8
Serratus Posterior Inferior G9 - 9	Levator Costae G9 - 10	Transversus Thoracis G9 - 11	-

Gluteus Maximus G10 - 1	Gluteus Medius G10 - 2	Gluteus Minimus G10 - 3	Piriformis G10 - 4
Gemellus Superior G10 – 5A	Obturator Internus G10 – 5B	Gemellus Inferior G10 – 5C	Obturator Externus G10 – 5D
Quadratus Femoris G10 – 5E	Iliacus G10 - 6	Psoas Major G10 - 7	Iliopsoas G10 – 6+7
Sartorius G11 - 1	Tensor Fascia Latae G11 - 2	Pectineus G11 - 3	Adductor Brevis G11 - 4
Adductor Longus G11 - 5	Adductor Magnus G11 - 6	Gracilis G11 - 7	-
Rectus Femoris G12 - 1	Vastus Lateralis G12 - 2	Vastus Intermedius G12 - 3	Vastus Medialis G12 - 4
Biceps Femoris G12 - 5	Semitendinosus G12 - 6	Semimembranosus G12 - 7	Popliteus G12 - 8
Gastrocnemius G13 - 1	Plantaris G13 - 2	Soleus G13 - 3	Tibialis Posterior G13 - 4
Flexor Digitorum Longus G13 - 5	Flexor Hallucis Longus G13 - 6	Fibularis Brevis (Peroneus Brevis) G13 - 7	Fibularis Longus (Peroneus Longus) G13 - 8
Tibialis Anterior G13 - 9	Extensor Digitorum Longus G13 - 10	Extensor Hallucis Longus G13 - 11	-
-	-	-	-

  Mastering Muscles & Movement

Bone Cards (Use to draw your own muscle flashcards or bony landmark flashcards)

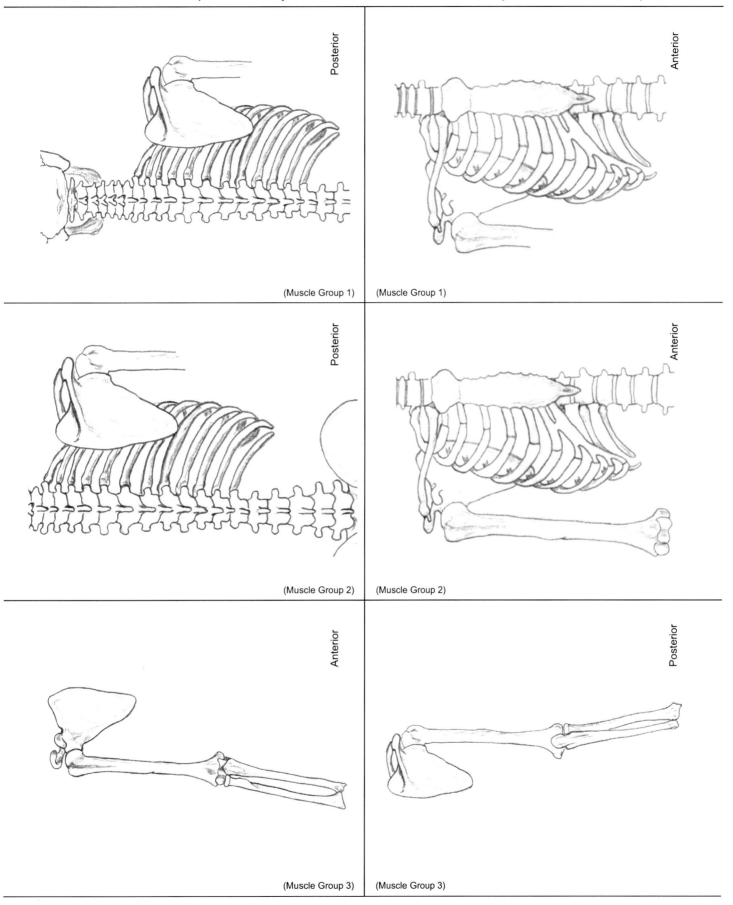

Posterior

Anterior

(Muscle Group 1)

(Muscle Group 1)

Posterior

Anterior

(Muscle Group 2)

(Muscle Group 2)

Anterior

Posterior

(Muscle Group 3)

(Muscle Group 3)

Bone Cards (Use to draw your own muscle flashcards or bony landmark flashcards)

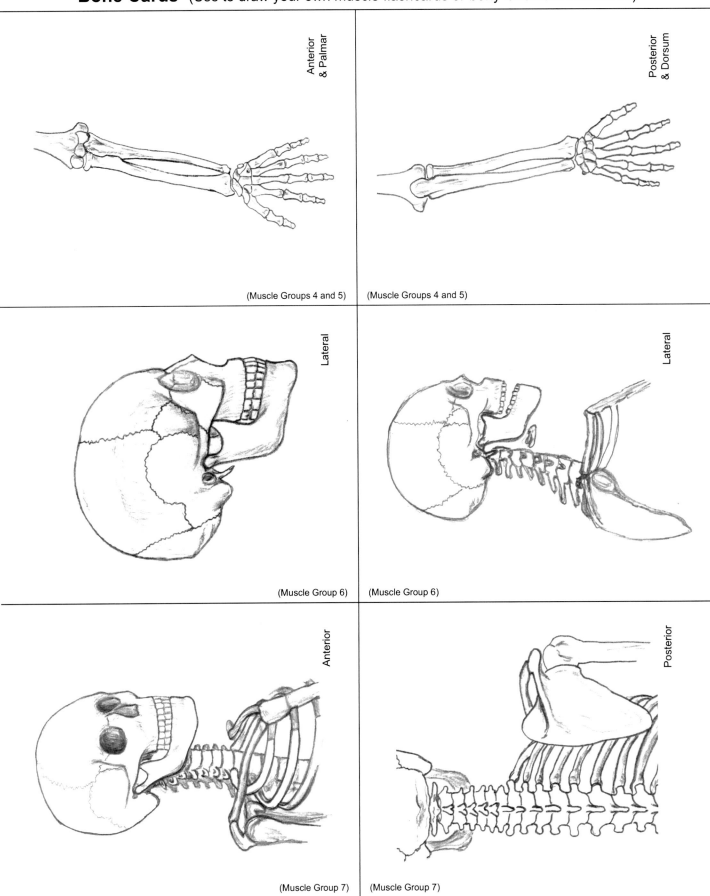

Anterior & Palmar

Posterior & Dorsum

(Muscle Groups 4 and 5)

(Muscle Groups 4 and 5)

Lateral

Lateral

(Muscle Group 6)

(Muscle Group 6)

Anterior

Posterior

(Muscle Group 7)

(Muscle Group 7)

 Mastering Muscles & Movement

Bone Cards (Use to draw your own muscle flashcards or bony landmark flashcards)

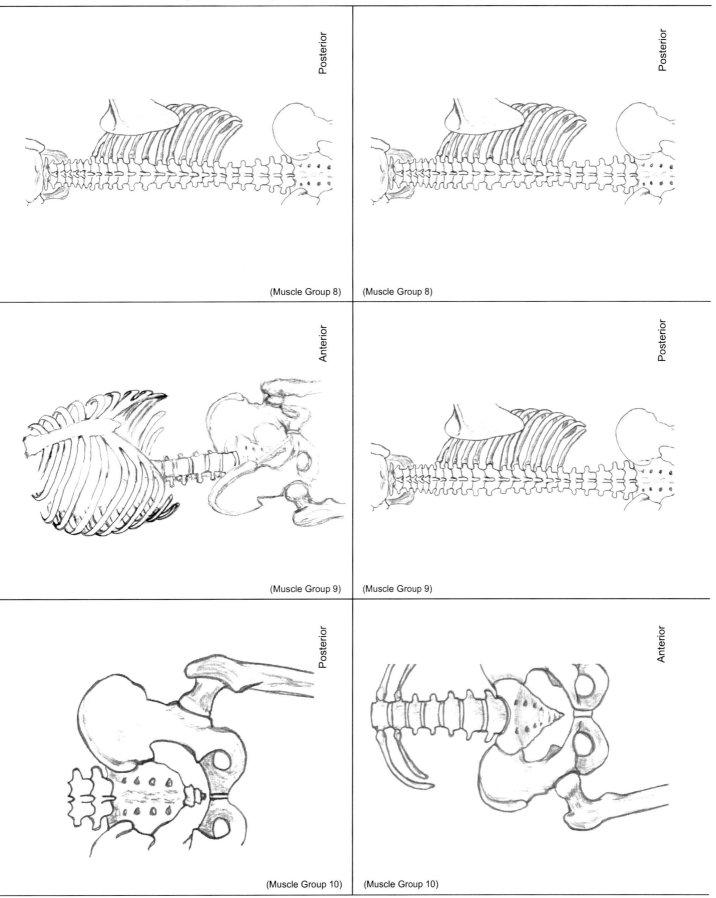

Posterior

(Muscle Group 8)

Posterior

(Muscle Group 8)

Anterior

(Muscle Group 9)

Posterior

(Muscle Group 9)

Posterior

(Muscle Group 10)

Anterior

(Muscle Group 10)

Bone Cards (Use to draw your own muscle flashcards or bony landmark flashcards)

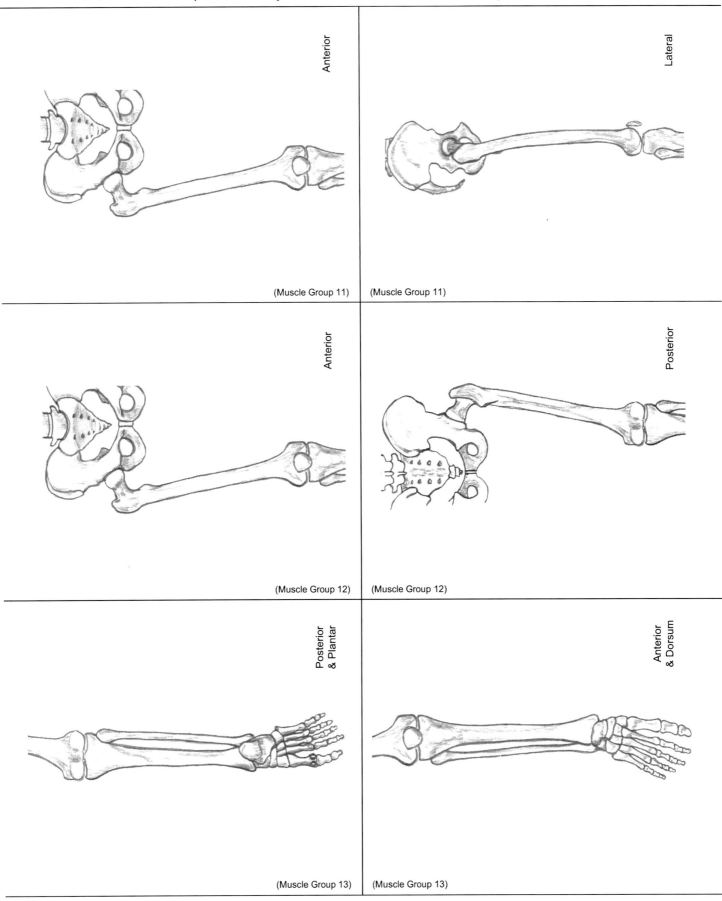

Anterior

(Muscle Group 11)

Lateral

(Muscle Group 11)

Anterior

(Muscle Group 12)

Posterior

(Muscle Group 12)

Posterior & Plantar

(Muscle Group 13)

Anterior & Dorsum

(Muscle Group 13)

Bibliography

The following list gives the main resources used in the development of this book.

1. Acland, Robert D., *DVD Atlas of Human Anatomy*, New York: Lippincott Williams & Wilkins, 2004

2. Archer, Pat and Nelson, Lisa, *Anatomy & Physiology for Manual Therapists*, New York: Lippincott Williams & Wilkins, 2013

3. Barcsay, Jeno, *Anatomy for the Artist*, New York: Barnes & Noble Books, 2002

4. Barral, Jean-Pierre and Croibier, Alain, *Manual Therapy for the Peripheral Nerves*, Edinburgh: Churchill Livingstone, 2007

5. Biel, Andrew, *Trail Guide to the Body: A hands-on guide to locating muscles, bones and more*, 4th ed., Boulder, CO: Books of Discovery, 2010

6. Calais-Germain, Blandine, *Anatomy of Movement*, Seattle: Eastland Press, 1993

7. Calais-Germain, Blandine, *The Female Pelvis: Anatomy & Exercises*, Seattle: Eastland Press, 2003

8. Clemente, Carmine D., *Anatomy – A Regional Atlas of the Human Body*, 4th ed., Baltimore: Williams & Wilkins, 1997

9. Drake, Richard L. et al., *Gray's Atlas of Anatomy*, Edinburgh: Churchill Livingstone, 2008

10. Duncan, Ruth, *Myofascial Release: Hands-on Guides for Therapists*, Champaign, IL: Human Kinetics, 2014

11. Gilroy, Anne M. et al., *Atlas of Anatomy*, 2nd ed., New York: Thieme Medical Publishers, Inc., 2012

12. Goldfinger, Eliot, *Human Anatomy for Artists*, New York: Oxford University Press, 1991

13. Goss, CM, ed. *Gray's Anatomy of the Human Body*, 28th ed., Philadelphia: Lea & Febiger, 1966

14. Hedley, Gil, *Integral Anatomy DVD Series*, Colorado Springs, CO: Integral Anatomy Productions, LLC, 2006-2009

15. Juhan, Deane, *Job's Body – A Handbook for Bodywork*, 3rd ed., Barrytown, NY: Station Hill Press, 2003

16. Kapandji, I.A., *The Physiology of the Joints, Volume 1 Upper Limb*, 5th ed., London: Churchill Livingstone, 1982

17. Kapandji, I.A., *The Physiology of the Joints, Volume 2 Lower Limb*, 5th ed., London: Churchill Livingstone, 1985

18. Kapandji, I.A., *The Physiology of the Joints, Volume 3 The Trunk and the Vertebral Column*, 2nd ed., London: Churchill Livingstone, 1974

19. Kapit, Wynn, and Elson, Lawrence M., *The Anatomy Coloring Book*, 3rd ed., San Francisco: Benjamin Cummings, 2002

20. Kendall, F.P., McCreary, E.K., and Provance, P.G., *Muscles, Testing and Function*, Baltimore: Williams & Wilkins, 1993

21. Lippert, Lynn S., *Clinical Kinesiology for Physical Therapy Assistants*, 3rd ed., Philadelphia: F. A. Davis Company, 2000

22. McMinn, R.M.H., and Hutchings, R.T., *Color Atlas of Human Anatomy*, Chicago: Year Book Medical Publishers, Inc., 1977

23. Myers, Thomas W., *Anatomy Trains: Myofascial Meridians for Manual and Movement Therapists*, 2nd ed., Edinburgh: Churchill Livingstone, 2009

24. Muscolino, Joseph E., *The Muscular System Manual*, Redding, CT: JEM Publications, 2002

25. Muscolino, Joseph E., *Kinesiology: The Skeletal System and Muscle Function*, St. Louis: Elsevier Mosby, 2011

26. Netter, Frank H., M.D., *Atlas of Human Anatomy*, 5th ed., Philadelphia: Elsevier, 2011

27. Netter, Frank H., M.D., *The CIBA Collection of Medical Illustrations, Volume 8: Musculoskeletal System*, New Jersey: CIBA-GEIGY Corporation, 1993

28. Neumann, Donald A., *Kinesiology of the Musculoskeletal System: Foundations for Rehabilitation*, 2nd ed., St. Louis: Mosby Elsevier, 2010

29. Platzer, Werner, *Color Atlas/Text of Human Anatomy, Vol. 1: Locomotor System*, 4th ed., New York: Thieme Medical Publishers, 1991

30. Pugh, Maureen Barlow, Ed., *Stedman's Medical Dictionary*, 27th ed., Baltimore: Lippincott Williams & Wilkins, 2000

31. Rohen, Yokochi and Lutjen-Drecoll, *Color Atlas of Anatomy*, 4th ed., Baltimore: Williams & Wilkins, 1998

32. Scheunke, Michael et al., *Thieme Atlas of Anatomy: General Anatomy and the Musculoskeletal System*, New York: Thieme Medical Publishers, 2010

33. Simons, David G., Travell, Janet G., and Simons, Lois S., *Myofascial Pain and Dysfunction: The Trigger Point Manual, Volume 1. Upper Half of Body*, 2nd Edition, Philadelphia: Lippincott Williams & Wilkins, 1999

34. Standring, Susan, *Gray's Anatomy – The Anatomical Basis of Clinical Practice*, 40th ed., Edinburgh: Churchill Livingstone, 2008

35. Stecco, Carla, *Functional Atlas of the Human Fascial System*, Edinburgh: Churchill Livingstone, 2015

36. Thibodeau, Gary A., and Patton, Kevin T., *The Human Body in Health & Disease*, 2nd ed., St. Louis: Mosby, 1997

37. Thompson, Clem W., and Floyd, R. T., *Manual of Structural Kinesiology*, 14th ed., New York: McGraw-Hill, 2001

38. Tortora, Gerard J., and Grabowski, Sandra Reynolds, *Principles of Anatomy and Physiology*, 7th ed., New York: Harper Collins, 1993

39. Travell, Janet G. and Simons, David G., *Myofascial Pain and Dysfunction: The Trigger Point Manual, Volume 2. The Lower Extremities*, Philadelphia: Lippincott Williams & Wilkins, 1983

Index

Index

Index

Index

Omohyoid, 129–134

Open chain movement, 29, 34

Opponens digiti minimi, 114–115

Opponens pollicis, 107–115, 205

Opposite side rotation, 121

Orbicularis oculi, 128

Orbicularis oris, 128

Origin, Insertion, Action (tables), 78, 86,
    94, 102, 110, 114, 130, 138, 146,
    154, 158, 170, 178, 186, 194, 198

P

Palmar Aponeurosis, 115

Palmar interossei, 108, 114

Palmaris longus, 99–106, 115, 205

Palpation, 68

Paraspinal muscles, 143

Passive insufficiency, 33, 92, 100, 184

Passive ROM, 32

Patellar tendon, see Ligaments, patellar

Pectineus, 163, 175–182, 208

Pectoralis major, 71, 83–90, 152, 204

Pectoralis minor, 75-82, 152, 204, 207

Pelvic brim, 158

Pelvic diaphragm, 158-159

Pelvic floor muscles, 158-159

Pelvic tilt, 47

Perineal body, 158-159

Perineal membrane, 159

Perineum, 158-159

Peripheral nervous system, 22

Peroneus muscles, see Fibularis

Pes anserinus, 48, 176–177, 184

PIP, 99, 191

Piriformis, 158–159, 163, 167–174, 208

Plane, 5-8

    cardinal, 5

    sagittal, 5-8

    median, 5

    midsagittal, 5

    transverse, 5-8

    frontal (coronal), 5-8

Plane/axis pairs, 10

Plantar aponeurosis, 199

Plantar interossei, 198

Plantaris, 163, 191–197, 200, 209

Platysma, 26, 127–134, 206

Plexus, 24, 172, 210–211

    brachial 24, 210–211

    cervical 24, 210

    lumbar 24, 148, 172, 210–211

    lumbosacral 24

    sacral 24, 172, 210–211

Pollux, 42, 107

Popliteus, 183–190, 209

Positional terms, 3

Posterior tilt (of pelvis), 47

Posterior scalene, 138, 140

Prevertebral muscles, 136

Primary curve of spine, 44, 118, 130

Prime mover, 31, 62

Procerus, 128

Pronator quadratus, 91-98, 205

Pronator teres, 91–98, 205

Proprioception, 25, 27

Psoas major, 153, 163, 167–174, 208

Psoas minor, 169

Pterygoid plates, 43, 122

Pterygoid, Lateral, 122, 127–134, 206

Pterygoid, Medial, 127–134, 206

Pubic symphysis, 47

Pubococcygeus, 158–159

Puborectalis, 158–159

Q

Quadratus femoris, 167–174

Quadratus lumborum, 143-150, 152–153,
    207

Quadratus plantae, 198

Quadriceps, 177, 183–190

R

Range of motion (ROM), 18, 28, 32–34

Reciprocal inhibition, 21

Recruitment

    motor units, 25

    muscles, 152

Rectus abdominis, 151–157, 207

Rectus capitis anterior, 136-137

Rectus capitis lateralis, 136–137

Rectus capitis posterior major, 137–141

Rectus capitis posterior minor, 137–141

Rectus femoris, 163, 183–190, 208–209

Rectus sheath, 153

Regions of the body, 4

Respiration, 152

Retinaculum, 100, 115

Reversed O/I action, 29, 80, 135, 138–
    140, 148, 172, 204, 206–209

Rhomboid major & minor, 75–82

Ribs, true/false/floating, 46

Risorius, 128

Roles muscles play, 31

ROM, see Range of motion

Rotator cuff muscles, 84, 86

Rotatores, 143–150, 206–207

S

Sacral plexus, 24, 172, 210–211

Sacrotuberous ligament, 126, 158, 169

Sagittal axis, 9

Sagittal plane, 5

Same side rotation, 121

Sartorius, 163, 175–182, 208–209

Scalenes, 135–142, 152, 206–207

Scapulahumeral rhythm, 83

Secondary curve of spine, 44, 118, 130

Semimembranosus, 163, 183–190, 208–
    209

Semispinalis capitis, 135–142, 206

Semispinalis, 143–150, 206–207

Semitendinosus, 163, 183–190, 208–209

Sensory nerves, 22, 25,

Serratus anterior, 71, 75–82, 154, 204

Serratus posterior inferior, 151–157

Serratus posterior superior, 151–157

Shoulder complex, 72, 83

Shoulder girdle, 40, 75

SITS, see Rotator cuff muscles

Skeletal system, 11

Skull, sutures of, 43

Soleus, 163, 191–197, 209

Sphincter urethrae, 158–159

Sphincter urethrovaginalis, 158-159

Spinal canal, 23, 119, 123–124

Spinal cord, 22-23, 119

Spinalis, 143–150, 206–207

Spine, curves of, 118, 130

Splenius capitis, 135-142, 206

Index

(this page intentionally blank)

Muscles – List by Group

Muscles are placed in groups based on the bones and joints they *move* as they contract.

----- Upper Extremity -----
(Chapter 4)

----- Axial Body -----
(Chapter 5)

----- Lower Extremity -----
(Chapter 6)

Group 1 – Scapula / Clavicle
Trapezius
Levator scapula   **p. 75-82**
Rhomboid major & minor
Serratus anterior
Pectoralis minor
Subclavius

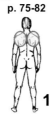
1

Group 2 – Shoulder Joint
Deltoid
Supraspinatus   **p. 83-90**
Infraspinatus
Teres minor
Subscapularis
Pectoralis major
Coracobrachialis
Latissimus dorsi
Teres major

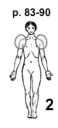
2

Group 3 – Elbow, Forearm
Biceps brachii   **p. 91-98**
Brachialis
Brachioradialis
Pronator teres
Pronator quadratus
Triceps brachii
Anconeus
Supinator

3

Group 4 – Wrist, Hand, Fingers
Flexor carpi radialis
Palmaris longus   **p. 99-106**
Flexor carpi ulnaris
Flexor digitorum superficialis
Flexor digitorum profundus
Extensor carpi radialis longus
Extensor carpi radialis brevis
Extensor carpi ulnaris
Extensor digitorum
Extensor indicis

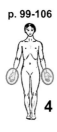
4

Group 5 – Thumb
Flexor pollicis longus   **p. 107-113**
Flexor pollicis brevis
Opponens pollicis
Adductor pollicis
Abductor pollicis brevis
Abductor pollicis longus
Extensor pollicis longus
Extensor pollicis brevis

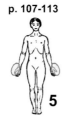
5

Bonus Group   **p. 114-115**
Intrinsic muscles of the hand

Group 6 – Face, Jaw
Masseter
Temporalis   **p. 127-134**
Lateral pterygoid
Medial pterygoid
Occipitofrontalis
Platysma
Suprahyoids Group
   Geniohyoid, Mylohyoid,
   Stylohyoid, Digastric
Infrahyoids Group
   Sternohyoid, Sternothyroid,
   Omohyoid, Thyrohyoid
Muscles of facial expression

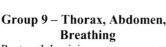
6

Group 7 – Neck, Head
Sternocleidomastoid
Scalenes group   **p. 135-142**
Longus capitis & longus colli
Suboccipital group
   Rectus capitis posterior major
   Rectus capitis posterior minor
   Oblique capitis superior
   Oblique capitis inferior
Splenius capitis
Splenius cervicis
Semispinalis capitis
Levator scapula*
Trapezius, upper fibers*
   *(revisited for reversed O/I actions)

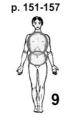
7

Group 8 – Spine   **p. 143-150**
Spinalis
Longissimus
Iliocostalis
Semispinalis
Multifidus
Rotatores
Quadratus lumborum
Interspinales & Intertransversarii

8

Group 9 – Thorax, Abdomen, Breathing
Rectus abdominis   **p. 151-157**
External oblique
Internal oblique
Transverse abdominis
Diaphragm
External intercostals
Internal intercostals
Serratus posterior superior
Serratus posterior inferior
Levator costae
Transversus Thoracis

9

Bonus Group   **p. 158-159`**
Muscles of the pelvic floor and perineum

Group 10 – Hip Joint (Part 1)
Gluteus maximus
Gluteus medius   **p. 167-174**
Gluteus minimus
Piriformis (1st lateral rotator)
The other 5 lateral rotators
   Gemellus superior
   Obturator internus
   Gemellus inferior
   Obturator externus
   Quadratus femoris
Iliopsoas
   (Iliacus & Psoas major)

10

Group 11 – Hip Joint (Part 2)
Sartorius
Tensor fascia latae   **p. 175-182**
Pectineus
Adductor brevis
Adductor longus
Adductor magnus
Gracilis

11

Group 12 – Knee (& Hip Joint, Part 3)
Rectus femoris
Vastus lateralis   **p. 183-190**
Vastus intermedius
Vastus medialis
Biceps femoris
Semitendinosus
Semimembranosus
Popliteus

12

Group 13 – Ankle, Foot, Toes
Gastrocnemius
Plantaris
Soleus   **p. 191-197**
Tibialis posterior
Flexor digitorum longus
Flexor hallucis longus
Fibularis longus (peroneus)
Fibularis brevis (peroneus)
Tibialis anterior
Extensor digitorum longus
Extensor hallucis longus

13

Bonus Group   **p. 198-199**
Intrinsic muscles of the foot

Muscles – Alphabetical Index